W9-CBN-007

Mathematics for Christian Living Series

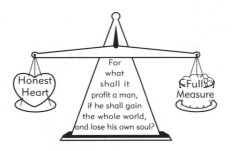

For what shall it profit a man, if he shall gain the whole world, and lose his own soul?

Honest Heart

Full Measure

Mathematics for Christian Living Series

Understanding Mathematics

Grade 6

Teacher's Manual
Part 2

Rod and Staff Publishers, Inc.
Hwy. 172, Crockett, Kentucky 41413
Telephone: (606) 522-4348

Acknowledgments

We are indebted to God for the vision of the need for a *Mathematics for Christian Living Series* and for His enabling grace. Charitable contributions from many churches have helped to cover the expenses for research and development.

This revision was written by Brother Glenn Auker. The brethren Marvin Eicher, Jerry Kreider, and Luke Sensenig served as editors. Brother Timothy Conley and Sister Amy Herr drew the illustrations. The work was evaluated by a panel of reviewers and tested by teachers in the classroom. Much effort was devoted to the production of the book. We are grateful for all who helped to make this book possible.

—The Publishers

Copyright, 1996
by

Rod and Staff Publishers, Inc.
P.O. Box 3, Hwy. 172
Crockett, Kentucky 41413

Printed in U.S.A

ISBN 978-07399-0478-7
Catalog no. 13692.3

9   10   11   —   23   22   21   20   19   18

Materials for this Course

Books and Worksheets
Pupil's textbook
2 Teacher's Manuals
Quizzes and Speed Tests
Chapter Tests

Tools Needed for Each Student
English ruler
Metric ruler
Protractor
Compass

To the Teacher

Basic Philosophy

Mathematics is a fundamental part of God's creation. Although a study of mathematics does not in itself lead to God and salvation, it can heighten one's awareness of the perfection in God's order. Because of that perfection, unchanging mathematical principles can be used to solve a host of everyday problems pertaining to quantity, length, size, proportion, and many other matters. The goal of this mathematics course is to develop in students the ability to solve mathematical problems so that they will be better able to serve the Lord.

May the Lord bless you as you teach this phase of the laws in His orderly world. Important as the mathematical concepts are which are presented in this course, they are superseded by the patience and wisdom that you will reveal as you present them. If you teach students to calculate well yet influence them in a wrong direction, you will teach them to calculate for wrong purposes. But if you teach them to calculate well *and* teach godly virtues by word and example, you will help to train valuable servants for the Lord. May your teaching be fruitful to this end.

Plan of the Course

This book contains 170 lessons in thirteen chapters. The first twelve chapters present the subject matter to be taught in the course. Chapter 13 consists mainly of review lessons designed to review the course and prepare the students for the final test.

This text is intended to be taught at the rate of one lesson per day. If you cannot have math class every school day, you will need to omit or combine some lessons in order to cover the material.

Pupil's Book

The lesson text presents explanations and illustrations of the new concepts. In teaching the lesson, briefly discuss the concepts in the explanation and then move promptly into solving several problems. Students learn most quickly by studying the examples, watching the teacher solve a few problems on the chalkboard, and then solving some problems themselves.

Class Practice is a set of problems to be used in teaching the lesson and providing class drill for the students. Solve one or two problems yourself, and then have the students solve the others either on paper or at the chalkboard. Check their work to make certain they are using the correct procedures.

Written Exercises are the homework problems, usually divided into part A, part B, and so on. The first several parts contain problems that develop the new concepts taught in the lesson. These are followed by a part containing six reading problems. Some of the reading problems relate to the new material, and some deal with review concepts.

Review Exercises give review of concepts taught in previous lessons. This textbook is designed to review more recent material more frequently and less recent material less frequently. Because of the review pattern and the pattern for introducing new material, it is important that the lessons are covered in consecutive order.

Pairing of problems. Most of the problems are arranged in pairs. That is, problems 1 and 2 are of the same kind, problems 3 and 4 are similar, and so on. If a lesson or set of problems is too long for the available time, the teacher can assign only the even-numbered or the odd-numbered problems with the confidence that all the main concepts will be drilled in those exercises. In general, each pupil should do at least the even- or odd-numbered problems in every part of the exercises.

Teacher's Guide

The teacher's guide provides a skeleton outline for each lesson. The order of the headings gives the suggested order to follow in presenting the lesson to the class.

Objectives lists the main concepts to be taught in the lesson. Watch especially for objectives that are marked with a star; they indicate concepts that are new in this math series. Plan to give special attention to these concepts as you teach.

Review gives concepts to be reviewed from previous lessons. Each item reviewed in the pupil's lesson has corresponding exercises in the teacher's guide. Use the examples in the teacher's guide to prepare the students for the review portion of their lesson assignment. Spend more time with difficult concepts such as percentages, and less time with simpler concepts such as carrying in addition.

When reviewing, be sure to allow sufficient time for the main part of the lesson—the new material.

Introduction provides an illustration, a theme, or a train of logic with which to introduce the lesson. The Introduction is not intended to be a lesson of its own, but rather a springboard to the lesson itself.

Teaching Guide contains a set of numbered points to be taught, along with helps for presenting them to the class. Boldface is used for main lesson concepts, and regular type for further explanations and other points. After each main teaching point are several related exercises for illustration and practice.

Plan ahead so that you have sufficient time to develop this part of the lesson. Use both these exercises and the Class Practice problems in the pupil's text to reinforce the concepts being taught. In math, experience is usually the best teacher.

An Ounce of Prevention warns of wrong ideas or procedures that students need to avoid. Be sure to point these out to your students. Even though they may seem trivial, they can be real pitfalls.

Further Study presents material that is intended to broaden the teacher's base of knowledge. Although you may occasionally decide to present these facts to the class, this section is designed primarily for the teacher's benefit.

General Class Procedure

Following is the recommended procedure for teaching a typical lesson in this course.

1. Correct the homework from the previous lesson. The answers are inserted in the teacher's guide.
2. Review previous lessons, using the Review section of the teachers' guide.
3. Teach the material for the new lesson, using the Class Practice problems to make certain the lesson is well learned.
4. Assign the homework.
5. Administer any speed test or quiz that is called for. If you have a multigrade classroom, it may fit your schedule better to give speed tests or quizzes before math class while you are teaching another class.

Naturally, an experienced teacher will sometimes vary his approach to teaching the lesson. However, it is recommended that beginning teachers give careful consideration to the instructions in the Teaching Guide.

Quizzes and Speed Tests

The quizzes and speed tests (found in a separate booklet) are an integral part of this course. Quizzes and Speed tests are numbered according to the lessons with which they belong, and should be given as indicated in the Review section of the teacher's guide.

Quizzes

The purpose of the 21 quizzes is to review things that students have previously learned. These quizzes are not timed, but are rather intended to reveal the understanding of concepts.

It is suggested that quizzes be given twice the value of homework grades when preparing report cards.

Speed Tests

The purpose of the 23 speed tests is to gauge students' ability to solve quickly the types of problems with which they are working. Speed tests are not given until the students have had a few days' practice with a certain type of problems.

The speed tests are timed tests. Students are expected to have all problems completed by the end of the time indicated on the speed test. Those problems not finished are counted incorrect, as are all problems with wrong answers.

It is suggested that speed test grades be given the same value as homework grades when preparing report cards.

Chapter Tests

A chapter test (found in a separate booklet) is to be given at the end of each chapter. Each test counts as a numbered lesson in the course. It is suggested that at the end of a marking period, the tests be averaged and that average be given at least equal weight with the homework average in determining the report card grade.

Following are a few pointers for testing.

1. Only the test, scratch paper, pencils, and an eraser should be on each student's desk.
2. Steps should be taken to minimize the temptation of dishonesty and the likelihood of accidentally seeing other students' answers. Following are some suggestions.
   a. Desk tops should be level. If the desks are very close to each other, have the students keep their work directly in front of them on the desk.
   b. Students should not look around more than necessary during test time.
   c. No communication should be allowed.

d. As a rule, students should remain seated during the whole test period. It is a good idea to sharpen a few extra pencils and have them on hand.

e. Students should hand in their tests before going on to any other work.

3. Encourage the students to do their work carefully and to go back over it as they have time. Do not allow them to hand in their tests too soon. On the other hand, some students are so meticulous that they can hardly finish their tests. If you have this problem, set a time when you will collect all the tests. Once 90% of the tests are completed, the rest of them should generally be finished in the next five or ten minutes. Of course there are exceptions for slower students.

4. A test is different from homework. Students should realize that they must rely on their own knowledge as they work. The teacher should not help them except to make sure that all instructions are clearly understood.

Evaluating Test Results

1. If you check the tests in class, have students check each others' work. Spot check the corrected tests.

2. Tests are valuable tools in determining what the students have grasped. Are there any places where the class is uniformly weak? If so, reinforcement is needed.

3. One effective way to discover the general performance of the class is to find the class median. This is done by arranging the scores in order from highest to lowest. The middle score is the class median. If there is an even number of students, find the average of the two middle scores.

Disposition of the Corrected Tests

1. As a rule, students should have the privilege to see their tests. Review any weak points and answer any questions about why an answer is wrong.

2. The teacher may use his discretion about whether the students should be allowed to keep their tests permanently. Some teachers prefer to collect them again so that there is no chance of students' younger siblings seeing the tests in later years.

Contents of Book 1

Table of Contents

Numbers given first are pupil page numbers.
Numbers at the far right are actual manual page numbers printed at the bottom of the pages.

Chapter 13   Number Sentences and Year-End Review

Many Bible illustrations and parables can be thought of as spiritual proportions. As we understand how these natural things relate, we can grasp the meaning of heavenly teaching.

Chapter 7

Decimals and Proportions

If God so clothe the grass of the field, which to day is, and to morrow is cast into the oven, shall he not much more clothe you?   (Matthew 6:30)

For we being many are one bread, and one body.   (1 Corinthians 10:17)

84. Dividing Decimals by 10, by 100, and by 1,000

In Lesson 78 you learned to multiply any number by 10, 100, or 1,000 by moving the decimal point to the right in the number. Dividing decimals by 10, by 100, and by 1,000 is just as easy. But instead of moving the decimal point to the right, it is moved to the left. Zeroes are annexed to the left of the number if they are needed.

Rule 1: To divide a decimal by 10,
move the decimal point one place to the left.

Rule 2: To divide a decimal by 100,
move the decimal point two places to the left.

Rule 3: To divide a decimal by 1,000,
move the decimal point three places to the left.

Example A $2.5 \div 10$
Think: Move the decimal point 1 place to the left.
2.5 $2.5 \div 10 = 0.25$

Example B $2.5 \div 100$
Think: Move the decimal point 2 places to the left.
2.5 = 02.5 $2.5 \div 100 = 0.025$

Example C $2.5 \div 1,000$
Think: Move the decimal point 3 places to the left.
2.5 = 002.5 $2.5 \div 1,000 = 0.0025$

General rule: To divide a decimal by 10, 100, or 1,000, move the decimal point to the left as many places as the number of zeroes in the divisor.

CLASS PRACTICE

Solve these problems.

a. $7.14 \div 10$ 0.714   b. $37.7 \div 10$ 3.77   c. $157.5 \div 100$ 1.575

d. $0.15 \div 100$ 0.0015   e. $783.9 \div 1,000$ 0.7839   f. $17.2 \div 1,000$ 0.0172

WRITTEN EXERCISES

A.   *Divide each number by 10. Annex a zero if it is needed.*

1. $3.45 \div 10$ 0.345   2. $4.12 \div 10$ 0.412   3. $3.892 \div 10$ 0.3892

4. $42.919 \div 10$ 4.2919   5. $0.6 \div 10$ 0.06   6. $0.48 \div 10$ 0.048

LESSON 84

Objective

- To teach *dividing decimals by 10, 100, and 1,000, by moving the decimal point to the left.

Review

1. *Multiplying decimals by 10, by 100, and by 1,000* (Lesson 78).
   a. 100×4.4 (440)
   b. 10×0.35 (3.5)
   c. $1,000 \times 6.78$ (6,780)
   d. $1,000 \times 3.3$ (3,300)

2. *Multiplying decimals by decimals* (Lessons 79, 80).

   a. $\begin{array}{r} 0.15 \\ \times\, 0.03 \\ \hline (0.0045) \end{array}$ b. $\begin{array}{r} 4.75 \\ \times\, 0.6 \\ \hline (2.850) \end{array}$

3. *Changing between fractions and decimals* (Lessons 73, 74).
   a. $\frac{3}{8} = (0.375)$
   b. $\frac{5}{16} = (0.3125)$
   c. $0.45 = (\frac{9}{20})$
   d. $0.36 = (\frac{9}{25})$

4. *Improper fractions* (Lesson 50). No class review is necessary.

5. *Multiplying fractions* (Lessons 60–64).
   a. $\frac{3}{4}$ of $24 = (18)$
   b. $\frac{3}{5} \times \frac{2}{3} = (\frac{2}{5})$
   c. $1\frac{1}{2} \times 4\frac{2}{3} = (7)$

Introduction

Write the following problems on the board, and solve them by division. Ask, "In what way are the quotients similar to the dividends? In what way are they different?" (The quotients have the same digits as the dividend except for annexed or dropped zeroes. The decimal point comes between different digits than it does in the dividend.)

$$10\overline{)\$214.00} \quad (\$21.40) \qquad 100\overline{)\$72.00} \quad (\$0.72)$$

Teaching Guide

1. Review the position of the decimal point in whole numbers such as 6, 25, and 120.
   a. $6 = (6.)$
   b. $25 = (25.)$
   c. $120 = (120.)$

2. **To divide a decimal by 10, move the decimal point one place to the left. To divide a decimal by 100, move the decimal point two places to the left. To divide a decimal by 1,000, move the decimal point three places to the left.** Annex zeroes if necessary.
   a. $3.4 \div 10 = (0.34)$
   b. $0.45 \div 10 = (0.045)$
   c. $23.5 \div 100 = (0.235)$
   d. $3.67 \div 100 = (0.0367)$
   e. $3,546 \div 1,000 = (3.546)$
   f. $4.7 \div 1,000 = (0.0047)$

B. **Divide each number by 100. Annex zeroes if they are needed.**

7. $11.47 \div 100$ 0.1147   **8.** $53.81 \div 100$ 0.5381   **9.** $475.29 \div 100$ 4.7529

10. $163.91 \div 100$ 1.6391   **11.** $0.9 \div 100$ 0.009   **12.** $0.12 \div 100$ 0.0012

C. **Divide these numbers by 1,000. Annex zeroes if they are needed.**

13. $135 \div 1,000$ 0.135   **14.** $465 \div 1,000$ 0.465   **15.** $191.9 \div 1,000$ 0.1919

16. $4,821.3 \div 1,000$ **17.** $8.7 \div 1,000$ **18.** $0.9 \div 1,000$

          4.8213   0.0087   0.0009

D. **Divide each number by 10, by 100, and by 1,000.**

Divide	by 10	by 100	by 1,000
12.3	**19.** 1.23	**20.** 0.123	**21.** 0.0123
174.9	**22.** 17.49	**23.** 1.749	**24.** 0.1749
4	**25.** 0.4	**26.** 0.04	**27.** 0.004
0.7	**28.** 0.07	**29.** 0.007	**30.** 0.0007

REVIEW EXERCISES

E. **Multiply these numbers mentally.** *(Lesson 78)*

31. 3.483×10 **32.** 2.683×100 **33.** $3.2 \times 1,000$ **34.** 5.2×100

          34.83   268.3   3,200   520

F. **Solve these multiplication problems.** *(Lessons 79, 80)*

35.	**36.**	**37.**	**38.**
3.5	5.2	0.02	0.04
$\times 0.3$	$\times 0.01$	$\times 0.04$	$\times 0.08$
1.05	0.052	0.0008	0.0032

G. **Change the fractions to decimals, and the decimals to fractions.** *(Lessons 73, 74)*

39. $\frac{5}{8}$ 0.625   **40.** $\frac{13}{40}$ 0.325   **41.** 0.55 $\frac{11}{20}$ **42.** 0.88 $\frac{22}{25}$

H. **Change these whole or mixed numbers to improper fractions.** *(Lesson 50)*

43. 9 $\frac{9}{1}$ **44.** 15 $\frac{15}{1}$ **45.** $5\frac{3}{5}$ $\frac{28}{5}$ **46.** $3\frac{3}{4}$ $\frac{15}{4}$

I. **Multiply these fractions.** *(Lessons 60–64)*

47. $\frac{5}{8}$ of 32 20   **48.** $\frac{3}{4} \times \frac{5}{8}$ $\frac{15}{32}$ **49.** $1\frac{1}{4} \times \frac{4}{5}$ 1   **50.** $3\frac{1}{3} \times 2\frac{2}{5}$ 8

85. Dividing a Decimal by a Whole Number

Dividing a decimal by a whole number is almost the same as dividing whole numbers. The only difference is that a decimal point must be placed in the quotient directly above the decimal point in the dividend. Study the following examples.

```
      3.3                    $37.81
  6)19.8                 4)$151.24
     18                     12
      18                    31
      18                    28
       0                    32
                            32
                            04
                             4
                             0
```

CLASS PRACTICE

Solve these problems.

```
        2.55                5.24               1.156              0.1555
  a. 5)12.75         b. 6)31.44        c. 14)16.184       d. 25)3.8875
```

WRITTEN EXERCISES

A.   Copy each division problem, and add the missing decimal point in the quotient.

```
         2.7                1.15              1.008              2.701
  1.  14)37.8         2.  23)26.45      3.  177)178.416    4.  35)94.535
```

B.   Solve these division problems, being careful to place the decimal points correctly. Check by casting out nines.

```
         2.41               12.4              0.29               0.675
  5.  4)9.64          6.  7)86.8        7.  3)0.87         8.  5)3.375

        0.1237             0.1087            0.0532             2.2846
  9.  8)0.9896       10.  9)0.9783     11.  6)0.3192      12.  2)4.5692

          $3.38              $3.68             $22.10             $4.21
  13.  11)$37.18     14.  12)$44.16    15.  15)$331.50    16.  25)$105.25
```

C.   Solve these reading problems.

17. One day 3.6 inches of rain fell in a 6-hour period. What was the average amount that fell in 1 hour?   0.6 inch

18. The Oakdale Mennonite School purchased 12 songbooks for $95.40. What was the cost of each songbook? $7.95

LESSON 85

Objective

- To review dividing a decimal by a whole number.

Review

1. *Dividing decimals by 10, by 100, and by 1,000* (Lesson 84).
   a. $34.2 \div 100$ (0.342)
   b. $32.91 \div 100$ (0.3291)
   c. $41.6 \div 1,000$ (0.0416)

2. *Multiplying decimals* (Lesson 79, 80).

   a. $\begin{array}{r} 15.5 \\ \times\, 0.06 \\ \hline (0.930) \end{array}$ b. $\begin{array}{r} 4.9 \\ \times\, 0.008 \\ \hline (0.0392) \end{array}$

3. *Comparing decimals by annexing zeroes* (Lesson 75).
   a. 0.01 (<) 0.0101
   b. 0.35 (>) 0.3499
   c. 0.29 (>) 0.2899

4. *Dividing fractions* (Lessons 65–67).
   a. $\frac{3}{4} \div \frac{1}{3} = (2\frac{1}{4})$
   b. $6 \div 1\frac{1}{6} = (5\frac{1}{7})$

5. *Mental multiplication* (Lessons 19, 20).
   a. 14×15 (210)
   b. 16×50 (800)
   c. 32×25 (800)
   d. $8 \times 5 \times 4$ (160)

Introduction

Place the following division problems on the board, and solve them without placing the decimal points. Challenge the students to tell you where the decimal points belong according to mental division by 10, 100, and 1,000. When all the problems are solved, ask the pupils what they notice about the position of the decimal points. (The ones in the quotients are directly above the ones in the dividends.)

a. $10\overline{)34.50}$ (3.45)   b. $100\overline{)32.300}$ (0.323)

c. $1,000\overline{)4.1000}$ (0.0041)

Teaching Guide

Dividing a decimal by a whole number is much like dividing whole numbers. The only difference is that a decimal point must be placed in the quotient directly above the decimal point in the dividend.

a. $5\overline{)12.5}$ (2.5)   b. $6\overline{)4.206}$ (0.701)

c. $4\overline{)\$3.84}$ (\$0.96)   d. $9\overline{)0.9189}$ (0.1021)

An Ounce of Prevention

Students often make the careless mistake of omitting the decimal point in an answer. Help them to avoid this problem by stressing the wisdom of placing the decimal point first. As a corrective measure, count any answer wrong which is correct except for the missing decimal point. The numbers 35 and 3.5 use the same two digits, but they are not the same number at all. Writing 35 for 3.5 is just as incorrect as writing 35 for 53.

Here is one way to get the point across. Ask a student for his age. Write it on the board, but put the decimal point at the wrong place. Is this your age? The students would probably far rather be 11 or 12 years old than 1.1 or 1.2 years old.

19. Ronald and Jerry often ride their bicycles to school on pleasant days. The round trip to school and home again is 9.6 miles. How far do the boys live from school?

4.8 miles

20. When Lucy went shopping with her mother, she saw an advertisement that read "Macaroni and cheese dinners, 4 for $1.00." What was the price of 1 dinner?

$0.25

21. The scale in the doctor's office showed that Henry weighed 68.4 pounds soon after his eleventh birthday. A year later it showed that he weighed 75.6 pounds. What was the average amount of weight that Henry gained each month that year?   0.6 pound

22. A night light uses $7\frac{1}{2}$ watts of electricity per hour. In how many hours will it use 50 watts? $6\frac{2}{3}$ hours

REVIEW EXERCISES

D.   Divide these numbers by 10, 100, or 1,000 as indicated. (*Lesson 84*)

23.   3.45 ÷ 10   0.345   24.   5 ÷ 10   0.5   25.   35.4 ÷ 100   0.354

26.   3.28 ÷ 100   0.0328   27.   415.3 ÷ 1,000 0.4153 28.   348.2 ÷ 1,000 0.3482

E.   Multiply these decimals. (*Lessons 79, 80*)

29.   17.2   30.   1.45   31.   0.15   32.   0.04
        × 0.15   × 0.05   × 0.02   × 0.05
        2.580   0.0725   0.0030   0.0020

F.   Copy each set of decimals, compare them, and write > or < between them.
     (*Lesson 75*)

33.   0.04 _>_ 0.0041   34.   0.5002 _<_ 0.51

35.   0.27 _>_ 0.2699   36.   0.4 _<_ 0.401

G.   Solve these division problems. (*Lessons 65–67*)

37. $8 ÷ \frac{2}{5}$ 20   38. $\frac{4}{5} ÷ \frac{4}{9}$ $1\frac{4}{5}$ 39. $6 ÷ 1\frac{1}{3}$ $4\frac{1}{2}$ 40. $5\frac{5}{6} ÷ 3\frac{1}{3}$ $1\frac{3}{4}$

H.   Solve these multiplication problems mentally. (*Lessons 19, 20*)

41.   22 × 15   330 42.   8 × 4 × 5   160 43.   24 × 50   1,200 44.   24 × 25   600

21

86. Dividing by a Decimal

Division by a decimal is like division by a whole number except that two extra steps are required before dividing. Study the following rules and examples.

> 1. Move the decimal point in the divisor to the far right of the divisor, and mark its new position with a caret (⌃).
> 2. Count the number of places that the decimal point in the divisor was moved, and move the decimal point in the dividend the same number of places. Annex zeroes if more places are needed. Mark this new position with a caret.
> 3. Place the decimal point for the quotient directly above the caret in the dividend.
> 4. Estimate and divide as usual.

Example A	Example B	Example C

$$0.45_\wedge\overline{)5.89_\wedge5}\quad\begin{array}{r}13.1\end{array}$$

Example A
```
        13.1
0.45 )5.89 5
       45
      ___
      139
      135
      ___
       45
       45
       ___
        0
```

Example B
```
          71.
$0.32 )$22.72
        224
        ___
         32
         32
         ___
          0
```

Example C
```
         14.
1.25 )17.50
       125
       ___
       500
       500
       ___
         0
```

Remember that when a decimal point is moved to the right, the number is multiplied by 10, 100, and so on. If both the divisor and the dividend are multiplied by the same number, the quotient does not change. For example, $8 \div 4$, $80 \div 40$, and $800 \div 400$ are all 2. This is why decimal points are moved when the divisor is a decimal.

When one sum of money is divided by another as in Example B, notice that the answer is not labeled as money. Such a division does not answer the question "How much money?" Rather, it answers the question "How many *times* is one sum of money contained in another?"

CLASS PRACTICE

Solve these problems.

a. $0.5\overline{)45.15}$ 90.3

b. $1.7\overline{)5.61}$ 3.3

c. $0.65\overline{)\$11.70}$ $18.

d. $2.75\overline{)\$1,276}$ $464.

WRITTEN EXERCISES

A. *Copy and solve these division problems. Check your work by casting out nines.*

1. $0.6\overline{)12}$ 20

2. $0.5\overline{)15}$ 30

3. $0.25\overline{)16}$ 64

4. $0.45\overline{)72}$ 160

LESSON 86

Objectives

- To teach *dividing by decimals.
- To teach *dividing one sum of money by another.

Review

1. *Dividing decimals by 10, by 100, and by 1,000* (Lesson 84).
   a. $4.2 \div 10$ (0.42)
   b. $4.2 \div 100$ (0.042)
   c. $4.2 \div 1,000$ (0.0042)

2. *Adding and subtracting decimals* (Lesson 76).

   a. $\begin{array}{r} 3.500 \\ + 0.876 \\ \hline (4.376) \end{array}$ b. $\begin{array}{r} 34.200 \\ - 15.984 \\ \hline (18.216) \end{array}$

3. *Adding fractions* (Lesson 54).

   a. $\begin{array}{r} 3\frac{3}{5} \\ + 1\frac{1}{2} \\ \hline (5\frac{1}{10}) \end{array}$ b. $\begin{array}{r} 3\frac{3}{4} \\ + 5\frac{1}{3} \\ \hline (9\frac{1}{12}) \end{array}$

Introduction

Write the following three problems on the board, and ask the students to solve them. The students should readily understand that the quotients are the same because the numbers in the second and third problems are 10 times as great as those in the preceding problem.

$$\overset{(4)}{4\overline{)16}} \qquad \overset{(4)}{40\overline{)160}} \qquad \overset{(4)}{400\overline{)1,600}}$$

Read the following problem, and challenge the students to tell you how the solution should be written on the board.

> Michael sold some pigeons at an auction and received $44.80 for them. If he received $2.80 per pigeon, how many pigeons did he sell?

After the problem is on the board, see if the students can find a way to change the divisor. Multiplying the divisor by 100 will remove the decimal point from it. If the divisor is multiplied by 100, the dividend must also be multiplied by 100. This is done by moving its decimal point two places to the right.

$$\overset{16 \text{ pigeons}}{\$2.80_{\wedge}\overline{)\$44.80_{\wedge}}}$$

Teaching Guide

Division by a decimal is like division by a whole number except that two extra steps are required before dividing. The procedure is as follows:

1. Move the decimal point in the divisor to the far right of the divisor, and mark its new position with a caret ($_{\wedge}$).

2. Count the number of places that the decimal point in the divisor was moved, and move the decimal point

in the dividend the same number of places. Annex zeroes if more places are needed. Mark this new position with a caret.

3. Place the decimal point for the quotient directly above the caret in the dividend.

4. Estimate and divide as usual.

a.
$$
\begin{array}{r}
(2.1) \\
0.15_\wedge\overline{)0.31_\wedge 5} \\
\underline{30} \\
15 \\
\underline{15} \\
0
\end{array}
$$

b.
$$
\begin{array}{r}
(26.) \\
3.25_\wedge\overline{)84.50_\wedge} \\
\underline{650} \\
1950 \\
\underline{1950} \\
0
\end{array}
$$

c.
$$
\begin{array}{r}
(2.5) \\
\$4.20_\wedge\overline{)\$10.50_\wedge 0} \\
\underline{840} \\
2100 \\
\underline{2100} \\
0
\end{array}
$$

An Ounce of Prevention

Stress the point that when dollars are divided by dollars, the answer is not dollars. For example, $4.00 ÷ $2.00 = 2. There are two sets of $2.00 in $4.00.

$$\begin{array}{r} 2 \\ 3.2\overline{)6.4} \end{array}$$
5.

$$\begin{array}{r} 3.5 \\ 4.5\overline{)15.75} \end{array}$$
6.

$$\begin{array}{r} 4.5 \\ 1.25\overline{)5.625} \end{array}$$
7.

$$\begin{array}{r} 3.6 \\ 2.9\overline{)10.44} \end{array}$$
8.

$$\begin{array}{r} 4.2 \\ 0.72\overline{)3.024} \end{array}$$
9.

$$\begin{array}{r} 3.6 \\ 0.48\overline{)1.728} \end{array}$$
10.

$$\begin{array}{r} 4.1 \\ 0.121\overline{)0.4961} \end{array}$$
11.

$$\begin{array}{r} 6.9 \\ 0.325\overline{)2.2425} \end{array}$$
12.

$$\begin{array}{r} 8 \\ \$0.55\overline{)\$4.40} \end{array}$$
13.

$$\begin{array}{r} 16 \\ \$0.85\overline{)\$13.60} \end{array}$$
14.

$$\begin{array}{r} 18 \\ \$0.27\overline{)\$4.86} \end{array}$$
15.

$$\begin{array}{r} 45 \\ \$2.35\overline{)\$105.75} \end{array}$$
16.

B.   Solve these reading problems.

17. It rained 0.4 inch one week and 3.6 inches the next week. How many times as much rain fell the second week as the first week?   9 times

18. When Brother Martin returned from the mission field, the Landis family drove to the airport to meet him. They drove 225 miles and used 12.5 gallons of gasoline. How many miles did they travel on each gallon of gasoline?   18 miles

19. It took the Landis family 4.5 hours to drive the 225 miles to the airport. What was their average speed in miles per hour?   50 miles per hour

20. Brother Martin said that he had flown 900 miles in $2\frac{1}{4}$ hours ($2\frac{1}{4} = 2.25$). What was the average speed of the plane?   400 miles per hour

21. Mother spent $11.25 to buy fabric that cost $3.75 per yard. How many yards of fabric did she buy?   3 yards

22. The Eberly family buys and raises feeder steers. A feeder steer may gain an average of 2.25 pounds per day. At that rate, how many days must a steer be fed until he gains 765 pounds?   340 days

REVIEW EXERCISES

C.   Divide each number by 10, 100, or 1,000 as indicated. *(Lesson 84)*

23. $4.5 \div 10$ 0.45

24. $3.8 \div 100$ 0.038

25. $46.2 \div 1,000$ 0.0462

26. $45.32 \div 10$ 4.532

27. $34.5 \div 1,000$ 0.0345

28. $0.25 \div 100$ 0.0025

D.   Solve these problems. Watch the signs! *(Lessons 54, 56, 76)*

29.
$$\begin{array}{r} 4.53 \\ -\ 2.7 \\ \hline 1.83 \end{array}$$

30.
$$\begin{array}{r} 3.7 \\ -\ 2.388 \\ \hline 1.312 \end{array}$$

31.
$$\begin{array}{r} 1.715 \\ 0.31 \\ 4.5 \\ +\ 2.608 \\ \hline 9.133 \end{array}$$

32.
$$\begin{array}{r} 5.3 \\ 12.89 \\ 0.009 \\ +\ 16.41 \\ \hline 34.609 \end{array}$$

33.
$$\begin{array}{r} 2\frac{5}{8} \\ +\ 4\frac{1}{2} \\ \hline 7\frac{1}{8} \end{array}$$

34.
$$\begin{array}{r} 4\frac{1}{3} \\ +\ 2\frac{4}{5} \\ \hline 7\frac{2}{15} \end{array}$$

35.
$$\begin{array}{r} 5\frac{7}{9} \\ -\ 2\frac{5}{6} \\ \hline 2\frac{17}{18} \end{array}$$

36.
$$\begin{array}{r} 6\frac{3}{8} \\ -\ 3\frac{1}{3} \\ \hline 3\frac{1}{24} \end{array}$$

87. More Challenging Decimal Divisors

When a division problem does not divide evenly, the remainder can easily be made a part of the quotient. This can be done with common fractions or decimal fractions. When you form a fraction with the remainder and divisor, the quotient is a mixed number that includes the remainder. In decimals, this is done by annexing zeroes to the right of the decimal point in the dividend and continuing to divide. The quotient is then a decimal, and the remainder is part of it.

In Example A, the problem is solved, and the remainder is expressed as a fraction. In Example B, the same problem is solved by annexing two zeroes and continuing to divide. Notice that the two answers are equal. In this lesson you will be using the method illustrated in Example B.

$$\textbf{Example A} \qquad 0.4_\wedge \overline{)\,1.3_\wedge} \;\; 3\tfrac{1}{4} \qquad\qquad \textbf{Example B} \qquad 0.4_\wedge \overline{)\,1.3_\wedge 00} \;\; 3.25$$

Example A:
$$
\begin{array}{r}
3\tfrac{1}{4} \\
0.4_\wedge \overline{)\,1.3_\wedge} \\
12 \\
\hline
1
\end{array}
$$

Example B:
$$
\begin{array}{r}
3.25 \\
0.4_\wedge \overline{)\,1.3_\wedge 00} \\
12 \\
\hline
10 \\
8 \\
\hline
20 \\
20 \\
\hline
0
\end{array}
$$

When you divide, no place value in the quotient to the right of the decimal point may be left blank. Sometimes you must write zeroes after the decimal point before you can write other digits in the quotient. In Example C, two zeroes are needed before the digit 5.

Example C:
$$
\begin{array}{r}
0.005 \\
0.45_\wedge \overline{)\,0.00_\wedge 225} \\
225 \\
\hline
0
\end{array}
$$

CLASS PRACTICE

Solve these problems.

a. $0.5\overline{)0.04}$ → 0.08

b. $7\overline{)0.0147}$ → 0.0021

c. $0.6\overline{)0.009}$ → 0.015

d. $1.105\overline{)1.326}$ → 1.2

WRITTEN EXERCISES

A. **Solve these division problems. Annex zeroes to the right of the dividend until the problem divides evenly. You will not need to annex more than three zeroes in any of them.**

1. $0.5\overline{)1.22}$ → 2.44

2. $1.4\overline{)4.97}$ → 3.55

3. $0.36\overline{)0.486}$ → 1.35

4. $0.8\overline{)0.3}$ → 0.375

5. $0.35\overline{)0.56}$ → 1.6

6. $0.25\overline{)5.01}$ → 20.04

7. $0.08\overline{)0.5}$ → 6.25

8. $0.8\overline{)0.7}$ → 0.875

LESSON 87

Objectives

- To teach *dividing decimals that require the annexing of zeroes.

- To work with *division problems in which the first quotient figure(s) to the right of the decimal point are zeroes.

Review

1. Give Lesson 87 Speed Test (Multiplying and Dividing by 10, by 100, and by 1,000).

2. *Subtracting decimals* (Lesson 77). Remind pupils to fill in zeroes as needed.

   a. $\begin{array}{r} 3.4 \\ -\ 1.7 \\ \hline (1.7) \end{array}$
   b. $\begin{array}{r} 6.397 \\ -\ 2.6 \\ \hline (3.797) \end{array}$

3. *Subtracting proper fractions* (Lessons 53, 56).

   a. $\begin{array}{r} \frac{1}{2} \\ -\ \frac{1}{3} \\ \hline (\frac{1}{6}) \end{array}$
   b. $\begin{array}{r} 9\frac{1}{6} \\ -\ 3\frac{4}{9} \\ \hline (5\frac{13}{18}) \end{array}$

4. *Area* (Lesson 36).
   a. 1 sq. ft. = (144) sq. in.
   b. 1 sq. yd. = (9) sq. ft.
   c. 1 a. = (43,560) sq. ft.
   d. 1 sq. mi. = (640) a.
   e. 4 sq. yd. = (36) sq. ft.
   f. 5 sq. ft. = (720) sq. in.

5. *Short division* (Lesson 22). No class review is necessary.

Introduction

Henry was almost finished with his math lesson when he came to this problem: $0.326 \div 4$. This is his work. Is the answer correct?

$$\begin{array}{r} 0.\ 81 = 0.81 \\ 4\overline{)0.326} \\ \underline{32} \\ 06 \\ \underline{4} \\ 2 \end{array}$$

Henry made two mistakes. He failed to write a zero above the 3 in 0.326, and he failed to deal with the remainder of 2. This lesson is about division problems like this one. (The problem is solved correctly as example *d* in Teaching Guide.)

Teaching Guide

1. **If a division problem results in a remainder, annex zeroes to the right of the decimal, and continue dividing.** The boldface zeroes in the following problems were annexed during calculation.

   a. $$\begin{array}{r} (0.8565) \\ 4\overline{)3.426\mathbf{0}} \\ \underline{32} \\ 22 \\ \underline{20} \\ 26 \\ \underline{24} \\ 20 \\ \underline{20} \\ 0 \end{array}$$

   b. $$\begin{array}{r} (0.6625) \\ 8\overline{)5.3\mathbf{000}} \\ \underline{48} \\ 50 \\ \underline{48} \\ 20 \\ \underline{16} \\ 40 \\ \underline{40} \\ 0 \end{array}$$

   c. $$\begin{array}{r} 17.6) \\ 0.25_\wedge\overline{)4.40_\wedge0} \\ \underline{25} \\ 190 \\ \underline{175} \\ 150 \\ \underline{150} \\ 0 \end{array}$$

2. When dividing, leave no place value blank in the quotient to the right of the decimal point. Zeroes must sometimes be written after the decimal point before other digits can be written.

d.
$$
\begin{array}{r}
(0.0815) \\
4\overline{)0.3260} \\
\underline{32} \\
06 \\
\underline{4} \\
20 \\
\underline{20} \\
0
\end{array}
$$

e.
$$
\begin{array}{r}
(0.0895) \\
6\overline{)0.5370} \\
\underline{48} \\
57 \\
\underline{54} \\
30 \\
\underline{30} \\
0
\end{array}
$$

f.
$$
\begin{array}{r}
(0.00875) \\
1.2_\wedge\overline{)0.0_\wedge10500} \\
\underline{96} \\
90 \\
\underline{84} \\
60 \\
\underline{60} \\
0
\end{array}
$$

28

B. **Solve these division problems. Be careful not to miss any zeroes in the answers.**

9. $\dfrac{0.0731}{8\overline{)0.5848}}$ 10. $\dfrac{0.0911}{9\overline{)0.8199}}$ 11. $\dfrac{0.0099}{6\overline{)0.0594}}$ 12. $\dfrac{0.0091}{5\overline{)0.0455}}$

13. $\dfrac{0.095}{0.15\overline{)0.01425}}$ 14. $\dfrac{0.0831}{1.2\overline{)0.09972}}$ 15. $\dfrac{0.068}{2.5\overline{)0.17}}$ 16. $\dfrac{0.07}{1.6\overline{)0.112}}$

C. **Solve these reading problems.**

17. Oscar walks 5.5 miles through the mountains to church for Sunday morning services. The trip takes 2.2 hours. How many miles per hour does he walk?

2.5 miles per hour

18. Father made a long-distance telephone call that cost $0.46. The cost of the call was $0.092 per minute. How many minutes long was the call?   5 minutes

19. Mother bought 4.2 pounds of bologna at the meat counter. The bologna cost $9.87. What was the price of the bologna per pound? $2.35 per pound

20. Mother also bought 5.2 pounds of ground beef for $8.06. What was the price of the meat per pound? $1.55 per pound

21. Mother's bill at the grocery store was $43.92 plus $0.41 sales tax. She handed the cashier $60.00. How much change did she receive? $15.67

22. On the way home, Mother stopped at the service station and bought 8.5 gallons of gasoline at $1.22 per gallon. What was the cost of the gasoline? $10.37

REVIEW EXERCISES

D. **Solve these subtraction problems.** *(Lesson 77)*

23. $\begin{array}{r} 4.843 \\ -\ 3.9 \\ \hline 0.943 \end{array}$ 24. $\begin{array}{r} 8.315 \\ -\ 2.7 \\ \hline 5.615 \end{array}$ 25. $\begin{array}{r} 11.5 \\ -\ 7.099 \\ \hline 4.401 \end{array}$ 26. $\begin{array}{r} 15.2 \\ -\ 6.935 \\ \hline 8.265 \end{array}$

E. **Subtract these fractions and mixed numbers.** *(Lessons 53, 56)*

27. $\begin{array}{r} \frac{3}{4} \\ -\frac{1}{6} \\ \hline \frac{7}{12} \end{array}$ 28. $\begin{array}{r} \frac{2}{3} \\ -\frac{3}{5} \\ \hline \frac{1}{15} \end{array}$ 29. $\begin{array}{r} 3\frac{1}{2} \\ -1\frac{1}{7} \\ \hline 2\frac{5}{14} \end{array}$ 30. $\begin{array}{r} 5\frac{1}{8} \\ -2\frac{1}{3} \\ \hline 2\frac{19}{24} \end{array}$

F. **Change these measures as indicated.** *(Lesson 36)*

31. 3 sq. ft. = __432__ sq. in.   32. 99 sq. ft. = __11__ sq. yd.

33. 2 a. = __87,120__ sq. ft.   34. 3 sq. mi. = __1,920__ a.

35. 8 sq. yd. = __72__ sq. ft.   36. 288 sq. in. = __2__ sq. ft.

G. **Solve by short division. Write any remainder with R.** *(Lesson 22)*

37. $\dfrac{586}{4\overline{)2,344}}$ 38. $\dfrac{939}{6\overline{)5,634}}$ 39. $\dfrac{1,591\ \text{R }3}{8\overline{)12,731}}$ 40. $\dfrac{3,980\ \text{R }1}{9\overline{)35,821}}$

88. Rounding Decimals

Like whole numbers, decimals can be rounded when exact amounts are not needed. The steps for rounding decimals are much like the steps for rounding whole numbers.

> 1. Decide to which place value you will round the number. Underline the digit in that place.
> 2. Look at the digit one place to the right. If it is 5 or more, round the underlined digit to the next higher number. If it is less than 5, leave the underlined digit the same.
> 3. Drop all digits to the right of the underlined digit.
>
> **Example A**   Round 1.83 and 1.87 to the nearest tenth.
> 1.8$\underline{3}$ = 1.8 to the nearest tenth (3 < 5)
> 1.8$\underline{7}$ = 1.9 to the nearest tenth (7 > 5)
>
> **Example B**   Round 3.168 and 3.162 to the nearest hundredth.
> 3.1$\underline{6}$8 = 3.17 to the nearest hundredth (8 > 5)
> 3.1$\underline{6}$2 = 3.16 to the nearest hundredth (2 < 5)

Rounding money to the nearest cent is the same as rounding to the nearest hundredth because a cent is one hundredth of a dollar.

> **Example C**
> Round $4.852, $5.575, $6.895, and $7.996 to the nearest cent.
> 4.8\underline{5}$2 = $4.85 to the nearest cent
> 5.5\underline{7}$5 = $5.58 to the nearest cent
> 6.8\underline{9}$5 = $6.90 to the nearest cent
> 7.9\underline{9}$6 = $8.00 to the nearest cent

Notice the last two amounts above. The next higher hundredth after 6.89 is 6.90, and the next higher hundredth after 7.99 is 8.00. That is why the rounded amounts end with zeroes. The zeroes are written to make it clear that the amounts are stated to the nearest hundredth.

Sometimes an amount is given in cents and a fraction of a cent, and you need to express it in dollar form. Then you can use the following steps.

1. Write the cents in decimal form.
2. Move the decimal point two places to the left.
3. Change the sign from cents to dollars.

> **Example D**   Express $16\frac{7}{10}$ ¢ in dollar form.
> $16\frac{7}{10}$¢ = 16.7¢
> 16.7¢ = 0_\wedge$16.7 = $0.167

LESSON 88

Objectives

- To teach *rounding decimals to the nearest tenth and the nearest hundredth.

- To teach *rounding money to the nearest cent.

- To teach *expressing tenths of a cent in terms of a dollar.

Review

1. *Dividing by 10, by 100, and by 1,000* (Lesson 84).
   a. $4.5 \div 10$ (0.45)
   b. $4.5 \div 100$ (0.045)
   c. $4.5 \div 1,000$ (0.0045)

2. *Multiplying by 10, by 100, and by 1,000* (Lesson 78).
   a. 10×4.5 (45)
   b. 100×4.5 (450)
   c. $1,000 \times 4.5$ (4,500)

3. *Adding mixed numbers* (Lesson 54).

   a. $3\frac{1}{5}$
       $+2\frac{1}{2}$
       $(5\frac{7}{10})$

   b. $2\frac{3}{4}$
       $+5\frac{1}{6}$
       $(7\frac{11}{12})$

Introduction

The Seibels buy milk at a neighboring farm for $1.25 a gallon. How much would 1/2 gallon cost?

$$2)\overline{\$1.250} \quad (\$0.625)$$

Ask the students how much the Seibels should pay for 1/2 gallon of milk. They should pay $0.63 because cents are hundredths, and 0.625 rounded to the nearest hundredth is 0.63.

Teaching Guide

1. **Decimals can be rounded when exact amounts are not needed.** The following steps are used.
   (1) Decide to which place value you will round the number. Underline the digit in that place.
   (2) Look at the digit one place to the right. If it is 5 or more, round the underlined digit to the next higher number. If it is less than 5, leave the underlined digit the same.
   (3) Drop all digits to the right of the underlined digit.

   Call attention to the following difference: When a decimal is rounded, all digits to the right of the designated place value are dropped. But when a whole number is rounded, all digits to the right of the designated place value are changed to zeroes.

   Also point out that when there is a zero in the place to which a number is rounded, that zero is not dropped. The zero shows that the number is rounded to that place value. See problems *c* and *h* below.

Round these decimals to the nearest tenth.
  a. 0.48 (0.5)
  b. 0.92 (0.9)
  c. 0.96 (1.0)
  d. 3.58 (3.6)

Round these decimals to the nearest hundredth.
  e. 0.831 (0.83)
  f. 0.765 (0.77)
  g. 0.989 (0.99)
  h. 2.995 (3.00)

2. **Rounding money to the nearest cent is the same as rounding to the nearest hundredth.** A cent is one hundredth of a dollar.
  a. $3.654 ($3.65)
  b. $5.827 ($5.83)
  c. $6.891 ($6.89)
  d. $6.896 ($6.90)
  e. $4.497 ($4.50)
  f. $7.997 ($8.00)

3. **If an amount is given in cents and a fraction of a cent, it can be expressed in dollar form.** The following steps are used.
  (1) Write the cents in decimal form.
  (2) Move the decimal point two places to the left.
  (3) Change the sign from cents to dollars.
  a. 56 7/10 ¢ = 56.7 = $0.567
  b. 98 9/10 ¢ = 98.9 = $0.989
  c. 139 4/10 ¢ = 139.4 = $1.394
  d. 283 3/10 ¢ = 283.3 = $2.833

4. **To round a quotient to a certain decimal place, carry the division one place farther than that place. Then round to the place indicated.**

  Round each quotient to the nearest tenth.

  a. $\overset{1.65\quad (1.7)}{2\overline{)3.3}}$

  b. $\overset{0.65\quad (0.7)}{4\overline{)2.6}}$

  c. $\overset{0.97\quad (1.0)}{4\overline{)3.9}}$

  Round each quotient to the nearest hundredth.

  d. $\overset{0.312\quad (0.31)}{8\overline{)2.5}}$

  e. $\overset{0.575\quad (0.58)}{8\overline{)4.6}}$

  f. $\overset{3.847\quad (3.85)}{4\overline{)15.39}}$

To round quotients to the nearest tenth, divide to the hundredths' place, and round to the nearest tenth (Example E). To round quotients to the nearest hundredth, divide to the thousandths' place, and round to the nearest hundredth (Example F).

Example E

Divide 51 by 4, and round the quotient to the nearest tenth.

$$\frac{12.75}{4)\overline{51.00}} = 12.8 \text{ to the nearest tenth}$$

$$\begin{array}{r} \underline{4} \\ 11 \\ \underline{8} \\ 30 \\ \underline{28} \\ 20 \\ \underline{20} \\ 0 \end{array}$$

Example F

Divide 43 by 3, and round the quotient to the nearest hundredth.

$$\frac{14.333}{3)\overline{43.000}} = 14.33 \text{ to the nearest hundredth}$$

$$\begin{array}{r} \underline{3} \\ 13 \\ \underline{12} \\ 10 \\ \underline{9} \\ 10 \\ \underline{9} \\ 10 \\ \underline{9} \end{array}$$

CLASS PRACTICE

Round these numbers to the nearest tenth and the nearest hundredth.

a. 0.454   0.5 0.45

b. 0.317   0.3 0.32

Round these to the nearest cent.

c. $6.212 $6.21

d. $8.089 $8.09

e. $3.199 $3.20

f. $4.996 $5.00

Express these cents as dollars.

g. $14\frac{3}{10}$¢ $0.143

h. $15\frac{9}{10}$¢ $0.159

i. $7\frac{1}{10}$¢ $0.071

j. $5\frac{3}{10}$¢ $0.053

Solve these problems, and round the quotient to the nearest tenth.

k. $\dfrac{3.7}{1.5)\overline{5.475}}$

l. $\dfrac{1.6}{0.14)\overline{0.217}}$

WRITTEN EXERCISES

A. Round the following numbers as indicated.

Round to the nearest tenth.

1. 0.34   0.3
2. 0.58   0.6
3. 1.17   1.2
4. 3.93   3.9
5. 4.07   4.1
6. 4.04   4.0

Round to the nearest hundredth.

7. 3.515   3.52
8. 8.821   8.82
9. 9.493   9.49
10. 9.997   10.00
11. 11.846   11.85
12. 8.739   8.74

Round to the nearest cent.

13. $3.815 $3.82
14. $9.743 $9.74
15. $8.312 $8.31
16. $1.217 $1.22
17. $3.128 $3.13
18. $5.696 $5.70

B.   Express these cents as dollars.

19. $18\frac{7}{10}$¢ $0.187 **20.** $23\frac{3}{10}$¢ $0.233 **21.** $25\frac{9}{10}$¢ $0.259 **22.** $8\frac{1}{10}$¢ $0.081

C.   Solve each problem, and round the quotient to the nearest tenth.

23. $\overset{4.5}{4\overline{)18.1}}$
 24. $\overset{3.1}{5\overline{)15.3}}$
 25. $\overset{5.7}{2.5\overline{)14.3}}$
 26. $\overset{2.3}{1.5\overline{)3.465}}$

D.   Solve each problem, and round the quotient to the nearest hundredth.

27. $\overset{0.38}{8\overline{)3}}$
 28. $\overset{5.13}{3.8\overline{)19.475}}$
 29. $\overset{0.88}{0.4\overline{)0.352}}$
 30. $\overset{3.38}{1.6\overline{)5.4}}$

E.   Solve these reading problems. Follow the instructions for rounding the answers.

31. During a 4-week period, 5.4 inches of rain fell. What was the average rainfall each week? Round your answer to the nearest tenth of an inch.   1.4 inches

32. Washington, D.C., receives an average of 39 inches of rain per year. What is the average amount that the city receives every month? Round your answer to the nearest tenth of an inch.   3.3 inches

33. Father went with a group of men to Oceanside to help repair houses damaged by a hurricane. If their van used 40 gallons of gasoline to go 575 miles, how many miles did it travel on each gallon? Round your answer to the nearest tenth of a mile.
                                    14.4 miles

34. The 40 gallons of gasoline cost $1.259 per gallon. What was the cost of gasoline to travel to Oceanside? $50.36

35. Three men took turns driving on the way to Oceanside. Father drove $3\frac{3}{4}$ hours, Brother Dwight drove 4 hours, and Brother Daniel drove $3\frac{5}{6}$ hours. What was the total driving time on the trip to Oceanside? $11\frac{7}{12}$ hours

36. A 1.25-pound loaf of bread costs $0.89. How much is that for one pound of bread? Round your answer to the nearest cent. $0.71

REVIEW EXERCISES

F.   Multiply or divide these numbers by 10, 100, or 1,000. *(Lessons 78, 84)*

37. 100 × 0.56   **38.** 10 × 4.5   **39.** 1,000 × 3.75   **40.**   100 × 0.6
                  56   45   3,750   60
41. 4.3 ÷ 100   **42.** 3.7 ÷ 10   **43.** 52.5 ÷ 1,000   **44.**   2.2 ÷ 1,000
                  0.043   0.37   0.0525   0.0022

G.   Add these mixed numbers. *(Lesson 54)*

45. $3\frac{3}{4}$ **46.** $6\frac{8}{10}$ **47.** $5\frac{5}{6}$ **48.** $2\frac{3}{5}$
  $+5\frac{7}{8}$ $+2\frac{1}{2}$ $+2\frac{4}{9}$ $+5\frac{1}{4}$
  $9\frac{5}{8}$ $9\frac{3}{10}$ $8\frac{5}{18}$ $7\frac{17}{20}$

LESSON 89

Objective

- To teach *changing fractions to non-terminating decimals.
  a. Expressing the remainder as a fraction.
  b. Rounding the quotient to the nearest hundredth.

Review

1. Give Lesson 89 Quiz (Multiplying and Dividing Decimals). Note that the quiz covers the same scope as the review below. You could do the review before giving the quiz.

2. *Dividing decimals* (Lessons 85–87).

   a. $\overset{(\$9.12)}{5)\overline{\$45.60}}$ b. $\overset{(43.)}{2.5)\overline{107.5_{\wedge}}}$

3. *Multiplying decimals* (Lessons 79, 80).

   a. $\begin{array}{r} 3.45 \\ \times\, 1.2 \\ \hline (4.14) \end{array}$ b. $\begin{array}{r} 0.45 \\ \times\, 0.07 \\ \hline (0.0315) \end{array}$

Introduction

Write the fraction 1/8 on the board and use division to express it as a decimal (0.125). Now do the same for the fraction 1/9. Once you have it calculated to the ten-thousandths' place (0.1111), the students should understand that the digit 1 will continue to repeat. A decimal that repeats and does not end is called a nonterminating decimal. This lesson teaches two ways to express nonterminating decimals.

Teaching Guide

1. **One way to express a nonterminating decimal is to write the remainder as a fraction.** Write the remainder over the divisor and reduce the fraction to lowest terms.

   a. $7)\overline{6.00}$ with quotient $(0.85\tfrac{5}{7})$
   $$\begin{array}{r} (0.85\tfrac{5}{7}) \\ 7)\overline{6.00} \\ \underline{56} \\ 40 \\ \underline{35} \\ 5 \end{array}$$

   b. $$\begin{array}{r} (0.18\tfrac{2}{11}) \\ 11)\overline{2.00} \\ \underline{11} \\ 90 \\ \underline{88} \\ 2 \end{array}$$

   c. $$\begin{array}{r} 0.53\tfrac{5}{15} = (0.53\tfrac{1}{3}) \\ 15)\overline{8.00} \\ \underline{75} \\ 50 \\ \underline{45} \\ 5 \end{array}$$

89. Working With Nonterminating Decimals

In Lesson 73 you learned that $\frac{1}{2}$ and $\frac{1}{4}$ can easily be changed to the decimals 0.5 and 0.25. But for many fractions, such as $\frac{1}{3}$ and $\frac{5}{7}$, there are no exact decimal equivalents. These are known as **nonterminating decimals** because the decimal equivalents never terminate or stop. That is, they never divide out evenly; there is always a remainder.

One way to express a nonterminating decimal is to write the remainder as a fraction. See Example A.

Example A

Express $\frac{1}{3}$ as a decimal to the hundredths' place, with the remainder as a fraction in lowest terms.

$$\frac{1}{3} = 3\overline{)1.00}^{\,0.33\frac{1}{3}}$$

$$\begin{array}{r} 9 \\ \hline 1\,0 \\ 9 \\ \hline 1 \end{array}$$

No matter how far the division is carried, there is always a remainder. Write the remainder (1) over the divisor (3). The fraction $\frac{1}{3}$ is already in lowest terms.

Another way to express a nonterminating decimal is to round the number to a given place value. Carry the division one place beyond the one specified, and then round it. See Example B.

Example B

Express $\frac{5}{7}$ as a decimal rounded to the nearest hundredth.

$$\frac{5}{7} = 7\overline{)5.000}^{\,0.714} = 0.71 \text{ to the nearest hundredth}$$

$$\begin{array}{r} 49 \\ \hline 10 \\ 7 \\ \hline 30 \\ 28 \\ \hline 2 \end{array}$$

CLASS PRACTICE

Change these fractions to decimals. Divide to the hundredths' place, and express the remainder as a fraction in lowest terms.

a. $\frac{5}{6}$ $0.83\frac{1}{3}$ **b.** $\frac{7}{15}$ $0.46\frac{2}{3}$ **c.** $\frac{5}{9}$ $0.55\frac{5}{9}$

Change each fraction to a decimal rounded to the nearest hundredth.

d. $\frac{6}{7}$ 0.86 **e.** $\frac{5}{13}$ 0.38 **f.** $\frac{8}{9}$ 0.89

WRITTEN EXERCISES

A.   *Change each fraction to a decimal. Divide to the hundredths' place, and express the remainder as a fraction in lowest terms.*

1. $\frac{2}{3}$ 2. $\frac{1}{6}$ 3. $\frac{1}{12}$ 4. $\frac{2}{9}$ 5. $\frac{5}{12}$ 6. $\frac{7}{9}$
    $0.66\frac{2}{3}$ $0.16\frac{2}{3}$ $0.08\frac{1}{3}$ $0.22\frac{2}{9}$ $0.41\frac{2}{3}$ $0.77\frac{7}{9}$

7. $\frac{4}{15}$ 8. $\frac{3}{11}$ 9. $\frac{8}{9}$ 10. $\frac{6}{11}$ 11. $\frac{11}{12}$ 12. $\frac{3}{7}$
    $0.26\frac{2}{3}$ $0.27\frac{3}{11}$ $0.88\frac{8}{9}$ $0.54\frac{6}{11}$ $0.91\frac{2}{3}$ $0.42\frac{6}{7}$

B.   *Change each fraction to a decimal rounded to the nearest hundredth.*

13. $\frac{1}{16}$ 14. $\frac{5}{9}$ 15. $\frac{1}{7}$ 16. $\frac{7}{11}$ 17. $\frac{9}{16}$ 18. $\frac{7}{32}$
     0.06   0.56   0.14   0.64   0.56   0.22

19. $\frac{4}{7}$ 20. $\frac{9}{11}$ 21. $\frac{5}{18}$ 22. $\frac{5}{24}$ 23. $\frac{5}{7}$ 24. $\frac{2}{7}$
     0.57   0.82   0.28   0.21   0.71   0.29

C.   *Solve these reading problems.*

25. Dwayne's father asked him to bring an $\frac{11}{16}$-inch wrench. Express $\frac{11}{16}$ as a decimal rounded to the nearest hundredth.   0.69

26. Asia contains $\frac{7}{12}$ of the population of the world. Write $\frac{7}{12}$ as a decimal to the hundredths' place, with the remainder as a fraction in lowest terms. $0.58\frac{1}{3}$

27. In math class one day, Thomas had 35 out of 38 answers correct. Write a fraction to show what part of the answers were correct (number correct over total number of answers). Then express the fraction as a decimal rounded to the nearest hundredth.
$\frac{35}{38}$ 0.92

28. Darlene had 24 out of 27 answers correct on a Bible test. Write a fraction to show what part of the answers were correct (number correct over total number of answers). Reduce the fraction to lowest terms; then express it as a decimal rounded to the nearest hundredth. $\frac{24}{27}$ $\frac{8}{9}$ 0.89

29. Brother Levi is planning to build a turkey house for 4,000 turkeys. How much floor space does he need if each turkey requires 3.5 square feet?   14,000 square feet

30. Turkey feed costs $10.70 per hundredweight (hundred pounds). What is the cost for a ton of turkey feed? $214.00

REVIEW EXERCISES

D.   *Solve these division problems. (Lessons 85–87)*

                $4.12   2.5   95   1.35
31. $9\overline{)\$37.08}$ 32. $\$3.20\overline{)\$8.00}$ 33. $0.8\overline{)76}$ 34. $0.29\overline{)0.3915}$

E.   *Solve these multiplication problems. (Lessons 79, 80)*

35.	$45.80	36.	31.1	37.	0.815	38.	2.83
	× 0.45		× 0.04		× 0.2		× 0.08
	$20.61		1.244		0.1630		0.2264

2. Another way to express a nonterminating decimal is to round the number to a given place value. This is done by dividing to one digit beyond the place specified and then rounding the quotient.

$$
\begin{array}{r}
0.714 \quad (0.71) \\
7\overline{)5.000} \\
\underline{49} \\
10 \\
\underline{7} \\
30 \\
\underline{28} \\
2
\end{array}
$$

a.

$$
\begin{array}{r}
0.437 \quad (0.44) \\
16\overline{)7.000} \\
\underline{64} \\
60 \\
\underline{48} \\
120 \\
\underline{112} \\
8
\end{array}
$$

b.

$$
\begin{array}{r}
0.933 \quad (0.93) \\
15\overline{)14.000} \\
\underline{135} \\
50 \\
\underline{45} \\
50 \\
\underline{45} \\
5
\end{array}
$$

c.

Nonterminating decimals are rounded to the nearest hundredth in this lesson. The same procedure is also used to round terminating decimals.

Further Study

Whenever division results in a nonterminating decimal, the quotient figures begin to repeat at some point. For example, the decimal equivalent of 1/13 starts repeating in the ten-millionths' place. The digits will continue repeating as 0.076923076923076923 . . . Often a repeating decimal is written with a line above the part that repeats, as shown below.

$$
\begin{array}{r}
0.07692307 = 0.\overline{076923} \\
13\overline{)1.00000000} \\
\underline{91} \\
90 \\
\underline{78} \\
120 \\
\underline{117} \\
30 \\
\underline{26} \\
40 \\
\underline{39} \\
100 \\
\underline{91} \\
9
\end{array}
$$

Some decimal equivalents are nonterminating and nonrepeating. One example is the square root of a whole number that is not a perfect square. (The square root of 8 is 2.8284271 . . .) Another example is the decimal form of pi (π). Computers have calculated π to more than 100 million decimal places, yet there is no pattern of repeating digits. Such decimals cannot be obtained by division. They are known as irrational numbers.

LESSON 90

Objective

- To teach *multiplying mentally by changing decimals to fractions.

Review

1. *Rounding decimals to the nearest tenth or hundredth* (Lesson 88).
   Nearest tenth
     a. 0.28   (0.3)
     b. 0.32   (0.3)
   Nearest hundredth
     c. 0.938   (0.94)
     d. 0.832   (0.83)

2. *Changing fractions to decimals and expressing the remainder as a fraction* (Lesson 89). Divide to the hundredths' place, and express the remainder as a fraction.
   a. $\frac{1}{12} = (0.08\frac{1}{3})$
   b. $\frac{5}{6} = (0.83\frac{1}{3})$

3. *Changing fractions to decimals rounded to the nearest hundredth* (Lesson 89). Divide to the thousandths' place, and round the quotient.
   a. $\frac{11}{12} = 0.916...$ (0.92)
   b. $\frac{1}{6} = 0.166...$ (0.17)

Introduction

Review the fraction–decimal equivalents that the students memorized in Lesson 73. Then read the following problem to them.

> Sarah had $24.00. She spent 0.25 of her money to buy a wall motto that read, "He careth for you." How much did she pay for the motto?

Ask the students how they would solve the problem. Challenge them to find an easier method than 0.25 × $24.00. It is much easier to change 0.25 to 1/4 and find the answer mentally. Sarah paid $6.00.

Teaching Guide

Multiplying by a decimal is sometimes much simpler if the decimal is changed to a fraction. This is especially true in two cases.

1. When the fraction is a simple one like 1/2 or 1/4.

2. When the decimal is nonterminating, such as 0.33 1/3.

Remind pupils of the procedure for multiplying mentally by a fraction. If the numerator of a fraction is 1, simply divide by the denominator. If the numerator is not 1, divide by the denominator and multiply the result by the numerator.
   a. 0.5 × 48 = 1/2 × 48 = 48 ÷ 2 = (24)
   b. 0.25 × 48 = 1/4 × 48 = 48 ÷ 4 = (12)
   c. 0.33 1/3 × 48 = 1/3 × 48 = 48 ÷ 3 = (16)
   d. 0.4 × 25 = 2/5 × 25 = 25 ÷ 5 × 2 = (10)
   e. 0.75 × 36 = 3/4 × 36 = 36 ÷ 4 × 3 = (27)
   f. 0.66 2/3 × 36 = 2/3 × 36 = 36 ÷ 3 × 2 = (24)

90. Using Fractional Equivalents to Multiply Mentally

When a multiplication problem includes a decimal, multiplying is sometimes much simpler if the decimal is changed to a fraction. This is especially true when the fraction is a simple one or the decimal is nonterminating. It is easier to find $\frac{1}{4}$ of a number than to find 0.25 of it, or to find $\frac{1}{3}$ of a number than to find $0.33\frac{1}{3}$ of it.

Example A	Example B
Find 0.25 of 32.	Find $0.66\frac{2}{3}$ of 24.
Think: $0.25 = \frac{1}{4}$	Think: $0.66\frac{2}{3} = \frac{2}{3}$
$\frac{1}{4}$ of $32 = 32 \div 4 = 8$	$\frac{2}{3}$ of $24 = 24 \div 3 \times 2 = 16$
0.25 of $32 = 8$	$0.66\frac{2}{3}$ of $24 = 16$

CLASS PRACTICE

Find the answers mentally.

a. 0.5 of 16
   8

b. 0.25 of 44
   11

c. $0.33\frac{1}{3}$ of \$27
   \$9

d. 0.8 of \$30
   \$24

WRITTEN EXERCISES

A.   *Write each decimal as a fraction in lowest terms.*

1. 0.1 $\frac{1}{10}$ 2. 0.2 $\frac{1}{5}$ 3. 0.25 $\frac{1}{4}$ 4. 0.3 $\frac{3}{10}$ 5. $0.33\frac{1}{3}$ $\frac{1}{3}$ 6. 0.4 $\frac{2}{5}$

7. 0.5 $\frac{1}{2}$ 8. 0.6 $\frac{3}{5}$ 9. $0.66\frac{2}{3}$ $\frac{2}{3}$ 10. 0.7 $\frac{7}{10}$ 11. 0.75 $\frac{3}{4}$ 12. 0.8 $\frac{4}{5}$

B.   *Solve these problems mentally by converting the decimals to fractions.*

13. 0.5 of 12 6   **14.** 0.25 of 24 6   **15.** $0.33\frac{1}{3}$ of 27 9   **16.** 0.1 of 70 7

17. 0.2 of 45 9   **18.** 0.75 of 32 24   **19.** $0.66\frac{2}{3}$ of 9 6   **20.** 0.4 of 35 14

21. 0.6 of 15 9   **22.** 0.8 of 20 16   **23.** 0.5 of 60 30   **24.** $0.33\frac{1}{3}$ of 36 12

25. 0.3 of \$40.00   \$12.00   26. 0.2 of \$25.00   \$5.00

27. 0.75 of \$24.00   \$18.00   28. $0.66\frac{2}{3}$ of \$18.00   \$12.00

C. *Solve these reading problems. Solve numbers 29–32 mentally.*

29. Father is ordering pens for the school. The pens cost $0.25 each. How much will 80 pens cost? $20.00

30. Father also ordered 15 boxes of staples that cost $0.60 per box. How much did the staples cost? $9.00

31. Brother Wenger said that 0.2 of the 60 students in school either walked or rode bicycles to school. How many students arrived on foot or on bicycles?   12 students

32. Brother Wenger also said that $0.33\frac{1}{3}$ of his 24 students were in Grade 6. How many sixth-grade students did Brother Wenger have?   8 students

33. Andrew's Farm Supply has a toll-free telephone number for its customers. One phone call was 1.6 minutes long, and the charge to Andrew's Farm Supply was $0.30. What was the charge per minute for this call? Round your answer to the nearest cent. $0.19

34. Andrew's Farm Supply was charged $2.02 for a 9-minute telephone call. What was the charge per minute for the call? Round your answer to the nearest cent. $0.22

REVIEW EXERCISES

D. *Round these decimals as indicated.* (Lesson 88)

To nearest tenth

35. 0.48   0.5   **36.** 0.22   0.2   **37.** 1.998   2.0   **38.** 4.479   4.5

To nearest hundredth

39. 3.775   3.78   **40.** 4.161   4.16   **41.** 6.996   7.00   **42.** 5.9909   5.99

E. *Write each fraction as a decimal to the hundredths' place, and express the remainder as a fraction in lowest terms.* (Lesson 89)

43. $\frac{5}{8}$ $0.62\frac{1}{2}$ **44.** $\frac{4}{9}$ $0.44\frac{4}{9}$ **45.** $\frac{7}{12}$ $0.58\frac{1}{3}$ **46.** $\frac{5}{11}$ $0.45\frac{5}{11}$

F. *Write each fraction as a decimal rounded to the nearest hundredth.* (Lesson 89)

47. $\frac{3}{7}$ 0.43   **48.** $\frac{1}{6}$ 0.17   **49.** $\frac{5}{13}$ 0.38   **50.** $\frac{2}{15}$ 0.13

LESSON 91

Objectives

- To teach the importance of placing decimal points correctly.
- To give practice with the use of decimals in everyday situations.

Review

(Since the material in this lesson does not require much class discussion, you may wish to spend more time in review.)

1. *Multiplying mentally by changing decimals to common fractions* (Lesson 90).
   a. 0.25 of 24   (6)
   b. 0.2 of 35   (7)
   c. 0.75 of 36   (27)
   d. 0.8 of 35   (28)

2. *Changing fractions to nonterminating decimals* (Lesson 89). Divide to the thousandths' place and round the answer to the nearest hundredth.
   a. $\frac{5}{6}$ = (0.83)
   b. $\frac{7}{6}$ = (1.17)

3. *Dividing decimals* (Lessons 85–87).

   a. $4.5\overline{)14.4}$ (3.2)   b. $22\overline{)1.32}$ (0.06)

4. *Changing decimals to fractions in lowest terms* (Lesson 74).
   a. 0.65 = $\left(\frac{13}{20}\right)$
   b. 0.52 = $\left(\frac{13}{25}\right)$
   c. 0.12 = $\left(\frac{3}{25}\right)$

Introduction

Write the numbers 347, 34.7, and 3.47 on the board. Ask the class, "Are these the same numbers?" A small child might think they are the same because they contain the same digits. But if the numbers are written in fraction form, it becomes clear that they have three completely different values: $\frac{347}{1}$, $34\frac{7}{10}$, $3\frac{47}{100}$. The placing of the decimal point is very important, as the exercises in this lesson illustrate.

Teaching Guide

When decimals are written, it is very important to place the decimal point correctly. A missing or misplaced decimal point makes a great difference in the value of a number.

Read the following statements, and challenge the students to decide where the decimal points should be placed.

a. Bricks of standard size usually weigh about (45, <u>4.5</u>, 0.45) pound.

b. Father needed to use a stepladder because the ceiling was (105, <u>10.5</u>, 1.05, 0.105) feet high.

91. Choosing the Reasonable Decimal Answer

The decimal point is a little mark that makes a great difference in the value of a number. For example, the numbers 1.25 and 125 contain exactly the same digits; but because of the decimal point, the second number is 100 times greater than the first.

When you write decimals, be careful to place the decimal point correctly. If you write no decimal point at all, it means that the decimal point is at the end of the number.

CLASS PRACTICE

Place the decimal point to make these statements sensible.

a. Stanley's math book is 105 inches long.   10.5

b. Galen's father said that their silo is 6.00 feet high.   60.0

c. When Father flew to a mission in Guatemala, the plane traveled at a speed of 36.5 miles per hour.   365

WRITTEN EXERCISES

A. *Find the numbers that are unreasonable, and write them correctly. If all the numbers in a statement are reasonable, write* correct.

1. David walks 75 miles one way to school every day.   0.75

2. Dwight is in sixth grade. He is 1.15 years old.   11.5

3. Marcus spent 125 hours mowing the lawn one afternoon.   1.25

4. When Mother was baking a cake, Marlene sifted 35 cups of flour for her.   3.5

5. Naomi's pencil is 4.875 inches long.   correct

6. When Ruth's family went visiting in another state, Father said that their car had traveled at an average speed of 4.95 miles per hour.   49.5

7. On the same trip, Father said that the car had gone 195 miles on each gallon of gasoline.   19.5

8. The price of gasoline was $125 per gallon. $1.25

9. The length of Grandmother's house is 325 feet.   32.5

10. One evening after a day of steady rain, Rhoda's father said that it had rained 275 inches that day.   2.75

11. There are 25 gallons in 1 quart.   0.25

12. One morning it took Father and Michael 15 hours to milk the cows.   1.5

13. The box of corn flakes weighed 1.25 pounds.   correct

14. The 350-page book was 13.75 inches thick.   1.375

45

B.   *Solve these reading problems. Do numbers 15 and 16 mentally.*

15. Marcia spent 8 hours helping her mother do housecleaning one week. She spent 0.25 of the time cleaning the living room. How many hours did she work in the living room?   2 hours

16. The chicken house on the Miller farm holds 30,000 chickens. How many chickens are in the building if it is $0.66\frac{2}{3}$ full?   20,000 chickens

17. In a report on weather, Dale said that in a recent year Anchorage, Alaska, had 236 cloudy days. That same year Phoenix, Arizona, had 51 cloudy days. The number of cloudy days at Anchorage was how many times greater than the number at Phoenix? Round your answer to the nearest tenth.   4.6 times

18. Phoenix, Arizona, had 221 clear days that year. That is 3.25 times as many clear days as Anchorage, Alaska, had. How many clear days did Anchorage have that year?   68 days

19. Dale reported that the highest wind speed ever measured was on Mount Washington, New Hampshire, where the wind blew at 231 miles per hour. The average wind speed on Mt. Washington is 35.3 miles per hour. How many times faster was the highest wind speed than the average wind speed? Round your answer to the nearest tenth.
                                                                              6.5 times

20. More rain falls on Mobile, Alabama, than on most other cities in the United States. The average rainfall at Mobile is 64.64 inches per year, while the average at Phoenix, Arizona, is 7.11 inches per year. How much greater is the average rainfall at Mobile than at Phoenix?   57.53 inches

REVIEW EXERCISES

C.   *Solve these problems mentally by changing the decimals to fractions and then multiplying.* (Lesson 90)

21. 0.2 of 40   **22.** 0.25 of 44   **23.** 0.6 of 40   **24.** 0.75 of 36
              8   11   24   27

D.   *Change each fraction to a decimal rounded to the nearest hundredth.* (Lesson 89)

25. $\frac{1}{6}$ 0.17   **26.** $\frac{13}{16}$ 0.81   **27.** $\frac{4}{3}$ 1.33   **28.** $\frac{5}{6}$ 0.83

E.   *Solve these division problems.* (Lessons 85–87)

            0.6 $3.75   34.1   1.5
29. $6\overline{)3.6}$ **30.** $1.2\overline{)\$4.50}$ **31.** $0.65\overline{)22.165}$ **32.** $0.32\overline{)0.48}$

F.   *Change these decimals to fractions in lowest terms.* (Lesson 74)

33. 0.15 $\frac{3}{20}$ **34.** 0.36 $\frac{9}{25}$ **35.** 0.44 $\frac{11}{25}$ **36.** 0.85 $\frac{17}{20}$

An Ounce of Prevention

Review the concept that if a reading problem asks "How many times larger is one number than another?" division is required. Problems 17–19 are of this type.

LESSON 92

Objective

- To teach writing simple ratios and reducing them to lowest terms.

Review

1. Give Lesson 92 Speed Test (Multiplying Mentally by Changing Decimals to Fractions).

2. *Multiplying mentally by changing decimals to fractions* (Lesson 90).
   a. 0.25 of 32   (8)
   b. 0.66 2/3 of 90   (60)
   c. 0.4 of 45   (18)

3. *Rounding decimals* (Lesson 88). Round to the nearest hundredth and to the nearest tenth.
   a. 0.356   (0.36, 0.4)
   b. 0.249   (0.25, 0.2)
   c. 0.472   (0.47, 0.5)
   d. 0.596   (0.60, 0.6)

4. *Comparing decimals* (Lesson 75). Put > or < between the decimals.
   a. 0.063 (>) 0.06
   b. 0.001 (<) 0.009

5. *Multiplying fractions* (Lesson 60–64). No class review is necessary.

6. *Finding averages* (Lesson 27). Express remainders as fractions.
   a. 12, 15, 18, 16   (15 1/4)
   b. 23, 28, 24, 26, 21   (24 2/5)

Introduction

Read the following problem to the class.

Paul has 7 blue marbles and 15 yellow marbles. Write a fraction comparing the number of blue marbles to the number of yellow marbles. (7/15)

This fraction is called a ratio. As a ratio, it is read "7 to 15." It can also be written *7 to 15* and *7:15.*

Teaching Guide

1. **A ratio is the relationship between two numbers.** It does not show merely the size of a quantity but the relationship between two quantities.

   Robert has 3 pencils, 2 pens, and 1 eraser.
   a. Write a ratio comparing the number of pens to the number of pencils.
      (2 to 3; that is, 2/3 as many pens as pencils)
   b. Write a ratio comparing the number of pens to the number of erasers.
      (2 to 1; that is, 2/1 times as many pens as erasers)
   c. Write a ratio comparing the number of pencils to the number of pens.
      (3 to 2; that is, 3/2 times as many pencils as pens)
   d. Write a ratio comparing the number of erasers to the number of pencils.
      (1 to 3; that is, 1/3 as many erasers as pencils)

92. Using Ratios to Compare Numbers

Numbers are used to state the sizes of various quantities. But it is not always enough to know just the size of a quantity. Sometimes we also need to know the relationship between two quantities.

For example, suppose you have $10 and your older brother has $100. If you should lose $5, you would think it a great loss because that is half of your money. But if your brother lost $5, the loss would not seem so great because $5 is only a small fraction of $100.

This is the idea of a **ratio.** A ratio is the relationship between two numbers. It shows the size of one quantity in relation to another quantity.

Ratios are used to compare numbers. They can be expanded and reduced just like fractions. In the example above, the first ratio is 5 to 10—that is, $\frac{5}{10}$ or $\frac{1}{2}$. The second ratio is 5 to 100, or $\frac{5}{100}$, which reduces to $\frac{1}{20}$. Two equal ratios are **equivalent ratios.**

David and Janice kept a record of the different kinds of birds they saw. One month they saw 3 blue jays, 8 cardinals, and 14 chickadees.

a. Write a ratio comparing the number of blue jays to the number of cardinals.

Answer: 3 blue jays to 8 cardinals = 3 to 8 or $\frac{3}{8}$
  (They saw $\frac{3}{8}$ as many blue jays as cardinals.)

b. Write a ratio comparing the number of chickadees to the number of cardinals.

Answer: 14 chickadees to 8 cardinals = 14 to 8 or $\frac{14}{8}$
  (This reduces to an equivalent ratio of $\frac{7}{4}$.)

c. Write a ratio comparing the number of cardinals to the number of chickadees.

Answer: 8 cardinals to 14 chickadees = 8 to 14 or $\frac{8}{14}$
  (This reduces to an equivalent ratio of $\frac{4}{7}$.)

In the answers above, the ratio $\frac{14}{8}$ is in the form of an improper fraction. Such a ratio is usually reduced to lowest terms ($\frac{14}{8} = \frac{7}{4}$). But then it is left in the form of an improper fraction; it is not changed to a mixed number.

The answers above also show different ways that ratios can be written. Following are three forms that are commonly used. All three forms mean the same thing, and all three are read "four to seven."

$$4 \text{ to } 7 \qquad \frac{4}{7} \qquad 4{:}7$$

CLASS PRACTICE

Reduce these ratios to lowest terms. Do not write mixed numbers.

a. 6 to 2   3 to 1   **b.** 15 to 5   3 to 1   **c.** 20:8   5:2   **d.** 14 to 7   2 to 1

Write ratios to compare these items. State each ratio in lowest terms.

e. Compare 12 apples to 4 boys.   3 to 1

f. Compare 12 apples to $1.20.   1 to $0.10

g. Compare 24 cows to 4 calves.   6 to 1

h. Compare 28 church benches to 168 people.   1 to 6

WRITTEN EXERCISES

A.   *Reduce each ratio to lowest terms. Do not write mixed numbers.*

1. $\frac{4}{6}$ $\frac{2}{3}$ 2. $\frac{9}{12}$ $\frac{3}{4}$ 3. $\frac{20}{16}$ $\frac{5}{4}$ 4. $\frac{12}{8}$ $\frac{3}{2}$

B.   *Reduce these ratios to lowest terms. Write each one in the same form as the form shown.*

5.   18 to 9   2 to 1   **6.**   8 to 14   4 to 7   **7.**   9 to 15   3 to 5   **8.**   20 to 8   5 to 2

9.   16:6   8:3   **10.**   50:20   5:2   **11.**   15:10   3:2   **12.**   100:40   5:2

13. $\frac{12}{4}$ $\frac{3}{1}$ 14. $\frac{18}{6}$ $\frac{3}{1}$ 15. $\frac{20}{14}$ $\frac{10}{7}$ 16. $\frac{21}{9}$ $\frac{7}{3}$

C.   *Write ratios comparing the numbers of books as indicated below. State each ratio in lowest terms.*

Major Divisions of Old Testament Books
Number of Books
Law 5
History.............................12
Poetry 5
Major Prophets 5
Minor Prophets 12
Total number of books.........39

17. Books of the Law to total books in the Old Testament. $\frac{5}{39}$

18. Books of the Law to books of History. $\frac{5}{12}$

19. Books of Minor Prophets to books of Major Prophets. $\frac{12}{5}$

20. Books of History to total books in the Old Testament. $\frac{4}{13}$

21. Books of History to books of Major Prophets. $\frac{12}{5}$

22. Books of the Law to books of Minor Prophets. $\frac{5}{12}$

23. Total books in the Old Testament to books of Minor Prophets. $\frac{13}{4}$

24. Total books in the Old Testament to books of Major Prophets. $\frac{39}{5}$

2. **Ratios are much like fractions, and they are used to compare numbers.** Ratios can be expanded and reduced just like fractions. Equal ratios are equivalent ratios.

$$\frac{4}{5} = \frac{8}{10} = \frac{12}{15}$$
$$\frac{12}{18} = \frac{4}{6} = \frac{2}{3}$$

3. **Ratios are usually written in lowest terms; but if a ratio is in the form of an improper fraction, it is not changed to a mixed number.** It is left in the form of an improper fraction.

$$\frac{4}{12} = \frac{1}{3}$$
$$\frac{10}{6} = \frac{5}{3} \quad \text{(not changed to } 1\frac{2}{3}\text{)}$$

4. **Ratios are written in three forms.**
   3 to 7 = 3:7 = $\frac{3}{7}$

An Ounce of Prevention

Students may think that a ratio in the form of an improper fraction should be changed to a mixed number. The reason for not changing it will become clear as they work with proportions in Lesson 93.

Further Study

1. All the parts of the ratios in this lesson are obvious. That is not always the case. Consider the following problem.

   For every three fifth-grade students in Brother David's classroom, there are two sixth-grade students. Write a ratio comparing the number of students in the fifth grade to the number in both grades together.

   Because there are 3 fifth graders for every 2 sixth graders, the ratio of fifth-graders to the total is 3 to (3 + 2), or 3 to 5.

2. Studying ratios lays the foundation for working with proportions, which are introduced in Lesson 93.

```
┌─────────────────────────────────────────┐
│      Books Used for School Devotions     │
│                        Number of Books   │
│   Bibles ............................24   │
│   Christian Hymnals...............12      │
│   Life Songs #2..................... 8    │
│   Total number of books........44         │
└─────────────────────────────────────────┘
```

25. Bibles to *Life Songs* books. $\frac{3}{1}$

26. Bibles to *Christian Hymnals*. $\frac{2}{1}$

27. Bibles to total number of books. $\frac{6}{11}$

28. *Life Songs* books to *Christian Hymnals*. $\frac{2}{3}$

29. *Life Songs* books to total of books. $\frac{2}{11}$

30. *Christian Hymnals* to total of books. $\frac{3}{11}$

REVIEW EXERCISES

D. *Solve these problems mentally by first changing the decimals to fractions.* (Lesson 90)

31. 0.25 of 40   **32.** 0.5 of 66   **33.** 0.6 of 55   **34.** $0.66\frac{2}{3}$ of 33

       10   33   33   22

E. *Round each decimal to the nearest hundredth.* (Lesson 88)

35. 0.352   0.35   **36.** 0.646   0.65   **37.** 0.6851   0.69 **38.** 0.599   0.60

F. *Copy these decimals, compare them, and write > or < between them.* (Lesson 75)

39. 0.357 _<_ 0.36   **40.** 0.27 _<_ 0.271

41. 0.8201 _>_ 0.82   **42.** 0.235 _>_ 0.2309

G. *Solve these multiplication problems.* (Lessons 60–64)

43. $\frac{3}{4} \times \frac{4}{5}$ $\frac{3}{5}$ **44.** $\frac{3}{8} \times \frac{5}{6}$ $\frac{5}{16}$ **45.** $1\frac{1}{3} \times 2\frac{1}{4}$ 3   **46.** $3\frac{1}{3} \times 2\frac{2}{5}$ 8

H. *Find the average of each set of numbers. Express any remainders as fractions.* (Lesson 27)

47. 12, 15, 18, 17 $15\frac{1}{2}$ **48.** 28, 29, 36, 37 $32\frac{1}{2}$

93. Writing Proportions

You have learned that equal ratios are called equivalent ratios. Two equivalent ratios joined by an equal sign are a **proportion.** Following are three examples of proportions.

$$\frac{3}{4} = \frac{6}{8} \qquad \frac{8}{14} = \frac{4}{7} \qquad \frac{5}{100} = \frac{1}{20}$$

Any proportion can be checked by cross multiplication. This is done by multiplying the numbers that are located diagonally ("across the corner") from each other. If the proportion is true, the two products will be equal. The following multiplications show that the proportions above are true.

$$3 \times 8 = 24, \text{ and } 4 \times 6 = 24$$
$$8 \times 7 = 56, \text{ and } 14 \times 4 = 56$$
$$5 \times 20 = 100, \text{ and } 100 \times 1 = 100$$

Example A

On a regular spelling test, Isaac correctly spelled 18 out of 20 words. On a review test he had 45 out of 50 words correct. Prove that he did equally well on both tests.

Step 1.   Begin by writing two parallel phrases to show the relationship of the numbers to each other.

18 correct out of 20 total

45 correct out of 50 total

Step 2.   Rewrite each phrase as a ratio.

18 correct out of 20 $= \frac{18}{20}$ 45 correct out of 50 $= \frac{45}{50}$

Step 3.   Combine the two ratios to form a proportion.

$\frac{18}{20} = \frac{45}{50}$

Step 4.   Use cross multiplication to check the proportion.

$18 \times 50 = 900$, and $45 \times 20 = 900$

The proportion is true. This shows that Isaac did equally well on both tests.

If three numbers in a proportion are given, cross multiplication can be used to find the fourth number by following the steps below.

---

1. Multiply the numbers that are diagonal to each other.

2. Divide the product by the remaining number.

3. Check the proportion by using cross multiplication.

LESSON 93

Objective

- To teach *writing simple proportions from word statements.

Review

1. *Changing fractions to decimals, with remainders in fraction form* (Lesson 89).

   a. $\frac{11}{12} = (0.91\frac{2}{3})$

   b. $\frac{5}{14} = (0.35\frac{5}{7})$

2. *Adding and subtracting decimals* (Lesson 76).

   a.   3.9
       + 2.15
        (6.05)

   b.   2.187
        1.3
       + 2.65
        (6.137)

Introduction

Write the two proportions shown below, but do not call them proportions. Ask, "Is the relationship between 1 and 2 the same as between 2 and 4? Is the relationship between 5 and 10 the same as between 6 and 12?" The answers are yes. In each ratio, the upper number is exactly half of the lower number.

$$\frac{1}{2} = \frac{2}{4}$$

$$\frac{5}{10} = \frac{6}{12}$$

Introduce the term *proportion*. A proportion is two equivalent ratios joined by an equal sign.

Teaching Guide

1. **Two equivalent ratios joined by an equal sign are a proportion.**

2. **Any proportion can be checked by cross multiplication.** This is done by multiplying the numbers that are located diagonally from each other. If the proportion is true, the two products will be equal.

3. **Proportions can be written by using the following steps.**

   Step 1. Begin by writing two parallel phrases to show the relationship of the numbers to each other.

   14 days in 2 weeks
   35 days in 5 weeks

   Step 2. Rewrite each phrase as a ratio.

   14 days in 2 weeks = $(\frac{14}{2})$
   35 days in 5 weeks = $(\frac{35}{5})$

   Step 3. Combine the two ratios to form a proportion.

   $\frac{14}{2} = \frac{35}{5}$

   Step 4. Use cross multiplication to check the proportion.

   $14 \times 5 = 70; \ 2 \times 35 = 70$

4. **If three numbers in a proportion are given, use cross multiplication to find the fourth number.**
   (1) Multiply the numbers that are diagonal to each other.
   (2) Divide the product by the remaining number.
   (3) Check the proportion by using cross multiplication.

   a. $\frac{15}{3} = \frac{45}{n}$

   $3 \times 45 = 135;$
   $135 \div 15 = 9$

   b. $\frac{63}{8} = \frac{n}{57}$

   $63 \times 57 = 3{,}591;$
   $3{,}591 \div 8 = 448\frac{7}{8}$

Note: A proportion can be set up in any of four ways and still be arranged correctly. The most important thing is to get the right numbers paired in diagonal positions from each other. The proportion for Example B in the lesson could be set up in any of the following ways.

$\frac{18}{20} = \frac{n}{60}$ $\frac{n}{60} = \frac{18}{20}$ $\frac{20}{18} = \frac{60}{n}$ $\frac{60}{n} = \frac{20}{18}$

This is the reason for the use of parallel phrases as taught in the lesson: they help students to get the numbers in the correct positions. It is not so important that the phrases contain certain words as that they are parallel. Therefore, the pupils' phrases will not always be the same as the ones in the Answer Key. The phrases for Example A in the lesson could also be written as follows:

   20 total and 18 correct
   50 total and 45 correct

Further Study

A letter such as *n* that stands for a number is known as a literal number (that is, a "letter number"). Your students should think of a literal number as representing an unknown value, usually the number that is the solution to a problem. Literal numbers are a basic element in the study of algebra.

Example B

$\frac{18}{20} = \frac{n}{60}$ The letter n stands for the missing number.

Step 1: $18 \times 60 = 1{,}080$

Step 2: $1{,}080 \div 20 = 54;$ $n = 54$

Step 3: $18 \times 60 = 1{,}080;$ $20 \times 54 = 1{,}080$
The proportion is true.

CLASS PRACTICE

Find the missing numbers by using the method shown in Example B.

a. $\frac{4}{7} = \frac{n}{28}$ 16   **b.** $\frac{4}{6} = \frac{n}{15}$ 10   **c.** $\frac{10}{6} = \frac{n}{15}$ 25   **d.** $\frac{18}{15} = \frac{n}{24}$ 28.8

WRITTEN EXERCISES

A.   **Check each proportion by cross multiplication, and write the two products that you obtain. Then write *true* if the proportion is true and *false* if it is false.**

Example: $\frac{4}{5} = \frac{16}{20}$ *Example:* $\frac{3}{4} = \frac{7}{10}$

Answer: 80, 80, true   *Answer:* 30, 28, false

1. $\frac{3}{5} = \frac{6}{10}$ 2. $\frac{2}{3} = \frac{10}{15}$ 3. $\frac{4}{9} = \frac{6}{12}$ 4. $\frac{6}{8} = \frac{9}{12}$

30, 30, true   30, 30, true   48, 54, false   72, 72, true

5. $\frac{3}{6} = \frac{7}{16}$ 6. $\frac{3}{8} = \frac{7}{18}$ 7. $\frac{6}{9} = \frac{10}{15}$ 8. $\frac{4}{12} = \frac{5}{15}$

48, 42, false   54, 56, false   90, 90, true   60, 60, true

B.   **Find the missing numbers by using the method shown in Example B.**

9. $\frac{2}{6} = \frac{n}{9}$ 3   10. $\frac{6}{8} = \frac{n}{12}$ 9   11. $\frac{12}{9} = \frac{n}{12}$ 16   12. $\frac{15}{6} = \frac{n}{10}$ 25

13. $\frac{4}{8} = \frac{10}{n}$ 20   14. $\frac{4}{6} = \frac{10}{n}$ 15   15. $\frac{10}{6} = \frac{25}{n}$ 15   16. $\frac{7}{21} = \frac{2}{n}$ 6

C.   **Write a proportion for each problem. Then write *true* if the proportion is true and *false* if it is false.**

Example: In a regular lesson, Isaac correctly answered 24 out of 30 questions. On a test he had 32 answers correct out of 40.

Think: 24 out of 30 = $\frac{24}{30}$ 32 out of 40 = $\frac{32}{40}$

Compute: $\frac{24}{30} = \frac{32}{40}$ $24 \times 40 = 960$ $30 \times 32 = 960$

Answer: true

17. Mark had 27 out of 30 math problems correct one day. The next day he had 36 out of 40 math problems correct. $\frac{27}{30} = \frac{36}{40}$ true

18. Mother had a picture 5 inches wide and 7 inches long enlarged to 6 inches wide and 9 inches long. $\frac{5}{7} = \frac{6}{9}$ false

19. For art class, the sixth grade pupils enlarged a motto, which read "God Is Love," from 4 inches wide and 6 inches long to 8 inches wide and 10 inches long.

$\frac{4}{6} = \frac{8}{10}$ false

20. The Gehman family is counting the number of birds they see at their bird feeder. One Saturday, 8 out of 15 birds were chickadees. On Sunday, 6 out of 14 were chickadees.

$\frac{8}{15} = \frac{6}{14}$ false

D.   Solve these reading problems.

21. In one week, the Gehman family counted the following numbers of chickadees at their feeder: Sunday, 6; Monday, 8; Tuesday, 4; Wednesday, 6; Thursday, 9; Friday, 7; and Saturday, 8. What was the average number of chickadees that they counted each day? Round your answer to the nearest whole number.   7 chickadees

22. The Gehman family fed 25 pounds of bird seed to the birds in $2\frac{2}{7}$ weeks. How much seed did the birds eat each week? $10\frac{15}{16}$ pounds

REVIEW EXERCISES

E.   Change these fractions to decimals. Divide to the hundredths' place and express the remainder as a fraction in lowest terms. *(Lesson 89)*

23. $\frac{5}{16}$ $0.31\frac{1}{4}$ **24.** $\frac{11}{15}$ $0.73\frac{1}{3}$ **25.** $\frac{7}{12}$ $0.58\frac{1}{3}$ **26.** $\frac{5}{18}$ $0.27\frac{7}{9}$

F.   Solve these addition and subtraction problems. *(Lesson 76)*

27.   3.45   28.   4.1   29.   4.82   30.   8.6
    + 3.87   3.55   - 2.9   - 4.861
    ‾‾‾‾‾‾   + 5.987   ‾‾‾‾‾‾   ‾‾‾‾‾‾‾
      7.32   ‾‾‾‾‾‾‾   1.92   3.739
                      13.637

LESSON 94

Objective

- To teach *using proportions to solve reading problems.

Review

1. *Multiplying mentally by changing decimals to fractions* (Lesson 90).
   a. 0.25×36 (9)
   b. $0.33\ 1/3$ of 66 (22)
   c. 0.8×40 (32)

2. *Subtracting decimals* (Lesson 77).

   a.   3.321   b.   4.5
       $- 1.67$ $- 2.778$
       (1.651)   (1.722)

Introduction

Review working with proportions (Lesson 93).

Are these true proportions?

a. $\frac{2}{3} = \frac{6}{8}$ (No)

b. $\frac{4}{6} = \frac{6}{9}$ (Yes)

c. $\frac{12}{9} = \frac{20}{15}$ (Yes)

d. $\frac{21}{18} = \frac{35}{30}$ (Yes)

Find the missing numbers in these proportions.

e. $\frac{3}{4} = \frac{15}{n}$ $n = (20)$

f. $\frac{4}{6} = \frac{22}{n}$ $n = (33)$

Teaching Guide

1. **Proportions are useful in solving problems that involve rates.** All the following are examples of rates. They suggest a few of the many practical applications of proportions.

   miles per hour
   gallons per minute
   miles per gallon
   bushels per acre
   cents per pound
   items per container
   teaspoons of concentrate per gallon of water
   square feet of surface per gallon of paint

2. **The following steps can be used to solve reading problems by writing proportions.**
   (1) Write two parallel phrases to show the relationship of the numbers to each other. Use n to stand for the missing number.
   (2) Rewrite each phrase as a ratio.
   (3) Combine the two ratios to form a proportion.
   (4) Use cross multiplication to find the value of n.

94. Reading Problems: Using Proportions

In many reading problems, you need to work with **rates** such as miles per hour or teaspoons per quart. Proportions are very useful in solving such problems. To find the answer, you need to set up the numbers as a proportion. Then you can use cross multiplication to find the missing number. The following example shows how this is done.

> Susan is operating the egg packer in the chicken house. She knows that 1 flat holds 30 eggs. How many flats does she need for 510 eggs?
>
> 1. Write two parallel phrases to show the relationship of the numbers to each other. Use n to stand for the missing number.
>   1 flat for 30 eggs
> n flats for 510 eggs
>
> 2. Rewrite each phrase as a ratio.
>   1 flat for 30 eggs $= \frac{1}{30}$
> n flats for 510 eggs $= \frac{n}{510}$
>
> 3. Combine the two ratios to form a proportion.
> $\frac{1}{30} = \frac{n}{510}$
>
> 4. Use cross multiplication to find the value of n.
> $1 \times 510 = 510$ $510 \div 30 = 17$ $\frac{1}{30} = \frac{17}{510}$
>
> Check: $1 \times 510 = 510$, and $17 \times 30 = 510$
> Susan needs 17 flats for 510 eggs.

CLASS PRACTICE

Solve these reading problems by using proportions.

a. To make syrup for canning, Erla mixes water and sugar to a ratio of 2 parts water to 1 part sugar. How much sugar will she need if she is planning to use 4 cups of water?
    2 parts water to 1 part sugar
    4 cups water to n cups sugar
    2 cups

b. Father has lived 4 years for every 7 years that Grandfather has lived. Father is 32. How old is Grandfather?
    56 years

WRITTEN EXERCISES

A. ***Solve these reading problems by using proportions. The phrases are written for you.***

1. Mr. Moyer mixes one gallon of antifreeze with enough water to make two gallons of coolant for his truck. If the radiator holds a total of 6 gallons of coolant, how much antifreeze will he need to fill the radiator?

    1 gallon antifreeze for 2 gallons coolant
    n gallons antifreeze for 6 gallons coolant   3 gallons

2. Rhoda mixed 1 cup of sugar with enough water to make 1 quart of canning syrup. How much sugar will Rhoda need to make 20 quarts of canning syrup?

    1 cup sugar for 1 quart syrup
    n cups sugar for 20 quarts syrup   20 cups

3. Clinton Zook needs to replace the shingles on his house roof. Three bundles of shingles cover 100 square feet. How many bundles does Clinton need to cover 1,800 square feet?

    3 bundles for 100 square feet
    n bundles for 1,800 square feet   54 bundles

4. One kind of insect spray is made by mixing 1 pint of insecticide with 32 gallons of water. At this rate, how much water should be mixed with 8 pints of insecticide?

    1 pint insecticide with 32 gallons water
    8 pints insecticide with n gallons water   256 gallons

5. Brother Carl got 625 bushels of corn from a 5-acre cornfield. At that rate, how much corn should he get from a 9-acre field?

    625 bushels from 5 acres
    n bushels from 9 acres   1,125 bushels

6. If 2 dwarf apple trees produce 7 bushels of apples, how many bushels of apples will 15 trees produce?

    7 bushels from 2 trees
    n bushels from 15 trees $52\frac{1}{2}$ bushels

Problem 1

One day Curvin had 5 of his 6 reading problems correct. If there were 30 problems in the entire assignment, how many must he have correct to do just as well as he did with the reading problems?

   a. 5 problems correct out of 6
       n problems correct out of 30

   b. $\frac{5}{6} = \frac{n}{30}$

   c. $5 \times 30 = 150;\ 150 \div 6 = 25$
      Curvin must have 25 problems correct to do just as well as he did with the reading problems.
      Check: $5 \times 30 = 150$,
           and $25 \times 6 = 150$.

Problem 2

Red delicious apples are priced at 6 for 88 cents. What would be the price of 15 apples?

   a. 6 apples for 88 cents
       15 apples for n cents

   b. $\frac{6}{88} = \frac{15}{n}$

   c. $15 \times 88 = 1,320:\ 1,320 \div 6 = 220$
      220 cents = $2.20
      The cost of 15 apples is $2.20.
      Check: $15 \times 88 = 1,320$,
           and $6 \times 220 = 1,320$.

Problem 3

Marla counted the flowers in a flower bed. Three out of five flowers were lilies. There were 35 flowers in all. How many of them were lilies?

   a. 3 lilies out of 5 flowers
       n lilies out of 35 flowers

   b. $\frac{3}{5} = \frac{n}{35}$

   c. $3 \times 35 = 105;\ 105 \div 5 = 21$
      There were 21 lilies.
      Check: $3 \times 35 = 105$,
           and $21 \times 5 = 105$.

An Ounce of Prevention

Students sometimes fail to see the relationship between the numbers in a proportion, and they may use any available numbers to write their ratios. Insist that they write parallel phrases as the first step in solving any proportion problem. Only after they are proficient in writing phrases will they be able to set up proportions directly from the numbers in the problem.

Further Study

Solving proportions can also be done algebraically. Following is the algebraic solution to Problem 3 above. This method is taught in Grade 7.

$$3 \cdot 35 = 5n$$
$$105 = 5n$$
$$\frac{105}{5} = \frac{5n}{5}$$
$$21 = n$$

B. *Solve each problem by writing two parallel phrases and then rewriting them in the form of a proportion. Show your work and your solution. Write any remainder as a fraction.*

(Other arrangements of phrases and proportions may be correct.)

7. To make pickles, Sister Jane needs 7 cups of sugar for each gallon of sliced pickles. How many gallons of pickles can she make with 30 cups of sugar?

   7 cups for 1 gallon, 30 cups for n gallons $\frac{7}{1} = \frac{30}{n}$ $n = 4\frac{2}{7}$ gallons

8. When Aunt Anna bakes bread, she uses 12 cups of flour to make 4 loaves of bread. How many cups of flour does she use to make 6 loaves of bread?

   12 cups for 4 loaves, n cups for 6 loaves $\frac{12}{4} = \frac{n}{6}$ $n = 18$ cups

9. Aunt Anna also uses 3 tablespoons of shortening when she makes 4 loaves of bread. How many tablespoons of shortening does she use to make 6 loaves of bread?

   3 tablespoons for 4 loaves, n tablespoons for 6 loaves $\frac{3}{4} = \frac{n}{6}$ $n = 4\frac{1}{2}$ tablespoons

10. Mother uses 6 cups of flour to make 24 rolls. How many cups of flour does she use for 60 rolls?

    6 cups for 24 rolls, n cups for 60 rolls $\frac{6}{24} = \frac{n}{60}$ $n = 15$ cups

11. Daniel is helping Father to build bookcases. If it takes 14 boards to build 3 bookcases, how many boards should Father buy to make 11 bookcases? (A fraction in your answer means that he needs to buy another whole board.)

    14 boards for 3 bookcases, n boards for 11 bookcases $\frac{14}{3} = \frac{n}{11}$ $n = 52$ boards

12. William picked 3 quarts of strawberries in 18 minutes. At that rate, how many quarts of strawberries can he pick in 60 minutes?

    3 quarts in 18 minutes, n quarts in 60 minutes $\frac{3}{18} = \frac{n}{60}$ $n = 10$ quarts

REVIEW EXERCISES

C. *Solve these problems mentally by changing the decimals to fractions and then multiplying.* (Lesson 90)

13. 0.5 of 46   14. 0.25 of 28   15. 0.33$\frac{1}{3}$ of 27   16. 0.2 of 55
          23   7   9   11

17. 0.75 of 20   18. 0.66$\frac{2}{3}$ of 33 19. 0.4 of 35   20. 0.8 of 45
          15   22   14   36

D. *Solve these subtraction problems.* (Lesson 77)

21.	2.354	22.	11.187	23.	6.2	24.	5.3
	− 1.19		− 8.9		− 4.857		− 3.914
	1.164		2.287		1.343		1.386

95. Chapter 7 Review

A. **Divide each number by 10, by 100, and by 1,000.** *(Lesson 84)*

Divide	by 10	by 100	by 1,000
11.5	**1.** 1.15	**2.** 0.115	**3.** 0.0115
4,593	**4.** 459.3	**5.** 45.93	**6.** 4.593

B. **Solve these division problems, being careful to place the decimal points correctly. Check by casting out nines.** *(Lessons 85–87)*

7. $6\overline{)13.2}$ = 2.2   **8.** $8\overline{)26.48}$ = 3.31   **9.** $12\overline{)\$16.92}$ = \$1.41   **10.** $14\overline{)\$25.06}$ = \$1.79

11. $2.8\overline{)16.52}$ = 5.9   **12.** $3.2\overline{)4.736}$ = 1.48   **13.** $0.58\overline{)1.914}$ = 3.3   **14.** $0.37\overline{)1.6946}$ = 4.58

15. $0.9\overline{)0.054}$ = 0.06   **16.** $0.36\overline{)0.01152}$ = 0.032   **17.** $0.4\overline{)0.7}$ = 1.75   **18.** $3.15\overline{)20.79}$ = 6.6

C. **Round these decimals as indicated.** *(Lesson 88)*

	To nearest tenth	To nearest hundredth
0.487	**19.** 0.5	**20.** 0.49
1.089	**21.** 1.1	**22.** 1.09
3.995	**23.** 4.0	**24.** 4.00

D. **Round each amount to the nearest cent.** *(Lesson 88)*

25. \$2.775   **26.** \$4.853   **27.** \$4.239   **28.** \$3.996

\$2.78   \$4.85   \$4.24   \$4.00

E. **Express these cents in dollar form.** *(Lesson 88)*

29. $22\frac{8}{10}$¢   **30.** $41\frac{1}{10}$¢   **31.** $53\frac{3}{10}$¢   **32.** $9\frac{4}{10}$¢

\$0.228   \$0.411   \$0.533   \$0.094

F. **Change these fractions to decimals. Divide to the hundredths' place, and express the remainder as a fraction in lowest terms.** *(Lesson 89)*

33. $\frac{4}{7}$ $0.57\frac{1}{7}$ **34.** $\frac{7}{12}$ $0.58\frac{1}{3}$ **35.** $\frac{17}{3}$ $5.66\frac{2}{3}$ **36.** $\frac{23}{6}$ $3.83\frac{1}{3}$

LESSON 95

Objective

- To review the concepts taught in Chapter 7.

Teaching Guide

This review covers Lessons 84–94.

G. **Write these fractions as decimals rounded to the nearest hundredth.**
(Lesson 89)

37. $\frac{3}{8}$ 0.38   **38.** $\frac{5}{16}$ 0.31   **39.** $\frac{11}{15}$ 0.73   **40.** $\frac{11}{12}$ 0.92

H. **Solve these problems mentally by converting the decimals to fractions and then multiplying.** *(Lesson 90)*

41. 0.5 of 42   **42.** $0.33\frac{1}{3}$ of 21   **43.** 0.75 of 88   **44.** 0.6 of 45
      21   7   66   27

I. **Write each ratio in lowest terms.** *(Lesson 92)*

45. $\frac{8}{10}$ $\frac{4}{5}$ **46.** $\frac{15}{21}$ $\frac{5}{7}$ **47.** $\frac{12}{8}$ $\frac{3}{2}$ **48.** $\frac{25}{15}$ $\frac{5}{3}$

J. **Check each proportion by using cross multiplication. Show your work on your paper. Then write whether the proportion is** *true or false. (Lesson 93)*

49. $\frac{4}{10} = \frac{10}{25}$ **50.** $\frac{2}{16} = \frac{3}{23}$ **51.** $\frac{7}{8} = \frac{17}{20}$ **52.** $\frac{20}{18} = \frac{50}{45}$
100, 100   true   46, 48   false   140, 136   false   900, 900   true

K. **Find the missing numbers in these proportions.** *(Lesson 93)*

53. $\frac{2}{8} = \frac{n}{20}$ 5   **54.** $\frac{6}{32} = \frac{n}{48}$ 9   **55.** $\frac{4}{14} = \frac{10}{n}$ 35   **56.** $\frac{6}{36} = \frac{8}{n}$ 48

L. **Write a proportion for each reading problem, and use it to find the answer. Show your proportion in your work.** *(Lesson 94)*   (Proportions may vary.)

57. There are 4 pints in 2 quarts. How many pints are in 9 quarts?
$\frac{4}{2} = \frac{n}{9}$ $n =$ 18 pints

58. There are 8 quarts in 2 gallons. How many quarts are in 13 gallons?
$\frac{8}{2} = \frac{n}{13}$ $n =$ 52 quarts

59. The sixth grade has geography class 3 times each school week (5 days). At that rate, how many geography classes do they have in a 180-day school year?
$\frac{3}{5} = \frac{n}{180}$ $n =$ 108 times

60. The sixth grade has music class 2 times each school week (5 days). At that rate, how many music classes do they have in a 45-day marking period?
$\frac{2}{5} = \frac{n}{45}$ $n =$ 18 classes

61. Brother Carl usually raises 6 batches of hogs in 2 years. At that rate, how many batches can he raise in 5 years? $\frac{6}{2} = \frac{n}{5}$ $n =$ 15 batches

62. If Brother Carl raises 6 batches of hogs every 2 years, in how many years will he raise 9 batches of hogs? $\frac{6}{2} = \frac{9}{n}$ $n =$ 3 years

96. Chapter 7 Test

LESSON 96

Objective

- To test the students' mastery of the concepts in Chapter 7.

Teaching Guide

1. Correct Lesson 95.
2. Review any areas of special difficulty.
3. Administer the test.

Careful measures and honest dealings are important in God's sight. For this reason, it is valuable to have an understanding of different measurement systems and be able to convert units from one system to another.

Chapter 8

Using the Metric System

Thou shalt have a perfect and just weight, a perfect and just measure shalt thou have: that thy days may be lengthened in the land which the LORD thy God giveth thee.

(Deuteronomy 25:15)

97. Using the Metric Ruler

In Chapter 3 you studied the English system of measures. This system is used only in the United States and a few other countries. Most countries in the world, including Canada, use the **metric system** of measures.

The metric system was developed during the 1790s by scientists in France. It is used in much of the world today because it is an easy system to learn.

The metric system is simpler than the English system because all related units are based on ten. In the English system, for example, there are 12 inches in 1 foot and 5,280 feet in 1 mile. But in the metric system there 100 centimeters in 1 meter and 1,000 meters in 1 kilometer. Since the metric system is based on ten, the same as our number system, it is easy to calculate with metric units.

These are some of the prefixes used in the metric system.

kilo-	thousand	1 kilometer	= 1,000 meters
hecto-	hundred	1 hectometer	= 100 meters
deka-	ten	1 dekameter	= 10 meters
		1 meter	= 1 meter
deci-	tenth	1 decimeter	= 0.1 meter
centi-	hundredth	1 centimeter	= 0.01 meter
milli-	thousandth	1 millimeter	= 0.001 meter

The table above shows seven metric units of linear measure. Only four of these units are in common use. They are the kilometer, the meter, the centimeter, and the millimeter.

Compound measures are not used in the metric system as in the English system. For example, instead of writing 2 centimeters 4 millimeters, people normally write 2.4 centimeters or 24 millimeters.

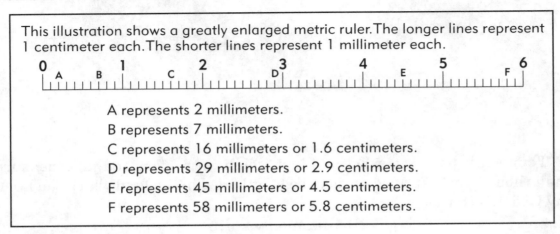

This illustration shows a greatly enlarged metric ruler. The longer lines represent 1 centimeter each. The shorter lines represent 1 millimeter each.

A represents 2 millimeters.
B represents 7 millimeters.
C represents 16 millimeters or 1.6 centimeters.
D represents 29 millimeters or 2.9 centimeters.
E represents 45 millimeters or 4.5 centimeters.
F represents 58 millimeters or 5.8 centimeters.

LESSON 97

Objectives

- To review the metric prefixes.
- To give practice with using the metric ruler to measure in centimeters and millimeters.

Review

1. *Writing ratios* (Lesson 92).
   a. Compare 5 song books to 9 students. (5 to 9)
   b. Compare 9 students to 5 song books. (9 to 5)

2. *Writing proportions to solve reading problems* (Lesson 94).

   In the Millers' garden there are 5 rows of sweet corn for every 2 rows of peas. If there are 7 rows of peas, how many rows of sweet corn are there?
   5 rows corn for 2 rows peas
   n rows corn for 7 rows peas
   $\frac{5}{2} = \frac{n}{7}$
   $5 \times 7 \div 2 = 17\frac{1}{2}$ rows of sweet corn

3. *Rounding decimals* (Lesson 88).
   Round to the nearest tenth.
   a. 0.38 (0.4)
   b. 0.24 (0.2)
   c. 0.99 (1.0)
   Round to the nearest hundredth.
   d. 0.566 (0.57)
   e. 0.678 (0.68)
   f. 0.997 (1.00)

4. *Multiplying decimals* (Lessons 79, 80).

   a. $\begin{array}{r} 3.4 \\ \times\, 0.5 \\ \hline (1.70) \end{array}$ b. $\begin{array}{r} 12.8 \\ \times\, 2.2 \\ \hline (28.16) \end{array}$

   c. $\begin{array}{r} 0.46 \\ \times\, 0.04 \\ \hline (0.0184) \end{array}$

Introduction

Briefly review the relationships between the various English measures.

> 12 inches = 1 foot
> 3 feet = 1 yard
> 1,760 yards = 1 mile
> 5,280 feet = 1 mile
> 16 tablespoons = 1 cup
> 2 cups = 1 pint
> 2 pints = 1 quart
> 4 quarts = 1 gallon
> 8 dry quarts = 1 peck
> 4 pecks = 1 bushel

How does one learn these relationships? By memorizing each of them individually. By contrast, relationships between units in the metric system are based on ten. For example, the meter is the basic unit of linear measure. Each of the other metric linear units is found by multiplying or dividing the meter by ten or a power of ten.

Teaching Guide

1. **The metric system of measures is based on the meter.** It was developed by French scientists in the 1790s, and it is the most widely used system of measures in the world today.

   Be sure that the students have metric rulers. Many rulers today have both English and metric units. You will also need a meter measure or a yardstick that shows metric units.

2. **In the metric system, all related units are based on ten.** Prefixes are used to show the relationship of each derived unit to the base unit. Use your meter measure to show the length of a meter, a decimeter, a centimeter, and a millimeter.

   Drill the meanings of the prefixes. Point out that they show exactly what the relationship is between a derived unit and the base unit. For example, *kilometer* means "thousand meters" and *centimeter* means "hundredth meter." If you know what the prefixes mean, you can easily tell how the units are related.

a.   1 kilometer = 1,000 meters
b.   1 hectometer = 100 meters
c.   1 dekameter = 10 meters
d.   1 decimeter = 0.1 meter
e.   1 centimeter = 0.01 meter
f.   1 millimeter = 0.001 meter

3.   **There are seven metric units of linear measure.** They are as follows: kilometer, hectometer, dekameter, meter, decimeter, centimeter, and millimeter. Only four of these are in common use: the kilometer, the meter, the centimeter, and the millimeter.

   The seven units were devised when the metric system was formulated. But when the system came into actual everyday use, the hectometer, dekameter, and decimeter were soon dropped.

4.   **Compound measures are not used in the metric system as in the English system.** Since all relationships are based on ten, any fraction of a unit can be written in decimal form.

   Give practice with using metric rulers. First show how to read in terms of millimeters, using letters A to F on the enlarged ruler. Then show how to read in terms of centimeters, using letters C to F. Have the students use their metric rulers and the meter measure to measure selected items in the classroom.

An Ounce of Prevention

   Examine your students' rulers. If the rulers include both English and metric units, they usually begin at opposite ends. When the students measure in millimeters, allow 1 millimeter of deviation in either direction. But since the centimeter is a larger unit, insist that all measurements to the nearest centimeter are exact.

Further Study

   The six metric prefixes given in the lesson are sufficient for most nonscientific purposes. A number of others can also be used, as shown below.

mega-	million
giga-	billion
tera-	trillion
peta-	quadrillion
exa-	quintillion
micro-	millionth
nano-	billionth
pico-	trillionth
femto-	quadrillionth
atto-	quintillionth

Answers to Part D. (Measure each student's lines.)

25. ─────────────────────────
26. ──────────────────────────────────────
27. ───────────────────────────────
28. ─────────────────────
29. ───────────────
30. ──────────

CLASS PRACTICE

Measure these lines in centimeters.

a. ____2 cm____   b. _____4 cm_____   c. _____5 cm_____

Draw lines of these lengths.   (Measure each student's lines.)

d. 4 centimeters   e. 7 centimeters   f. 1.1 centimeters

WRITTEN EXERCISES

A. **Write the correct number for each blank. Use the chart of metric prefixes if you need help.**

1. 1 dekameter = __10__ meters

2. 1 kilometer = __1,000__ meters

3. 1 centimeter = __0.01__ meter

4. 1 millimeter = __0.001__ meter

5. 1 meter = __10__ decimeters

6. 1 meter = __1,000__ millimeters

7. 1 hectometer = __100__ meters

8. 1 meter = __100__ centimeters

9. 1 decimeter = __0.1__ meter

10. 2 meters = __20__ decimeters

B. **Measure each line to the nearest centimeter, and write the measurement on your paper.**

11. ———————————— 5 cm

12. ———————————————— 7 cm

13. ——————— 3 cm

14. ————————————————— 8 cm

15. ——————————— 4 cm

16. ————— 2 cm

17. —————————————————— 10 cm

18. ————————————————— 9 cm

19. —— 1 cm

20. ————————————————————————— 13 cm

C. **Measure each line to the nearest millimeter, and write the measurement on your paper.**

21. ———————————— 88 mm

22. ——— 15 mm

23. ——— 25 mm

24. ————— 34 mm

D. **Draw lines of the lengths given below. Be exact in your work.**   (See facing page.)

25. 6 centimeters

26. 14 centimeters

27. 1 decimeter

28. 5.2 centimeters

29. 3.7 centimeters

30. 2.3 centimeters

E. Solve these reading problems. You may use your metric ruler for help.

31. When the sixth grade studied arthropods in science class, they learned that most spiders are less than 1 centimeter long. How many millimeters are in 1 centimeter?
10 millimeters

32. The tarantula is a spider that may grow to be 25 centimeters across. How many millimeters are in 25 centimeters?
250 millimeters

33. The sixth grade also learned that some ants grow to be as long as 2.5 centimeters. How many millimeters are in 2.5 centimeters?
25 millimeters

34. The American ants go hunting for their food in swarms. These swarms move about 30 centimeters a minute. How many decimeters are in 30 centimeters?
3 decimeters

REVIEW EXERCISES

F. Write ratios for these reading problems. *(Lesson 92)*

35. There are 39 books in the Old Testament and 27 books in the New Testament. Write a ratio in lowest terms to compare the number of books in the Old Testament to the number in the New Testament. $\frac{13}{9}$

36. The Book of Matthew contains 28 chapters, and the Book of Mark contains 16 chapters. Write a ratio in lowest terms to compare the number of chapters in Mark to the number in Matthew. $\frac{4}{7}$

G. Use proportions to solve these reading problems. *(Lesson 93)*

37. When the spies searched the land of Canaan, 2 spies brought a good report, and 10 spies brought an evil report. For every 1 spy who brought a good report, how many brought an evil report? $\frac{2}{10} = \frac{1}{n}$ $n = 5$ spies

38. There have been about 2 years before the birth of Christ for every 3 years of history in all. If 4,000 years passed before Christ's birth, what is the total number of years in history? $\frac{2}{3} = \frac{4,000}{n}$ $n = 6,000$ years

H. Round these decimals as indicated. *(Lesson 88)*

To the nearest tenth

39. 3.67   3.7   **40.** 5.83   5.8   **41.** 7.98   8.0   **42.** 6.09   6.1

To the nearest hundredth

43. 5.071   5.07   **44.** 3.887   3.89   **45.** 3.995   4.00   **46.** 5.699   5.70

I. Multiply these decimal fractions. *(Lessons 79, 80)*

47.	3.5	48.	4.21	49.	0.21	50.	0.15
	× 4.6		× 1.4		× 0.05		× 0.09
	16.10		5.894		0.0105		0.0135

LESSON 98

Objectives

- To review the metric units of linear measure.
- To review changing linear measures from one metric unit to another.
- To teach that *1 meter equals about 39 3/8 inches.

Review

1. *Measuring with a metric ruler* (Lesson 97). This concept will probably be reviewed sufficiently if you have the students check Lesson 97 in class.

2. *Proportion problems* (Lesson 93).

   a. $\frac{4}{6} = \frac{n}{15}$ ($n = 10$)

   b. $\frac{4}{12} = \frac{n}{48}$ ($n = 16$)

3. *Changing fractions to decimals rounded to the nearest hundredth* (Lesson 89).

   a. $\frac{3}{7}$ (0.43)

   b. $\frac{5}{11}$ (0.45)

   c. $\frac{1}{12}$ (0.08)

4. *Multiplying fractions and mixed numbers* (Lessons 60–64). No class review is necessary.

Introduction

Practice changing from one English linear measure to another. This will help to prepare the students for the study of metric linear measures as well as for some of the review exercises in the lesson. It should also help them to appreciate the simplicity of changing from one metric unit to another.

   a.   14 ft. = (168) inches
   b.   180 inches = (5) yards
   c.   6 miles = (31,680) ft.
   d.   14 yd. = (42) ft.

Ask the pupils why it is easy to change metric measures from one unit to another. Call attention to the chart of metric linear units in the text. Explain that 10 of a smaller unit always equals 1 of the next larger unit, 100 of a smaller unit equals 1 of the second larger unit, and 1,000 of a smaller unit equals 1 of the third larger unit.

Teaching Guide

1. **The meter is the basic unit of linear measure in the metric system.** It is a few inches longer than a yard.

2. **Of the seven metric units of linear measure, only four are in common use.** They are the kilometer, the meter, the centimeter, and the millimeter.

3. **To change from a larger unit to a smaller unit, multiply.**
   When changing to a metric measure one unit smaller, multiply by 10.
      a.   60 cm = (600) mm
      b.   3.7 cm = (37) mm
   When changing to a metric measure two units smaller, multiply by 100.
      c.   5 m = (500) cm
      d.   4.6 m = (460) cm

98. Metric Units of Linear Measure

The meter is the basic unit of measure in the metric system. It is a few inches longer than a yard. Following are the metric units of linear measure from largest to smallest, with their abbreviations. Notice that no periods are used with metric abbreviations.

Metric Units of Linear Measure	
1 kilometer (km)	= 1,000 meters
1 hectometer (hm)	= 100 meters
1 dekameter (dkm)	= 10 meters
1 meter (m)	= 1 meter
1 decimeter (dm)	= 0.1 meter
1 centimeter (cm)	= 0.01 meter
1 millimeter (mm)	= 0.001 meter

Remember that only four of the units above are in common use. Their lengths are given below.

1 millimeter	= -
1 centimeter	= ——
1 meter	= about $39\frac{3}{8}$ inches
1 kilometer	= about $\frac{5}{8}$ mile

Converting from one metric unit to another is easy because it always takes 10 smaller units to make one unit of the next larger size. Because of this, conversion simply requires multiplying or dividing by 10, by 100, by 1,000, and so forth.

To change from a larger unit to a smaller unit, multiply.

When changing to a metric measure one unit smaller, multiply by 10.
Example: Changing from centimeters to millimeters
5 cm = 50 mm   8.4 cm = 84 mm

When changing to a metric measure two units smaller, multiply by 100.
Example: Changing from meters to centimeters
7 m = 700 cm   6.2 m = 620 cm

When changing to a metric measure three units smaller, multiply by 1,000.
Examples: Changing from meters to millimeters
          Changing from kilometers to meters
          11 m = 11,000 mm   2.3 km = 2,300 m

To change from a smaller unit to a larger unit, divide.

When changing to a metric measure one unit larger, divide by 10.
Example: Changing from millimeters to centimeters
            500 mm = 50 cm   82 mm = 8.2 cm

When changing to a metric measure two units larger, divide by 100.
Example: Changing from centimeters to meters
            300 cm = 3 m   40 cm = 0.4 m

When changing to a metric measure three units larger, divide by 1,000.
Examples: Changing from millimeters to meters
            Changing from meters to kilometers
            500 mm = 0.5 m   280 mm = 0.28 m
            2,000 m = 2 km   96 m = 0.096 km

Converting metric units is a practical application of moving the decimal point to multiply or divide by 10, 100, or 1,000. Remember to annex zeroes if more decimal places are needed. But if the result is a decimal with one or more zeroes to the right, those zeroes are usually dropped. For example, 40 cm = 0.4 m (not 0.40 m), and 500 mm = 0.5 m (not 0.500 m).

CLASS PRACTICE

Change these metric measures as indicated.

   a. 5 m = <u> 500 </u> cm   **b.** 3 km = <u> 3,000 </u> m   **c.** 5.2 m = <u> 520 </u> cm

   d. 4,000 m = <u> 4 </u> km   **e.** 220 cm = <u> 2.2 </u> m   **f.** 55 mm = <u> 5.5 </u> cm

WRITTEN EXERCISES

A. **Write the abbreviation for each term, and the meaning of each term except the meter.**
        Example: kilometer
        Answer: km, 1,000 meters

   1. hectometer   **2.** dekameter   **3.** meter
            hm, 100 meters   dkm, 10 meters   m
   4. decimeter   **5.** centimeter   **6.** millimeter
            dm, 0.1 meter   cm, 0.01 meter   mm, 0.001 meter

B. **Change these metric measures to smaller units by multiplying.**

   7. 4 cm = <u> 40 </u> mm   **8.** 2.4 cm = <u> 24 </u> mm

   9. 7.5 m = <u> 750 </u> cm   **10.** 38 m = <u>3,800</u> cm

   11. 0.25 m = <u> 250 </u> mm   **12.** 6 m = <u>6,000</u> mm

   13. 5 km = <u>5,000</u> m   **14.** 6.3 km = <u>6,300</u> m

When changing to a metric measure three units smaller, multiply by 1,000.

    e.   5 m = (5,000) mm

    f.   6.7 m = (6,700) mm

    g.   15.3 km = (15,300) m

    h.   0.75 km = (750) m

4. **To change from a smaller unit to a larger unit, divide.**

When changing to a metric measure one unit larger, divide by 10.

    a.   60 mm = (6) cm

    b.   8 mm = (0.8) cm

When changing to a metric measure two units larger, divide by 100.

    c.   600 cm = (6) m

    d.   73 cm = (0.73) m

When changing to a metric measure three units larger, divide by 1,000.

    e.   4,000 m = (4) km

    f.   2,800 m = (2.8) km

    g.   5,000 mm = (5) m

    h.   450 mm = (0.45) m

Note: Have grocery labels, showing both the English weight and the metric weight, ready to show to the class in the next lesson. Possibly you could assign the students to find the labels and bring them to class.

Further Study

The prefix *deka-* is often spelled *deca-;* it is related to the word *decade.* The spelling *deka-* is used to help avoid confusion between this prefix and the prefix *deci-,* especially in abbreviations (such as *dm* versus *dkm*).

C. Change these metric measures to larger units by dividing.

15. 30 mm = ___3___ cm   **16.** 52 mm = ___5.2___ cm

17. 420 cm = ___4.2___ m   **18.** 36 cm = ___0.36___ m

19. 640 mm = ___0.64___ m   **20.** 1,300 mm = ___1.3___ m

21. 1,500 m = ___1.5___ km   **22.** 780 m = ___0.78___ km

D. Solve these reading problems.

23. Father is 175 centimeters tall. How many meters tall is he?   1.75 meters

24. Mother is 1.62 meters tall. How many centimeters tall is she?   162 centimeters

25. One meter equals 39.37 inches. How many inches tall is John if he is 1.45 meters tall? (Multiply and round your answer to the nearest inch.)   57 inches

26. John's Bible workbook is 26 centimeters long. What part of a meter is that?   0.26 meter

27. Jason lives 4 kilometers from church. How many meters are in 4 kilometers?   4,000 meters

28. If a postage stamp is 22 millimeters wide, what is its width in centimeters?   2.2 centimeters

REVIEW EXERCISES

E. Measure each line to the nearest centimeter, and write the measurement on your paper. *(Lesson 97)*

29. ——— 2 cm ———   **30.** ——— 10 cm ———

31. ——— 4 cm ———   **32.** ——— 9 cm ———

F. Find the missing numbers in these proportions. *(Lesson 93)*

33. $\frac{4}{12} = \frac{n}{30}$ $n = 10$ **34.** $\frac{12}{27} = \frac{44}{n}$ $n = 99$

G. Change each fraction to a decimal rounded to the nearest hundredth. *(Lesson 89)*

35. $\frac{7}{9}$ 0.78   **36.** $\frac{7}{16}$ 0.44

H. Solve these multiplication problems. *(Lessons 60–64)*

37. $\frac{3}{5} \times 7$ $4\frac{1}{5}$ **38.** $\frac{2}{3} \times \frac{1}{4}$ $\frac{1}{6}$ **39.** $3\frac{3}{5} \times 1\frac{1}{2}$ $5\frac{2}{5}$ **40.** $3\frac{3}{4} \times 2\frac{1}{3}$ $8\frac{3}{4}$

I. Change these English linear measures as indicated. *(Lesson 32)*

41. 4 ft. = ___48___ in.   **42.** 156 in. = ___13___ ft.

43. 27 yd. = ___81___ ft.   **44.** 3 mi. = _15,840_ ft.

Math Challenger

45. How many millimeters are in 1 kilometer?   1,000 × 1,000 = 1,000,000 millimeters

99. Metric Units of Weight

The basic unit of metric weight is the gram. A gram is a very small unit; 1 ounce is more than 28 grams. A large paper clip weighs a little more than 1 gram.

Because the gram is so small, the kilogram is used more frequently than the gram. One kilogram equals about 2.2 pounds. A large Bible weighs about one kilogram.

The same prefixes are used with metric units of weight as with the units of linear measure. The method for changing from one unit to another is also the same.

Metric Units of Weight	
1 metric ton (m.t.)	= 1,000 kilograms
1 kilogram (kg)	= 1,000 grams
1 hectogram (hg)	= 100 grams
1 dekagram (dkg)	= 10 grams
1 gram (g)	= 1 gram
1 decigram (dg)	= 0.1 gram
1 centigram (cg)	= 0.01 gram
1 milligram (mg)	= 0.001 gram

Only four of the units above are in common use. They are the metric ton, the kilogram, the gram, and the milligram. Each of these units is 1,000 times larger or smaller than the unit of the next size. Therefore, conversions with metric units of weight usually involve multiplying or dividing by 1,000.

To change from a larger unit to a smaller unit, multiply.
33 m.t. = 33,000 kg   3.3 kg = 3,300 g   0.33 g = 330 mg

To change from a smaller unit to a larger unit, divide.
450 mg = 0.45 g   45 g = 0.045 kg   4,500 kg = 4.5 m.t.

CLASS PRACTICE

Change these metric measures as indicated.

a. 5 g = <u>5,000</u> mg

b. 7,000 mg = <u> 7 </u> g

c. 3.6 kg = <u>3,600</u> g

d. 450 mg = <u> 0.45 </u> g

e. 4,200 g = <u> 4.2 </u> kg

f. 3,600 kg = <u> 3.6 </u> m.t.

g. 4.3 g = <u>4,300</u> mg

h. 5.4 m.t. = <u>5,400</u> kg

i. 750 kg = <u> 0.75 </u> m.t.

LESSON 99

Objectives

- To review the metric units of weight.
- To review changing weights from one metric unit to another.
- To teach that 1 kilogram equals about 2.2 pounds.

Review

1. *Writing proportions to solve reading problems* (Lesson 93).

    a. Kaylene carried 3 jars of peaches to the basement for every 5 jars that Denise carried. If Kaylene carried 27 jars of peaches to the basement, how many did Denise carry?

    3 jars by Kaylene for 5 jars by Denise

    27 jars by Kaylene for n jars by Denise

    $\frac{3}{5} = \frac{27}{n}$ $5 \times 27 \div 3 =$

    (45) jars carried by Denise

    b. Father knows that for every 100 pounds of coal burned in the coal furnace, 3 pounds of ash must be carried out of the basement. At that rate, how many pounds of ash will result from burning 1 ton of coal?

    3 lb. ash from 100 lb. coal

    n lb. ash from 2,000 lb. coal

    $\frac{3}{100} = \frac{n}{2,000}$ $3 \times 2,000 \div 100 =$

    (60) lb. ash

2. *Multiplying decimals mentally by changing the decimal to a fraction* (Lesson 90).

    a. $0.33\frac{1}{3} \times 27$ (9)

    b. 0.4×45 (18)

    c. 0.75×48 (36)

Introduction

Begin by reviewing conversions of English weights from one unit to another. This will help to introduce metric weights and to prepare students for some of the review exercises in the lesson.

    a.   4 lb. = (64) oz.

    b.   8 tons = (16,000) lb.

    c.   160 oz. = (10) lb.

Then discuss metric linear measure, both to review Lesson 98 and to introduce metric weight.

    d.   5 m = (500) cm

    e.   90 cm = (900) mm

    f.   8.7 km = (8,700) m

    g.   500 mm = (0.5) m

    h.   350 cm = (3.5) m

    i.   4,800 m = (4.8) km

Show the students some grocery labels that give the weight in grams or kilograms. Even in the United States, the weight of many groceries, such as prepared cereals, is shown in both English and metric units.

Teaching Guide

1. **The gram is the basic unit of weight in the metric system.** The same prefixes are used for units of weight as for units of linear measure. Use the chart in the lesson to drill the relationships among metric units of weight.

2. **Of the eight metric units of weight, only four are in common use.** The most common units are the metric ton, the kilogram, the gram, and the milligram. Less common are the hectogram, the dekagram, the decigram, and the centigram.

3. **To change from a larger unit to a smaller unit, multiply.** Each of the common units is 1,000 times larger than the next smaller common unit. Therefore, these conversions usually involve multiplying by 1,000.
   a.   3 g = (3,000) mg
   b.   0.145 g = (145) mg
   c.   5.5 kg = (5,500) g
   d.   0.82 m.t. = (820) kg

4. **To change from a smaller unit to a larger unit, divide.** Each of the common units is 1,000 times smaller than the next larger common unit. Therefore, these conversions usually involve dividing by 1,000.
   a.   3,000 g = (3) kg
   b.   4,500 mg = (4.5) g
   c.   275 g = (0.275) kg
   d.   5,150 kg = (5.15) m.t.

Note: Have containers showing both the English and the metric measures of capacity for the next lesson. This could also be assigned to the students.

Further Study

How is the gram related to the meter? The gram was originally defined as the weight or mass of one cubic centimeter of pure water at 4 degrees Celsius (39.2 degrees Fahrenheit) at sea level. One kilogram was then the weight of one cubic decimeter of pure water under the same conditions.

Later, the International Bureau of Weights and Measures constructed a cylinder of platinum-iridium with a mass of exactly 1 kilogram. This cylinder became the official standard, and today the gram is defined as 0.001 kilogram.

WRITTEN EXERCISES

A. *Write the abbreviation for each term, and the meaning of each term except the gram.*

> *Example:* milligram
> *Answer:* mg, 0.001 gram

1. centigram
   cg, 0.01 gram

2. decigram
   dg, 0.1 gram

3. gram
   g

4. dekagram
   dkg, 10 grams

5. hectogram
   hg, 100 grams

6. kilogram
   kg, 1,000 grams

B. *Change these metric measures to smaller units by multiplying.*

7. 5 g = _5,000_ mg

8. 0.4 g = _400_ mg

9. 0.7 kg = _700_ g

10. 17 kg = _17,000_ g

11. 0.38 m.t. = _380_ kg

12. 1.3 m.t. = _1,300_ kg

C. *Change these metric measures to larger units by dividing.*

13. 1,300 mg = _1.3_ g

14. 250 mg = _0.25_ g

15. 4,250 g = _4.25_ kg

16. 350 g = _0.35_ kg

17. 8,400 kg = _8.4_ m.t.

18. 530 kg = _0.53_ m.t.

D. *Change these metric measures as indicated.*

19. 15 g = _15,000_ mg

20. 5.5 kg = _5,500_ g

21. 760 kg = _0.76_ m.t.

22. 75 mg = _0.075_ g

23. 400 g = _0.4_ kg

24. 3 m.t. = _3,000_ kg

E. *Solve these reading problems.*

25. Father purchased a 45-kilogram bag of feed at the mill. How many grams of feed did he buy?
    45,000 grams

26. A kilogram equals about 2.2 pounds. How many pounds of feed are in a 45-kilogram bag?
    99 pounds

27. According to 1 Samuel 17:5, Goliath's armor weighed 5,000 shekels. That weight is thought to equal about 57 kilograms. How many grams are in 57 kilograms?
    57,000 grams

28. In 1 Samuel 17:7 it is stated that the head of Goliath's spear weighed 600 shekels. That is thought to be about 7,000 grams. How many kilograms are in 7,000 grams?
    7 kilograms

89

REVIEW EXERCISES

F. *Change these metric measures as indicated.* (Lesson 98)

29. 5 km = <u>5,000</u> m   **30.** 80 mm = <u>0.08</u> m

31. 28 m = <u>2,800</u> cm   **32.** 12 mm = <u>1.2</u> cm

G. *Measure each line to the nearest centimeter, and write the measurement on your paper.* (Lesson 97)

33. ————————————   5 cm

34. ——————————————   7 cm

H. *Write proportions to solve these reading problems.* (Lesson 93)

35. A smaller box has 2 grams of cereal for every 3 grams in a larger box. The smaller box has 454 grams of cereal. How many grams are in the larger box?

$$\frac{2}{3} = \frac{454}{n} \qquad n = 681 \text{ grams}$$

36. Of every 9 hogs that the Moyers shipped to market one week, 6 hogs weighed over 100 kilograms. How many of the 39 hogs shipped that week weighed over 100 kilograms?

$$\frac{9}{6} = \frac{39}{n} \qquad n = 26 \text{ hogs}$$

I. *Solve these problems mentally by first changing the decimals to fractions.* (Lesson 90)

37. 0.25 of 20   5   **38.** 0.5 of 60   30

39. $0.66\frac{2}{3}$ of 18   12   **40.** 0.75 of 80   60

J. *Change these measures as indicated.* (Lesson 33)

41. 12 lb. = <u>192</u> oz.   **42.** 7 tons = <u>14,000</u> lb.

43. 8 tons 900 lb. = <u>16,900</u> lb.   **44.** 4 lb. 8 oz. = <u>72</u> oz.

Math Challenger

45. How many milligrams are in 1 metric ton?

$$1,000 \times 1,000 \times 1,000 = 1,000,000,000 \text{ milligrams}$$

LESSON 100

Objectives

- To review the metric units of capacity.
- To review changing measures of capacity from one metric unit to another.
- To teach that *1 liter equals about 1.06 liquid quarts.

Review

1. Give Lesson 100 Quiz (Metric Units of Linear Measure).

2. *Changing metric units of linear measure and weight* (Lessons 98, 99).
   a. 7 cm = (70) mm
   b. 45 cm = (0.45) m
   c. 1,420 m = (1.42) km
   d. 4 g = (4,000) mg
   e. 130 mg = (0.13) g
   f. 800 kg = (0.8) m.t.

3. *Writing ratios* (Lesson 92).
   a. The shortest psalm is Psalm 117, which has 2 verses. The longest psalm is Psalm 119, with 176 verses. Write a ratio in lowest terms to compare the number of verses in Psalm 117 to the number of verses in Psalm 119.
      (2 to 176 = 1 to 88)
   b. The shortest verse in the Bible is John 11:35, which has 2 words. The longest verse in the Bible is Esther 8:9, with 90 words. Write a ratio in lowest terms to compare the number of words in the longest verse to the number in the shortest verse.
      (2 to 90 = 1 to 45)

4. *Dividing fractions* (Lesson 65–67). No class review is necessary.

Introduction

Review the English units of liquid and dry capacity. Ask the students, "Is there any reason that one measure would not work for both liquid and dry measure?" In the metric system, the liter is both a liquid and a dry measure.

Bring some containers to class that show the capacity in liters. Even in the United States, many liquids, such as vegetable oil, are labeled in liters as well as English units.

Teaching Guide

1. **The liter is the basic unit of capacity in the metric system.** Other units of capacity are the kiloliter, the hectoliter, the dekaliter, the deciliter, the centiliter, and the milliliter. Only the liter and the milliliter are in common use, though the kiloliter is also used sometimes for very large quantities.

2. **To change from one unit of capacity to another, the same two rules are used as for making changes with other units of measure.**
   To change from a larger unit to a smaller unit, multiply.
   To change from a smaller unit to a larger unit, divide.

   Conversions with metric units of capacity usually involve multiplying or dividing by 1,000.
   a. 4.5 l = (4,500) ml
   b. 7 kl = (7,000) l
   c. 0.35 kl = (350) l
   d. 580 l = (0.58) kl
   e. 440 ml = (0.44) l
   f. 4,450 ml = (4.45) l

100. Metric Units of Capacity

Unlike the English system, the metric system has one unit for both liquid and dry measures. The basic unit of measure is the liter. This unit is a little larger than 1 liquid quart. One liter equals 1.06 liquid quarts.

The same prefixes and the same methods of conversion apply to the units of capacity as to the other metric units that you have studied.

Metric Units of Capacity

1 kiloliter (kl)	= 1,000 liters
1 hectoliter (hl)	= 100 liters
1 dekaliter (dkl)	= 10 liters
1 liter (*l*)	= 1 liter
1 deciliter (dl)	= 0.1 liter
1 centiliter (cl)	= 0.01 liter
1 milliliter (ml)	= 0.001 liter

Only two of the units above are in common use. They are the liter and the milliliter, though the kiloliter is also used sometimes for very large quantities. Each of these units is 1,000 times larger or smaller than the unit of the next size. Therefore, conversions with metric units of capacity usually involve multiplying or dividing by 1,000.

To change from a larger unit to a smaller unit, multiply.
27 kl = 27,000 *l*   0.27 *l* = 270 ml

To change from a smaller unit to a larger unit, divide.
540 ml = 0.54 *l*   5,400 *l* = 5.4 kl

CLASS PRACTICE

Change these metric measures as indicated.

a. 5 *l* = <u>5,000</u> ml   b. 8.1 cl = <u>81</u> ml   c. 1.4 kl = <u>1,400</u> *l*

d. 9,000 ml = <u>9</u> *l*   e. 950 ml = <u>0.95</u> *l*   f. 350 dkl = <u>3,500</u> *l*

g. 425 ml = <u>0.425</u> *l*   h. 27.5 dl = <u>2.75</u> *l*   i. 2.5 *l* = <u>250</u> cl

93

WRITTEN EXERCISES

A. *Write the abbreviation for each term, and the meaning of each term except the liter.*

    Example: kiloliter
      Answer: kl; 1,000 liters

1. hectoliter	2. dekaliter	3. liter
hl, 100 liters	dkl, 10 liters	*l*
4. deciliter	5. centiliter	6. milliliter
dl, 0.1 liter	cl, 0.01 liter	ml, 0.001 liter

B. *Change these metric measures to smaller units by multiplying.*

  7. $3\,l = \underline{3{,}000}$ ml   8. $1.66\,l = \underline{1{,}660}$ ml   9. $0.07\,l = \underline{70}$ ml

10. $15\text{ kl} = \underline{15{,}000}\ l$ 11. $2.4\text{ kl} = \underline{2{,}400}\ l$ 12. $0.11\text{ kl} = \underline{110}\ l$

C. *Change these metric measures to larger units by dividing.*

13. $7{,}000\,l = \underline{7}$ kl   14. $430\,l = \underline{0.43}$ kl   15. $1{,}500\,l = \underline{1.5}$ kl

16. $15{,}100$ ml $= \underline{15.1}\ l$ 17. $1{,}700$ ml $= \underline{1.7}\ l$ 18. 350 ml $= \underline{0.35}\ l$

D. *Change these metric measures as indicated.*

19. $3.6\text{ kl} = \underline{3{,}600}\ l$ 20. $3{,}200$ ml $= \underline{3.2}\ l$ 21. $1.35\,l = \underline{1{,}350}$ ml

22. $350\,l = \underline{0.35}$ kl   23. $15\,l = \underline{15{,}000}$ ml   24. 850 ml $= \underline{0.85}\ l$

E. *Solve these reading problems.*

25. Mother gives baby Sarah 1.5 milliliters of vitamins each day. What part of a liter of vitamins would Sarah take in 4 weeks?   0.042 liter

26. The bottle contains 50 milliliters of vitamins. If 1 teaspoon contains 5 milliliters, how many teaspoons of vitamins are in the bottle?   10 teaspoons

27. When 3-year-old James had a fever, Mother gave him 2.5 milliliters of infant's pain medicine. What part of a liter is that?   0.0025 liter

28. Father put 68.2 liters of gasoline into the family car on Saturday so that they could travel to a distant church on Sunday. If the gasoline cost $0.39 per liter, how much did Father pay? Round your answer to the nearest cent. $26.60

29. The 68.2 liters of gasoline replaced the fuel that the car had used since Father last filled the tank. He said that the car had traveled an average of 10.5 kilometers for each liter of that gasoline. At that rate, how many kilometers had the car traveled since the tank was last filled?   716.1 kilometers

30. A fuel deliveryman filled two tanks with heating fuel for the winter. He put 850 liters into one tank and 700 liters into the other tank. How many kiloliters of fuel did he deliver?   1.55 kiloliters

Further Study

The liter is used instead of the quarts and gallons in English measure, and the milliliter is used instead of teaspoons and tablespoons for small items such as medicine. A grocery item that is less than 1 liter is usually labeled either as part of a liter (0.95 liter) or in milliliters (124 ml).

There is a relationship between the meter and the liter. One liter is equal to the quantity of one cubic decimeter. In Lesson 99 it was noted that one cubic decimeter of pure water under specified conditions weighs 1 kilogram. Thus 1 liter = 1 cubic decimeter = 1 kilogram of pure water. And for most practical purposes, 1 milliliter of water = 1 cubic centimeter = 1 gram.

REVIEW EXERCISES

F. *Change these measures as indicated.* (*Lessons 98, 99*)

31. 720 m = _0.72_ km

32. 1,500 mm = _1.5_ m

33. 1,450 kg = _1.45_ m.t.

34. 0.75 kg = _750_ g

G. *Write a ratio for each problem.* (*Lesson 92*)

35. Abraham lived 175 years, and Methuselah lived 969 years. Write a ratio comparing the life span of Abraham to the life span of Methuselah. $\frac{175}{969}$

36. When Gideon first called the Israelites to fight the Midianites, 32,000 men responded to the call. The Lord revealed to Gideon that He had chosen only 300 of these men. Write a ratio in lowest terms, comparing the number of men who first responded to the men whom the Lord chose. $\frac{320}{3}$

H. *Solve these division problems.* (*Lessons 65–67*)

37. $5 \div \frac{3}{8}$ $13\frac{1}{3}$ **38.** $\frac{3}{4} \div \frac{7}{8}$ $\frac{6}{7}$ **39.** $7 \div 1\frac{3}{4}$ 4 **40.** $3\frac{3}{5} \div 1\frac{2}{9}$ $2\frac{52}{55}$

I. *Change these English measures as indicated.* (*Lesson 34*)

41. 5 bu. = _20_ pk.

42. 8 pk. = _64_ qt.

43. 48 tbsp. = _3_ cups

44. 7 pt. = _14_ cups

101. Metric Units of Area

Area is the amount of surface that an object covers. Area is different from linear measure because it involves both length and width. Therefore, area is not measured with linear units such as meters and centimeters, but with square units such as square meters and square centimeters. Except for the hectare (hĕk' tĕr'), all metric units of area are named as square units.

In the English system, the abbreviation for *square inch* is *sq. in*. But in the metric system, the exponent 2 is used instead of the abbreviation *sq*. An exponent is a small raised number such as the 2 in cm^2. It shows that the abbreviation refers to a square measure.

The relationships between metric units of area are based on ten, the same as other metric units. But since area involves two dimensions, a change from one unit to another requires multiplying or dividing by 100 (10 × 10) or 10,000 (100 × 100). Study the table below.

1 square meter (m^2)	= 10,000 square centimeters (cm^2)
1 hectare (ha)	= 10,000 square meters
1 square kilometer (km^2)	= 100 hectares

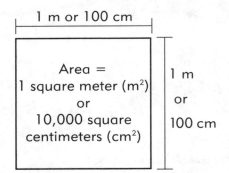

The block to the left shows the relationship of a square meter to a square centimeter. A square meter is the area covered by a square 1 meter by 1 meter. Because 1 meter equals 100 centimeters, 1 square meter is equal to the area of a square measuring 100 centimeters by 100 centimeters, or 10,000 square centimeters.

A hectare is actually a square hectometer (100 meters by 100 meters). But *hectare* is in common use while *hectometer* is not. One hectare equals about 2.5 acres.

Changing from one metric unit of area to another is done by the same rules that you have been using. Since some of the conversions involve multiplying or dividing by 10,000, the decimal point must be moved *four* places to the left or right.

LESSON 101

Objectives

- To teach the *metric units of area.
- To teach *changing measures of area from one metric unit to another.

Review

1. *Metric measures* (Lessons 98–100).
   a. 15 km = (15,000) m
   b. 6.25 m = (625) cm
   c. 4.5 g = (4,500) mg
   d. 6,300 g = (6.3) kg
   e. 900 ml = (0.9) *l*
   f. 5 kl = (5,000) *l*

2. *Measuring with a metric ruler* (Lesson 97). Give practice with using a metric ruler to measure lines if the students have had trouble with this.

3. *Writing proportions to solve reading problems* (Lesson 93).
   a. Mother mixes 1 cup of sugar with 2 cups of water to make canning syrup. At that rate, how much sugar should be added to 9 cups of water?

      1 cup sugar with 2 cups water
      n cups sugar with 9 cups water
      $\frac{1}{2} = \frac{n}{9}$ $1 \times 9 \div 2 = (4\ 1/2)$ cups

   b. Brandon measured a bush and its shadow at noon one spring day. He found that the 6-foot bush cast an 8-foot shadow. How tall was a tree that cast a 36-foot shadow at the same time?

      6-foot bush cast 8-foot shadow
      n-foot tree cast 36-foot shadow
      $\frac{6}{8} = \frac{n}{36}$ $6 \times 36 \div 8 = (27)$ feet

Introduction

Give some practice with changing English measures of area from one unit to another (Lesson 36).
   a. 1 sq. ft. = (144) sq. in.
   b. 1 sq. yd. = (9) sq. ft.
   c. 90 sq. ft. = (10) sq. yd.
   d. 4 sq. mi. = (2,560) acres

Ask the students what English unit would be used to measure the length of the classroom. (foot or yard) What English unit is used to measure how much carpet is needed to cover a floor? (usually square yard)

What metric unit is used to measure the length of a room? (meter) What metric unit would be used to measure how much carpet is needed to cover a floor? (square meter)

Teaching Guide

1. **The square meter is the basic unit for measuring area in the metric system.** Other common units are the square centimeter, the hectare, and the square kilometer.

2. **In metric abbreviations, the exponent 2 is used to indicate "square."** The exponent indicates that the square measures have two dimensions—length and width.

   km^2 = square kilometer
   m^2 = square meter
   cm^2 = square centimeter

3. **Metric units of square measure are based on ten but are actually related by hundreds.** Because the units have two dimensions, the conversion numbers are 100 (10×10) or 10,000 (100×100).
   a. 5 m^2 = (50,000) cm^2
   b. 15 ha = (150,000) m^2

c. $3 \text{ km}^2 = (300) \text{ ha}$
d. $525 \text{ ha} = (5.25) \text{ km}^2$
e. $15,000 \text{ cm}^2 = (1.5) \text{ m}^2$
f. $2.5 \text{ ha} = (25,000) \text{ m}^2$
g. $18,000 \text{ m}^2 = (1.8) \text{ ha}$
h. $45 \text{ ha} = (0.45) \text{ km}^2$

Further Study

The hectare is based on the *are* (ĕr), which equals a square 10 meters by 10 meters (100 square meters). One hectare equals 100 ares, or a square 100 meters by 100 meters.

> **To change from a larger unit to a smaller unit, multiply.**
> $3 \text{ m}^2 = 30,000 \text{ cm}^2$ $2.4 \text{ ha} = 24,000 \text{ m}^2$ $3.8 \text{ km}^2 = 380 \text{ ha}$

> **To change from a smaller unit to a larger unit, divide.**
> $42,000 \text{ cm}^2 = 4.2 \text{ m}^2$ $2,500 \text{ m}^2 = 0.25 \text{ ha}$ $675 \text{ ha} = 6.75 \text{ km}^2$

CLASS PRACTICE

Change these metric measures as indicated.

a. $5 \text{ m}^2 = \underline{50,000} \text{ cm}^2$ b. $8 \text{ km}^2 = \underline{800} \text{ ha}$ c. $3.1 \text{ m}^2 = \underline{31,000} \text{ cm}^2$

d. $22,000 \text{ m}^2 = \underline{2.2} \text{ ha}$ e. $568 \text{ ha} = \underline{5.68} \text{ km}^2$ f. $4,800 \text{ cm}^2 = \underline{0.48} \text{ m}^2$

g. $475 \text{ ha} = \underline{4.75} \text{ km}^2$ h. $3.4 \text{ m}^2 = \underline{34,000} \text{ cm}^2$ i. $38,000 \text{ m}^2 = \underline{3.8} \text{ ha}$

WRITTEN EXERCISES

A. Write the abbreviation for each unit.

1. square centimeter cm^2
2. square meter m^2
3. hectare   ha
4. square kilometer km^2

B. Change these metric measures to smaller units by multiplying.

5. $7 \text{ m}^2 = \underline{70,000} \text{ cm}^2$
6. $4 \text{ km}^2 = \underline{400} \text{ ha}$
7. $15 \text{ ha} = \underline{150,000} \text{ m}^2$
8. $2.5 \text{ m}^2 = \underline{25,000} \text{ cm}^2$
9. $0.55 \text{ km}^2 = \underline{55} \text{ ha}$
10. $3.75 \text{ ha} = \underline{37,500} \text{ m}^2$

C. Change these metric measures to larger units by dividing.

11. $50,000 \text{ m}^2 = \underline{5} \text{ ha}$
12. $900 \text{ ha} = \underline{9} \text{ km}^2$
13. $30,000 \text{ cm}^2 = \underline{3} \text{ m}^2$
14. $35,000 \text{ m}^2 = \underline{3.5} \text{ ha}$
15. $745 \text{ ha} = \underline{7.45} \text{ km}^2$
16. $2,500 \text{ cm}^2 = \underline{0.25} \text{ m}^2$

D. Change these metric measures as indicated.

17. $800 \text{ ha} = \underline{8} \text{ km}^2$
18. $34 \text{ m}^2 = \underline{340,000} \text{ cm}^2$
19. $30,000 \text{ m}^2 = \underline{3} \text{ ha}$
20. $350 \text{ ha} = \underline{3.5} \text{ km}^2$
21. $5.1 \text{ m}^2 = \underline{51,000} \text{ cm}^2$
22. $25,000 \text{ m}^2 = \underline{2.5} \text{ ha}$

E. Solve these reading problems.

23. How many square meters are in a 37-hectare farm?   370,000 square meters

24. The top of the large desk in Father's study has an area of 1.8 square meters. What is this area in square centimeters?   18,000 square centimeters

25. A large factory building covers 5.25 hectares. How many square meters does it cover?   52,500 square meters

26. There are 8,500 square meters in a tract of land. What is its area in hectares?
      0.85 hectare

REVIEW EXERCISES

F. Change these measures as indicated. *(Lessons 36, 98–100)*

27. 2 sq. ft. = __288__ sq. in.   **28.** 6 sq. yd. = __54__ sq. ft.

29. 1,920 a. = __3__ sq. mi.   **30.** 72 sq. ft. = __8__ sq. yd.

31. 4.5 m = __450__ cm   **32.** 0.15 km = __150__ m

33. 2,400 ml = __2.4__ l **34.** 2.3 kg = __2,300__ g

35. 3.2 m.t. = __3,200__ kg   **36.** 0.45 l = __450__ ml

G. Measure each line to the nearest centimeter, and write the measurement on your paper. *(Lesson 97)*

37. ——————————————— 4 cm

38. —————————————————————— 8 cm

H. Write a proportion to solve each reading problem. *(Lesson 93)*

39. Father uses 16 pounds of salt to mix 2 tons of feed. At that rate, how much salt should he mix into 5 tons of feed? $\frac{16}{2} = \frac{n}{5}$ $n = 40$ pounds

40. God commanded Noah to build an ark that was 5 cubits wide for every 3 cubits of height. The ark was 30 cubits high. How wide was it? $\frac{5}{3} = \frac{n}{30}$ $n = 50$ cubits

LESSON 102

Objective

- To give practice with reading problems that involve metric measures.

Review

1. *Metric units of measure* (Lessons 98–101).
   a. 15 m = (1,500) cm
   b. 250 mm = (0.25) m
   c. 1.3 km = (1,300) m
   d. 27.5 cm = (275) mm
   e. 5 l = (5,000) ml
   f. 250 ml = (0.25) l
   g. 470 l = (0.47) kl
   h. 1.85 kl = (1,850) l
   i. 5 ha = (50,000) m^2
   j. 250 ha = (2.5) km^2
   k. 1.5 m^2 = (15,000) cm^2
   l. 8,500 cm^2 = (0.85) m^2

2. *Units of time* (Lesson 37).
   a. 5 min. = (300) sec.
   b. 4 hr. = (240) min.
   c. 4,000 yr. = (400) decades
   d. 96 mo. = (8) yr.

3. *Writing proportions to solve reading problems* (Lesson 94).
   a. In Omaha, Nebraska, an average of 2 out of every 5 days are cloudy. How many days are cloudy in an average year?
      2 cloudy days out of 5 days
      n cloudy days out of 365 days
      $\frac{2}{5} = \frac{n}{365}$ 2 × 365 ÷ 5 =
         (146) cloudy days per year
   b. In Richmond, Virginia, an average of 1 out of every 5 days is clear. How many days are clear in an average year?
      1 clear day out of 5 days
      n clear days out of 365 days
      $\frac{1}{5} = \frac{n}{365}$ 1 × 365 ÷ 5 =
         (73) clear days per year

Introduction

Give a thorough review of converting metric measures from one unit to another. Use Class Practice and the problems listed under Review.

Teaching Guide

This lesson gives further practice with reading problems that involve metric measures, and it also gives additional practice with metric unit conversions. Address any particular difficulty that your students may have with reading problems.

None of the exercises deal with new concepts. However, a few of the reading problems do require a more involved working with metric units than in previous lessons.

102. Metric Measures in Reading Problems

CLASS PRACTICE

Solve these reading problems.

    a. The church house and the school building are 3.5 kilometers apart. How many meters apart are they?   3,500 meters

    b. Douglas's pencil is 64 millimeters long. How many centimeters long is it?   6.4 centimeters

    c. Three of the Millers' steers weigh an average of 522 kilograms each. How many metric tons do they weigh in all?   1.566 metric tons

    d. The Baers drove 396 kilometers in 4.5 hours. How many kilometers per hour did they travel?   88 kilometers per hour

WRITTEN EXERCISES

A.   *Solve these reading problems.*

    1. A jet plane cruised at an altitude of 12,700 meters above sea level. How many kilometers above sea level was it flying?   12.7 kilometers

    2. An American quarter has a diameter of about 24 millimeters. How many centimeters are in 24 millimeters?   2.4 centimeters

    3. Brother Hess spent three days traveling in church work. He traveled 482 kilometers on the first day, 519 kilometers on the second day, and 367 kilometers on the third day. What was the average distance that he traveled each day?   456 kilometers

    4. A customer came to Mr. Daniels' lumberyard to buy a plank 4 meters long. The first plank Mr. Daniels measured was 389.7 centimeters long. How much shorter was it than 4 meters?   10.3 centimeters

    5. The Masts live 2.3 kilometers from church. The Myers live 4 times as far away as the Masts do. How far is the Myers' home from the church?   9.2 kilometers

    6. A bag of sugar weighs 2,264 grams. How many kilograms does it weigh?   2.264 kilograms

    7. Fifteen persons in an elevator weighed an average of 64 kilograms each. Find the total weight of these people in metric tons.   0.96 metric ton

    8. A truck was loaded with 65 bags of potatoes weighing 20 kilograms each. How many metric tons of potatoes were on the truck?   1.3 metric tons

    9. A 2-liter container of milk cost $1.18. What was the price per liter for the milk? $0.59

10. A bottle of gravy flavoring contained 60 milliliters. Express 60 milliliters as liters.
0.06 liter

11. The Welland family's car went 390 kilometers on 78 liters of gasoline. How many kilometers per liter did it travel?
5 kilometers per liter

12. Brother Martin has a small vehicle that averages 8.5 kilometers for each liter of diesel fuel it uses. At that rate, how many liters of diesel fuel did it use on a 238-kilometer trip?
28 liters

13. Holmes County, Ohio, has an area of about 1,100 square kilometers. What is this area in hectares?
110,000 hectares

14. The Hidden Valley Christian Day School is located on 1.825 hectares of land. How many square meters is that?
18,250 square meters

15. A 48.4-hectare farm sold for $4,500 per hectare. What was the selling price of the farm?
$217,800.00

16. Uncle Larry plants 90 kilograms of wheat per hectare in his fields. One field covers 75,000 square meters. How many kilograms of wheat does Uncle Larry plant in this field?
675 kilograms

REVIEW EXERCISES

B.   Change these measures as indicated. *(Lessons 37, 98, 101)*

17. 5 m = __500__ cm

18. 3,500 m = __3.5__ km

19. 0.6 l = __600__ ml

20. 1,300 l = __1.3__ kl

21. 8 l = __8,000__ ml

22. 8,800 m = __8.8__ km

23. 500 ha = __5__ km²

24. 3 ha = __30,000__ m²

25. 25 min. = __1,500__ sec.

26. 660 min. = __11__ hr.

27. 119 days = __17__ wk.

28. 15 decades = __150__ yr.

C.   Write proportions to solve these reading problems. *(Lesson 94)*

29. There is much less water in snow than in rain. It takes a 6-inch layer of moist snow to equal the water in 1 inch of rainfall. Nine inches of moist snow is equal to how many inches of rain?
$\frac{6}{1} = \frac{9}{n}$ $n = 1\frac{1}{2}$ inches

30. Dry snow contains much less water than moist snow. It takes a 30-inch layer of dry snow to equal the water in 6 inches of moist snow. How many inches of dry snow would be needed to have as much water as a 9-inch layer of moist snow?
$\frac{30}{6} = \frac{n}{9}$ $n = 45$ inches

LESSON 103

Objective

- To teach *making conversions between metric and English units of linear measure and weight.

Review

1. Give Lesson 103 Quiz (Metric Units of Weight, Capacity, and Area).

2. *Metric units of measure* (Lessons 99, 101).
   Units of weight
   a. 1.5 kg = (1,500) g
   b. 450 kg = (0.45) m.t.
   Units of square measure
   a. 5 ha = (50,000) m²
   b. 450 ha = (4.5) km²
   c. 2.1 m² = (21,000) cm²
   d. 3.2 ha = (32,000) m²

3. *Dividing decimals* (Lessons 85–87).

   a. $\overset{(3.51)}{5\overline{)17.55}}$ b. $\overset{(34.)}{0.4\overline{)13.6}}$

   c. $\overset{(41.)}{0.55\overline{)22.55}}$

4. *Time zones* (Lesson 38).
   a. Miami, Florida—8:45 A.M.
      Denver, Colorado—(6:45 A.M.)
   b. Seattle, Washington—9:15 A.M.
      New York City—(12:15 P.M.)

Introduction

Ask the students if 5 feet is nearer 1 meter or 1.5 meters. Is 80 pounds nearer to 25 or 35 kilograms? Is 55 miles per hour closer to 70, 80, 90, or 100 kilometers per hour? This lesson helps to answer those questions.

Teaching Guide

1. Use the Metric-to-English table to give practice with changing metric measures to English measures. Find the metric unit, and multiply the number of units in the metric measure by the conversion number that is given. Label the product with the English unit shown after the conversion number.
   a. 4 m = (13.12) ft.   [4 × 3.28]
   b. 15 cm = (5.85) in.   [15 × 0.39]
   c. 4 m = (157.6) in.   [4 × 39.4]
   d. 4 km = (2.48) mi.   [4 × 0.62]
   e. 110 g = (3.85) oz.   [110 × 0.035]
   f. 3 kg = (6.6) lb.   [3 × 2.2]

2. Use the English-to-Metric table to give practice with changing English units to metric units. Find the English unit, and multiply the number of units in the English measure by the conversion number that is given. Label the product with the metric unit shown after the conversion number.

   Problems *a–c* below help to answer the questions in the Introduction.
   a. 5 ft. = (1.5) m   [5 × 0.3]
   b. 80 lb. = (36) kg   [80 × 0.45]
   c. 55 m.p.h. = (88.55) km/h
      [55 × 1.61]
   d. 11 in. = (27.94) cm   [11 × 2.54]
   e. 6 mi. = (9.66) km   [6 × 1.61]
   f. 9 oz. = (254.7) g   [9 × 28.3]

Note: Students will not be tested on their memory of the English-metric relationships, but on their ability to change measures by using a chart.

103. Conversions Between Metric and English Units: Linear Measure and Weight

Because metric and English measures are both widely used, it is sometimes necessary to change a measure in one system to its equivalent in the other system. The tables below give the approximate relationships between English and metric units of linear measure and weight.

To change metric units to English units, use the Metric-to-English table below. Find the metric unit, and multiply the number of units in the metric measure by the conversion number that is given. Label the product with the English unit shown after the conversion number.

To change English units to metric units, use the English-to-Metric table below. Find the English unit, and multiply the number of units in the English measure by the conversion number that is given. Label the product with the metric unit shown after the conversion number.

Metric to English	**English to Metric**
Linear Measure 1 cm = 0.39 in. 1 m = 39.4 in. 1 m = 3.28 ft. 1 km = 0.62 mi. *Weight* 1 g = 0.035 oz. 1 kg = 2.2 lb.	*Linear Measure* 1 in. = 2.54 cm 1 ft. = 0.3 m 1 mi. = 1.61 km *Weight* 1 oz. = 28.3 g 1 lb. = 0.45 kg
Example A 3 m = ___ in. $3 \times 39.4 = 118.2$ in.	**Example B** 50 lb. = ___ kg $50 \times 0.45 = 22.5$ kg

CLASS PRACTICE

Change these measures as indicated.

a. 3 m = __9.84__ ft. b. 4 m = __157.6__ in. c. 14 km = __8.68__ mi.

d. 45 g = __1.575__ oz. e. 25 kg = __55__ lb. f. 11 ft. = __3.3__ m

g. 48 lb. = __21.6__ kg. h. 10 mi. = __16.1__ km i. 17 kg = __37.4__ lb.

WRITTEN EXERCISES

A.   *Change these metric measures to English measures by using the Metric-to-English table.*

1. 2 m = <u>78.8</u> in.   2. 5 m = <u>16.4</u> ft.   3. 3 km = <u>1.86</u> mi.

4. 60 g = <u>2.1</u> oz.   5. 4 kg = <u>8.8</u> lb.   6. 7 m = <u>22.96</u> ft.

B.   *Change these English measures to metric measures by using the English-to-Metric table.*

7. 6 in. = <u>15.24</u> cm   8. 2 mi. = <u>3.22</u> km   9. 2 ft. = <u>0.6</u> m

10. 100 lb. = <u>45</u> kg   11. 20 lb. = <u>9</u> kg   12. 6 oz. = <u>169.8</u> g

C.   *Change these measures as indicated.*

13. 12 m = <u>39.36</u> ft.   14. 12 ft. = <u>3.6</u> m   15. 9 lb. = <u>4.05</u> kg

16. 95 g = <u>3.325</u> oz.   17. 8 oz. = <u>226.4</u> g   18. 8 mi. = <u>12.88</u> km

D.   *Solve these reading problems.*

19. Daniel is 1.45 meters tall. How many inches tall is he?   57.13 inches

20. Daniel weighs 38 kilograms. How many pounds does he weigh?   83.6 pounds

21. The Kauffman family traveled to western Canada to visit a mission church there. On some interstate highways in the United States, the speed limit was 65 miles per hour. How many kilometers per hour is that?   104.65 kilometers per hour

22. In some parts of Canada, the speed limit was 100 kilometers per hour. How many miles per hour is that?   62 miles per hour

23. Father bought a 50-pound bag of feed. How many kilograms of feed is that?   22.5 kilograms

24. Father sold a steer that weighed 720 kilograms. What was its weight in pounds?   1,584 pounds

REVIEW EXERCISES

E.   *Change these measures as indicated. (Lessons 99, 101)*

25. 300 ha = <u>3</u> km²   26. 2.2 ha = <u>22,000</u> m²

27. 2.5 g = <u>2,500</u> mg   28. 2,300 g = <u>2.3</u> kg

F.   *Solve these division problems. (Lessons 85–87)*

29.
$$\begin{array}{r} \$3.15 \\ 5\overline{)\$15.75} \end{array}$$

30.
$$\begin{array}{r} 19.925 \\ 0.8\overline{)15.94} \end{array}$$

G.   *When it is the time given for the first city, what time is it in the second city? (Lesson 38)*

31. Atlanta, Georgia—4:15 P.M.; Portland, Oregon— ?   1:15 P.M.

32. Denver, Colorado—3:30 A.M.; Rochester, New York— ?   5.30 A.M.

LESSON 104

Objective

- To teach *making conversions between metric and English units of capacity and area.

Review

1. *Adding, subtracting, and dividing compound English units* (Lessons 39, 41).

   a. $\begin{array}{r} 5 \text{ ft. } 9 \text{ in.} \\ + 8 \text{ ft. } 6 \text{ in.} \\ \hline (14 \text{ ft. } 3 \text{ in.}) \end{array}$ b. $\begin{array}{r} 8 \text{ gal. } 2 \text{ qt.} \\ - 2 \text{ gal. } 3 \text{ qt.} \\ \hline (5 \text{ gal. } 3 \text{ qt.}) \end{array}$

   c. $\overset{(3 \text{ qt.})}{9)\overline{6 \text{ gal. } 3 \text{ qt.}}}$

2. *Metric units of capacity* (Lesson 100).
   a. 450 ml = (0.45) l
   b. 5,600 l = (5.6) kl

3. *Rounding decimals* (Lesson 88).
   To the nearest tenth
       a. 0.47   (0.5)
       b. 1.83   (1.8)
       c. 4.96   (5.0)
   To the nearest hundredth
       d. 0.387   (0.39)
       e. 3.379   (3.38)
       f. 4.495   (4.50)

Introduction

Ask the students if they have ever watched a fuel pump that measured the fuel in liters. How many liters might be put into the fuel tank of a car? Ten? Twenty? Fifty? One hundred? They might be surprised to know that a 15-gallon tank can hold over 50 liters of fuel.

If your students are more familiar with metric units than English units, you could reverse the situation described above and have them guess how many gallons are in 55 liters.

Teaching Guide

1. Use the Metric-to-English table to give practice with changing metric measures to English measures. Find the metric unit, and multiply the number of units in the metric measure by the conversion number that is given. Label the product with the English unit shown after the conversion number.

   Problem *g* below answers the question in the second paragraph of the Introduction.

   a. 4 l = (4.24) qt.   [4 × 1.06]
   b. 15 l = (15.9) qt.   [15 × 1.06]
   c. 6 ha = (15) a.   [6 × 2.5]
   d. 45 ha = (112.5) a.   [45 × 2.5]
   e. 25 km^2 = (9.75) sq. mi.   [25 × 0.39]
   f. 175 km^2 = (68.25) sq. mi.
       [175 × 0.39]
   g. 55 l = (58.3) qt. = (14.575) gallons
       [55 × 1.06 ÷ 4]

2. Use the English-to-Metric table to give practice with changing English units to metric units. Find the English unit, and multiply the number of units in the English measure by the conversion

104. Conversions Between Metric and English Units: Capacity and Area

Measures of capacity and area must sometimes be changed from metric units to English units or from English units to metric units. These changes are made by the same method as that described in Lesson 103.

Metric to English	**English to Metric**
Capacity	*Capacity*
1 l = 1.06 qt. (liquid)	1 qt. (liquid) = 0.95 l
Area	*Area*
1 ha = 2.5 a.	1 a. = 0.4 ha
1 km² = 0.39 sq. mi.	1 sq. mi. = 2.59 km²

Example A
3 l = ____ qt.
3 × 1.06 = 3.18 qt.

Example C
35 km² = ____ sq. mi.
35 × 0.39 = 13.65 sq. mi.

Example B
5 a. = ____ ha
5 × 0.4 = 2 ha

Example D
75 sq. mi. = ____ km²
75 × 2.59 = 194.25 km²

CLASS PRACTICE

Change these measures as indicated.

a. 3 ha = __7.5__ a.
b. 3 l = __3.18__ qt.
c. 2 km² = __0.78__ sq. mi.
d. 7 qt. = __6.65__ l
e. 15 a. = __6__ ha
f. 20 sq. mi. = __51.8__ km²
g. 18 l = __19.08__ qt.
h. 13 ha = __32.5__ a.
i. 7 sq. mi. = __18.13__ km²

WRITTEN EXERCISES

A. **Change these metric measures to English measures by using the Metric-to-English table.**

1. 2 ha = __5__ a.
2. 5 l = __5.3__ qt.
3. 10 ha = __25__ a.
4. 9 l = __9.54__ qt.
5. 5 ha = __12.5__ a.
6. 50 l = __53__ qt.

B.   Change these English measures to metric measures by using the English-to-Metric table.

7.   2 qt. = __1.9__ l 8.   30 a. = __12__ ha   9.   5 sq. mi. = __12.95__ km²

10.   20 qt. = __19__ l 11.   100 a. = __40__ ha   12.   80 sq. mi. = __207.2__ km²

C.   Change these measures as indicated.

13.   20 a. = __8__ ha   14.   5 km² = __1.95__ sq. mi.   15.   7 qt. = __6.65__ l

16.   9 sq. mi. = __23.31__ km²   17.   12 l = __12.72__ qt.   18.   45 ha = __112.5__ a.

D.   Solve these reading problems.

19.   The Wenger family lives on a 125-acre farm. How large is their farm in hectares?
                                                                            50 hectares

20.   The Commonwealth of Pennsylvania has an area of 45,308 square miles. How many square kilometers is that?   117,347.72 square kilometers

21.   Mother bought 1 gallon of milk. How many liters of milk did she buy? (Remember to first change gallons to quarts.)   3.8 liters

22.   The Laddsburg Mennonite School is on 1.5 hectares of land. How many acres is that?   3.75 acres

23.   While driving to an ordination service at a distant church, Father bought 72.2 liters of gasoline. How many quarts of gasoline did he buy? How many gallons?
                                                76.532 quarts   19.133 gallons

24.   The province of Prince Edward Island has an area of 5,657 square kilometers. What is its area in square miles?   2,206.23 square miles

REVIEW EXERCISES

E.   Solve these problems. *(Lessons 39, 41)*

25. 6 ft. 8 in.   26.   6 lb.   7 oz.   2 ft. 5 in.
     + 5 ft. 9 in.   − 3 lb.   9 oz.   27.   4)9 ft. 8 in.
     12 ft. 5 in.   2 lb. 14 oz.

F.   Change these measures as indicated. *(Lesson 100)*

28.   270 ml = __0.27__ l 29.   3,400 l = __3.4__ kl

G.   Round these decimals as indicated. *(Lesson 88)*

30.   0.38 to the nearest tenth   0.4   31.   0.797 to the nearest hundredth   0.80

number that is given. Label the product with the metric unit shown after the conversion number.

Problem *g* below answers the question in the first paragraph of the Introduction.

a.   66 qt. = (62.7) *l*   [66 × 0.95]
b.   8 qt. = (7.6) *l*   [8 × 0.95]
c.   25 a. = (10) ha   [25 × 0.4]
d.   115 a. = (46) ha   [115 × 0.4]
e.   40 sq. mi. = (103.6) km²   [40 × 2.59]
f.   15,000 sq. mi. = (38,850) km²
         [15,000 × 2.59]
g.   15 gal. = (60) qt. = (57) *l*   [60 × 0.95]

LESSON 105

Objectives

- To introduce the term *formula*. (Previous experience: Use of the rule *distance = rate × time,* without calling it a formula.)

- To teach the formula for distance, rate, and time, *including the form $d = r \times t$.

Review

1. Give Lesson 105 Speed Test (Metric Units of Measure).

2. *Changing between metric and English units of measure* (Lessons 103, 104). Use the conversion ratios found on the charts in Lessons 103 and 104.
   a. 5 km = (3.1) mi.
   b. 20 kg = (44) pounds
   c. 15 qt.= (14.25) *l*
   d. 18 a. = (7.2) ha

3. *Metric units of square measure* (Lesson 101).
   a. 2.5 km² = (250) ha
   b. 175 ha = (1.75) km²
   c. 1.67 m² = (16,700) cm²
   d. 2,800 cm² = (0.28) m²

4. *Measuring with a metric ruler* (Lesson 97). Have the students measure the length and width of their math books to the nearest centimeter.

5. *Changing fractions to decimals rounded to the nearest hundredth* (Lesson 88).
   a. $\frac{3}{16}$ = (0.19)
   b. $\frac{9}{11}$ = (0.82)
   c. $\frac{11}{15}$ = (0.73)

Introduction

Read the following problems to the students to test their understanding of distance, rate, and time.

a. The Gehman family left their home early one morning to visit their uncle in a distant state. They traveled 6 hours at an average speed of 50 miles per hour. How far did they travel? (6 × 50 = 300 miles)

b. That afternoon the Gehmans traveled 250 miles in 5 hours. What was their average speed in miles per hour? (250 ÷ 5 = 50 miles per hour)

c. In the evening they traveled 216 miles at an average rate of 54 miles per hour. How many hours did they travel? (216 ÷ 54 = 4 hours)

You will probably find that most of the students are quite comfortable with problems of this kind. The term *rate* may be new, but it is used for a familiar concept.

Teaching Guide

1. Discuss the terms *distance, rate,* and *time.*
   > Distance—How far
   > Rate—How fast
   > Time—How long

2. Discuss the units used in expressing rates of speed. Several common ones are shown here.
   > miles per hour (m.p.h.)
   > miles per minute (m.p.m.)
   > kilometers per hour (km/h)
   > feet per second (f.p.s.)

   These units can be discussed in relation to the three types of problems taught in the lesson.

105. Working With Distance, Rate, and Time

Sometimes you need to know **how far** you can travel in a given amount of time. It is often interesting to know **how fast** you have traveled. And you may you need to know **how long** it takes to get to a certain place.

These three facts—how far, how fast, and how long—are all related to each other. If you know any two of the three facts, you can find the one that is unknown. The three facts are named by the following terms.

Distance—How far (in miles or kilometers)

Rate—How fast (in miles or kilometers per hour)

Time—How long (in hours or minutes)

The relationship between distance, rate, and time can be stated with words or letters as shown below. Such a statement is called a **formula.**

$$\text{distance} = \text{rate} \times \text{time, or } d = r \times t$$

The formula above is used to find the distance when the rate and time are known. This is the basic way that the formula is written. To find the rate or the time, the formula is rewritten in the following two ways.

$$\text{rate} = \text{distance} \div \text{time, or } r = d \div t$$

$$\text{time} = \text{distance} \div \text{rate, or } t = d \div r$$

Example A

   The Mast family traveled 3 hours at an average speed of 50 miles per hour. How far did they travel?

Think: distance = rate × time, or $d = r \times t$

   50 miles per hour × 3 hours = 150 miles

Example B

   The Mast family traveled 150 miles in 3 hours. What was their average rate of speed?

Think: rate = distance ÷ time, or $r = d \div t$

   150 miles ÷ 3 hours = 50 miles per hour

Example C

   The Mast family traveled 150 miles at an average speed of 50 miles per hour. What was their traveling time?

Think: time = distance ÷ rate, or $t = d \div r$

   150 miles ÷ 50 miles per hour = 3 hours

CLASS PRACTICE

	Rate	Time	Distance
a.	52 m.p.h.	3 hr.	156 mi.
b.	46 m.p.h.	2.5 hr.	115 mi.
c.	52 m.p.h.	7 hr.	364 mi.
d.	54 m.p.h.	3.5 hr.	189 mi.
e.	40 m.p.h.	6 hr.	240 mi.
f.	45 m.p.h.	5.2 hr.	234 mi.

WRITTEN EXERCISES

A.   *Find the missing numbers for the chart below.*

	Rate	Time	Distance		Rate	Time	Distance
1.	48 m.p.h.	4 hr.	192 mi.	2.	50 m.p.h.	3.5 hr.	175 mi.
3.	48 m.p.h.	5 hr.	240 mi.	4.	52 m.p.h.	4.5 hr.	234 mi.
5.	50 m.p.h.	7 hr.	350 mi.	6.	48 m.p.h.	7.5 hr.	360 mi.
7.	44 m.p.h.	2.5 hr.	110 mi.	8.	42 m.p.h.	3.5 hr.	147 mi.
9.	52 m.p.h.	8.5 hr.	442 mi.	10.	82 km/h	5 hr.	410 km
11.	80 km/h	3.75 hr.	300 km	12.	87.5 km/h	8 hr.	700 km
13.	7 m.p.m.	12 min.	84 mi.	14.	5 m.p.m.	15 min.	75 mi.
15.	8 m.p.m.	8 min.	64 mi.	16.	7 m.p.m.	45 min.	315 mi.

B.   *Solve these reading problems.*

17. A man can usually walk at a steady pace of 3 miles per hour. At that rate, how many hours would it take to walk 15 miles?   5 hours

18. The Landis family traveled 350 miles to visit their grandparents. It took them 7 hours to drive that distance. What was their average rate of travel?   50 miles per hour

19. When Brother Mark went to visit an outreach church, the Miller family took him to the airport. They drove $2\frac{1}{2}$ hours at an average speed of 44 miles per hour. How far did they drive to the airport?   110 miles

20. Brother Mark's plane flew 1,350 miles in 3.6 hours. What was the average speed of the plane?   375 miles per hour

3. Work with the formula for distance, rate, and time. Write its three forms on the board, and use them to solve the examples in the text and the problems below.

distance = rate × time, or $d = r \times t$

    a. 3 hr. at 45 m.p.h. (135 mi.)

    b. 4 hr. at 79 km/h (316 km)

rate = distance ÷ time, or $r = d \div t$

    c. 255 mi. in 5 hr. (51 m.p.h.)

    d. 480 mi. in 10 hr. (48 m.p.h.)

time = distance ÷ rate, or $t = d \div r$

    e. 567 km at 81 km/h (7 hr.)

    f. 315 km at 70 km/h (4.5 hr.)

When you assign the written work, call attention to problems 13–16. These deal with minutes and miles per minute rather than with hours and miles per hour.

Note: Students will not be tested on their memory of the distance-rate-time formula, but on their ability to use it in solving problems.

Further Study

This lesson introduces the students to formulas by presenting one that is quite simple. Understanding this formula will prepare them for the geometric formulas taught later in the book. Basic formulas like these will acquaint students with the use of symbols to represent unknown numbers, as is done in algebraic equations.

21. When Elijah fled from Queen Jezebel (1 Kings 19), he traveled from Beersheba to Mt. Horeb in 41 days. If the distance from Beersheba to Mt. Horeb is 200 miles, what was his rate of travel in miles per day? Express your answer as a decimal rounded to the nearest tenth of a mile.   4.9 miles per day

22. One morning after family devotions, Father drove to Millville for some farm supplies. He traveled the 18 kilometers in 15 minutes. What was his speed in kilometers per minute? Express your answer as a decimal.

1.2 kilometers per minute

REVIEW EXERCISES

C. Use the tables given in Lessons 103 and 104 to change these measures as indicated.

23. 4 km = __2.48__ mi.   24. 25 mi. = __40.25__ km   25. 5 l = __5.3__ qt.

26. 8 qt. = __7.6__ l 27. 40 kg = __88__ lb.   28. 90 lb. = __40.5__ kg

D. Change these metric measures of area as indicated. *(Lesson 101)*

29. 4 km² = __400__ ha   30. 150 ha = __1.5__ km²   31. 4.2 ha = __42,000__ m²

32. 195 ha = __1.95__ km²   33. 35,000 cm² = __3.5__ m²   34. 12 km² = __1,200__ ha

E. Measure these lines to the nearest centimeter. *(Lesson 97)*

35. ———————   2 cm

36. ————————————————————————   12 cm

F. Change each fraction to a decimal rounded to the nearest hundredth. *(Lesson 88)*

37. $\frac{5}{6}$ 0.83   **38.** $\frac{5}{7}$ 0.71   **39.** $\frac{7}{15}$ 0.47   **40.** $\frac{7}{18}$ 0.39

106. Distance, Rate, and Time in Reading Problems

> distance = rate × time or $d = r \times t$
> rate = distance ÷ time, or $r = d \div t$
> time = distance ÷ rate, or $t = d \div r$

CLASS PRACTICE

Solve these reading problems.

a. The *Eight Metroliner* is one of the fastest trains in the United States. It can make the trip from Wilmington, Delaware, to Baltimore, Maryland, in 0.7 hour at an average rate of 97.7 miles per hour. Find the length of this trip, to the nearest mile.

68 miles

b. Another train, the *Express Metroliner*, makes the 135-mile trip from New York City to Baltimore in 2.05 hours. What is its average rate of speed? Round your answer to the nearest tenth mile per hour.   65.9 miles per hour

c. A Canadian train, the *York*, travels the 174 kilometers between Cornwall and Kingston, Ontario, at an average rate of 134 kilometers per hour. How long does the trip take? Round your answer to the nearest tenth of an hour.   1.3 hours

WRITTEN EXERCISES

A. *Solve these reading problems.*

1. Father drove to Auburn for supplies one morning. The trip took $\frac{1}{2}$ hour, and his average speed was 48 miles per hour. How far is it to Auburn?   24 miles

2. The Landis family drove 196 miles to attend a Bible conference at Lakeview. If their traveling time was 4 hours, what was their average rate of speed?   49 miles per hour

3. One morning Mark rode his bicycle to school in 0.25 hour at an average speed of 16 miles per hour. How many miles did Mark ride to school?   4 miles

4. The pony express carried mail 1,966 miles from St. Joseph, Missouri, to Sacramento, California. One of the fastest trips was made in 8 days. In that case, how many miles per day did the riders travel? Round your answer to the nearest tenth of a mile.

245.8 miles

5. When European Mennonites began moving to America, one of the first groups sailed from Gravesend, England, to Philadelphia, Pennsylvania, in 86 days. If the distance is 4,000 miles, what was their average speed in miles per day? Round your answer to the nearest whole number.   47 miles per day

LESSON 106

Objective

- To give practice with reading problems that involve distance, rate, and time.

Review

1. *Conversions between metric and English units of measure* (Lessons 103, 104).
   a. 4 km = (2.48) mi.
   b. 15 m = (49.2) ft.
   c. 10 oz. = (283) g
   d. 4.5 kg = (9.9) lb.
   e. 9 qt. = (8.55) l
   f. 15 acres = (6) ha

2. *Multiplying and dividing compound English units* (Lessons 40, 41).

   a.   5 ft. 6 in.   b.   4 lb. 9 oz.
          × 7   × 6
     (38 ft. 6 in.)   (27 lb. 6 oz.)

         (2 ft. 5 in.)   (1 lb. 12 oz.)
   c. 4)9 ft. 8 in.   d. 7)12 lb. 4 oz.

3. *Metric units of linear measure* (Lesson 98).
   a. 15 m = (1,500) cm
   b. 230 mm = (0.23) m
   c. 1.8 cm = (18) mm
   d. 2,500 m = (2.5) km

Introduction

This lesson reviews Lesson 105. Spend time briefly reviewing the formula for distance, rate, and time.
   a. 3 hr. at 15 m.p.h. (45 mi.)
   b. 3 hr. at 80 km/h (240 km)
   c. 180 mi. in 4 hr. (45 m.p.h.)
   d. 196 mi. at 49 m.p.h. (4 hr.)

Teaching Guide

Spend most of the class period giving practice with identifying distance, rate, and time in reading problems. If the students can identify these facts, they should have little trouble with the written work.

a. Duane went with his father to deliver eggs to stores. They were on the egg route for 3 hours. During that time they drove 69 miles. What was their average speed?
   time—3 hr.
   distance—69 mi.
   rate—unknown
   rate = distance ÷ time
   69 ÷ 3 = (23 m.p.h.)

b. Andrew was traveling with his father by train to a mission station. How far did they travel in 5 hours if the speed of the train was 80 miles per hour?
   time—5 hr.
   rate—80 m.p.h.
   distance—unknown
   distance = rate × time
   5 × 80 = (400 miles)

c. The Burkholder family drove 450 miles to visit their aunt who was teaching school. Their average speed was 50 miles per hour. How long did they travel?

>   distance—450 mi.
>   rate—50 m.p.h.
>   time—unknown

time = distance ÷ rate

450 ÷ 50 = (9 hr.)

d. Mervin biked the 4 miles to school in 1/3 hour. At that rate, how fast could he travel in miles per hour?

>   distance—4 mi.
>   time—1/3 hour
>   rate—unknown

rate = distance ÷ time

4 ÷ 1/3 = 4 × 3 = (12 m.p.h.)

Note: Problem *d* lends itself to mental calculation by multiplication. Do not discourage students from thinking: "There are three 1/3's in 1 hour; therefore, Mervin will bike 3 times 4 miles, or 12 miles in 1 hour." Learning to solve a math problem in several different ways is a skill you should strive to teach your pupils.

6. Today ships travel the distance between England and North America much more rapidly. In 1952, a ship traveled from western England to the New York harbor in 83 hours. If the ship traveled 3,386 miles, what was its average speed in miles per hour? Round your answer to the nearest whole number.   41 miles per hour

7. The fastest passenger planes travel between Europe and America in even less time. The Concorde jet can make the flight between London, England, and Washington, D.C., in about 3.58 hours at an average speed of 1,023 miles per hour. Find the distance that the Concorde flies, to the nearest whole number.   3,662 miles

8. When the Weaver family visited relatives out of state, they traveled 240 miles in 5 hours. What was their average rate of speed?   48 miles per hour

9. Joab and his armed men once traveled all night on foot from Bethlehem to Hebron (2 Samuel 2:32). If they covered the distance in 8 hours, and if Bethlehem and Hebron are 14 miles apart, how fast did they travel?   1.75 miles per hour

10. Acts 28:13 records Paul's journey by ship from Rhegium to Puteoli on his way to Rome. If the distance was 205 miles and the trip took 40 hours, what was the average speed at which the ship sailed? Answer in miles per hour, to the nearest tenth.   5.1 miles per hour

REVIEW EXERCISES

B.   Use the tables given in Lessons 103 and 104 to change these measures as indicated.

11.   14 kg = _30.8_ lb.   12.   8 mi. = _12.88_ km

13.   12 m = _39.36_ ft.   14.   6 qt. = _5.7_ l

15.   8 ha = _20_ a.   16.   8 sq. mi. = _20.72_ km²

C.   Solve these problems. *(Lessons 40, 41)*

17.   6 ft. 8 in.
        × 6
        ‾‾‾‾‾
       40 ft.

18.   6 lb. 7 oz.
        × 3
        ‾‾‾‾‾
       19 lb. 5 oz.

19.   5)9 lb. 6 oz.   →   1 lb. 14 oz.

20.   4)9 ft. 8 in.   →   2 ft. 5 in.

D.   Change these measures as indicated. *(Lesson 98)*

21.   150 cm = _1.5_ m   22.   3.5 m = _3,500_ mm

23.   3 km = _3,000_ m   24.   1,020 mm = _1.02_ m

25.   340 m = _0.34_ km   26.   9 m = _900_ cm

107. Using a Scale of Miles

A good map helps us accurately picture a certain area. It can be used to find not only the location of places but also the distance between places. The scale of miles on a map shows the ratio that the map maker used. For example, a scale of 1 inch = 40 miles means that one inch on the map is equal to 40 miles of actual distance.

The following steps explain how to find distances by using a scale of miles.

1. Using a ruler, measure carefully the distance on the map.
2. Divide the measurement found in Step 1 by the first part of the scale of miles. If the first part of the scale is 1, this step can be omitted.
3. Multiply the answer in Step 2 by the second part of the scale of miles. Label your answer with the unit used in the second part of the scale.

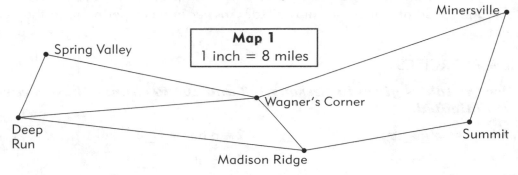

Map 1
1 inch = 8 miles

Example A
On Map 1, find the distance from Spring Valley to Wagner's Corner.
   a. Distance on map: $2\frac{1}{4}$ in.
   b. (Dividing by 1 is not needed.)
   c. $2\frac{1}{4} \times 8 = 18$ miles

Example B
On Map 2, find the distance from Plains to Lakeville.
   a. Distance on map: $1\frac{3}{4}$ in.
   b. $1\frac{3}{4} \div \frac{1}{4} = 7$
   c. $7 \times 12 = 84$ miles

CLASS PRACTICE

Give the actual distance represented by each measurement on a map if the scale is 1 inch = 24 miles.

  a. 4 in.   96 miles   **b.** $\frac{1}{2}$ in.   12 miles   **c.** $2\frac{1}{4}$ in.   54 miles   **d.** $3\frac{1}{8}$ in.   75 miles

LESSON 107

Objective

- To review finding actual distances by using the scale on a map.

Review

1. Give Lesson 107 Quiz (Conversions Between Metric and English Units).

2. *Changing decimals to fractions in lowest terms* (Lesson 74).
   a. $0.55 = (\frac{11}{20})$
   b. $0.28 = (\frac{7}{25})$
   c. $0.78 = (\frac{39}{50})$

3. *Changing fractions to decimals* (Lesson 73). Division for these does not need to be carried further than the ten-thousandths' place.
   a. $\frac{7}{20} = (0.35)$
   b. $\frac{7}{8} = (0.875)$
   c. $\frac{15}{16} = (0.9375)$

4. *Prime and composite numbers* (Lesson 45).
   a. 51 (composite)
   b. 52 (composite)
   c. 53 (prime)

5. *Adding and subtracting decimals* (Lesson 76). No class review is necessary.

Introduction

Call the students' attention to a wall map of North America. Ask them if they know how to use the map to find the distance from Los Angeles, California, to Washington, D.C. Measure the distance on the map, and use the scale of miles to find the actual distance. Also find the distances between other points of interest if you have time. (Be careful if you do this on a world map. Many wall maps—especially those of the Mercator projection—are greatly distorted in the polar regions.)

Teaching Guide

1. **A scale of miles shows the ratio of a distance on a map to the actual distance it represents.** On Map 1 in the text, 1 inch represents 8 miles. On Map 2, 1/4 inch represents 12 miles. If the students have geography books with a good set of maps, you could call attention to the different scales on the various maps.

2. **The scale of miles can be used to find the actual distance between any two points shown on the map.** The following steps are used.
   (1) *Using a ruler, measure carefully the distance on the map.* Have the students practice actually measuring on maps.
   (2) *Divide the measurement found in step 1 by the first part of the scale of miles.* If the first part of the scale is 1, this step can be omitted.
   (3) *Multiply the answer in step 2 by the second part of the scale of miles.* Label your answer with the unit used in the second part of the scale.

Problem A
   Measured distance: 3 1/2 in.
   Scale: 1/8 in. = 15 mi.
   3 1/2 ÷ 1/8 × 15 = (420) mi.

Problem B
   Measured distance: 2 1/4 in.
   Scale: 1/4 in. = 8 mi.
   2 1/4 ÷ 1/4 × 8 = (72) mi.

Problem C
   Measured distance: 1 1/4 in.
   Scale: 1/8 in. = 25 mi.
   1 1/4 ÷ 1/8 × 25 = (250) mi.

Problem D
   Measured distance: 3 1/2 in.
   Scale: 1/8 in. = 20 mi.
   3 1/2 ÷ 1/8 × 20 = (560) mi.

1. 3 in., 24 mi.   **2.** $2\frac{1}{2}$ in., 20 mi.

3. $2\frac{3}{4}$ in., 22 mi.   **4.** $\frac{3}{4}$ in., 6 mi.

5. $1\frac{3}{4}$ in., 14 mi.   **6.** $1\frac{1}{4}$ in., 10 mi.

7. $\frac{3}{4}$ in., 6 mi.

8. $\frac{3}{4}$ in., 36 mi.   **9.** $1\frac{3}{4}$ in., 84 mi.

10. $2\frac{1}{2}$ in., 120 mi.   **11.** 3 in., 144 mi.

12. $\frac{3}{4}$ in., 36 mi.   **13.** $1\frac{1}{4}$ in., 60 mi.

14. $2\frac{1}{4}$ in., 108 mi.

WRITTEN EXERCISES

A.   **Use Map 1 to find the distances between the places named below. First measure the length of the line between each pair of villages to the nearest $\frac{1}{4}$ inch, and write the measurement on your paper. Then find the distance in miles.**   (Answers on facing page)

1. Deep Run to Madison Ridge
2. Deep Run to Wagner's Corner
3. Wagner's Corner to Minersville
4. Spring Valley to Deep Run
5. Madison Ridge to Summit
6. Summit to Minersville.
7. Wagner's Corner to Madison Ridge

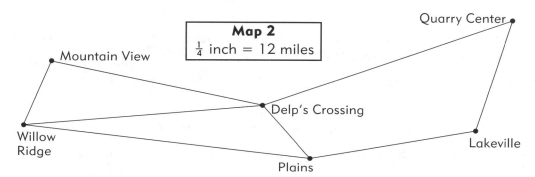

Map 2
$\frac{1}{4}$ inch = 12 miles

B.   **Use Map 2 to find the distance between each pair of villages named below. Measure to the nearest $\frac{1}{4}$ inch, write the measurement on your paper, and find the distance in miles.**   (Answers on facing page)

8. Willow Ridge to Mountain View
9. Plains to Lakeville
10. Willow Ridge to Delp's Crossing
11. Willow Ridge to Plains
12. Plains to Delp's Crossing
13. Quarry Center to Lakeville
14. Mountain View to Delp's Crossing

C.   **Solve these reading problems.**

Louise was studying a map in her father's Bible. The scale of miles was 1 inch = 32 miles. Use this scale to find the distances for numbers 15–18.

15. Louise measured the distance on the map between Jerusalem and the nearest point on the Dead Sea. The distance was $\frac{1}{2}$ inch.   16 miles

16. The distance on the map between Jerusalem and Beersheba was $1\frac{1}{2}$ inches.   48 miles

17. The distance on the map from the northernmost to the southernmost point in Israel was about $6\frac{1}{2}$ inches.   208 miles

18. The distance on the map from the Sea of Chinnereth (Sea of Galilee) to the Dead Sea was $2\frac{1}{8}$ inches.   68 miles

19. If an airplane flies 650 miles in $2\frac{1}{2}$ hours, what is its average rate of speed?   260 miles per hour

20. The Miller family is taking a 275-mile trip. If they travel at an average rate of 50 miles per hour, how long will the trip take? $5\frac{1}{2}$ hours

REVIEW EXERCISES

D.   *Solve these addition and subtraction problems.* (Lesson 76)

21.	**22.**	**23.**	**24.**
3.78	4.76	8.37	5.8
+ 4.92	+ 5.717	− 6.79	− 2.895
8.70	10.477	1.58	2.905

E.   *Change these decimals to fractions or mixed numbers in the simplest form.* (Lesson 74)

25. 0.44 $\frac{11}{25}$ **26.** 0.65 $\frac{13}{20}$ **27.** 4.45 $4\frac{9}{20}$ **28.** 3.04 $3\frac{1}{25}$

F.   *Change these fractions to decimals. You will not need to divide further than the ten-thousandths' place.* (Lesson 73)

29. $\frac{19}{25}$ 0.76   **30.** $\frac{5}{8}$ 0.625   **31.** $\frac{17}{40}$ 0.425   **32.** $\frac{7}{16}$ 0.4375

G.   *Identify each number as prime or composite.* (Lesson 45)

33. 31 prime   **34.** 32 composite   **35.** 33 composite   **36.** 34 composite

LESSON 108

Objective

- To review finding actual measurements by using the scale on a blueprint.

Review

1. *Conversions between metric and English units of measure* (Lessons 103, 104).
   a. 7 l = (7.42) qt.
   b. 9 qt. = (8.55) l
   c. 10 km² = (3.9) sq. mi.
   d. 11 a. = (4.4) ha
   e. 8 kg = (17.6) lb.
   f. 9 oz. = (254.7) g
   g. 13 km = (8.06) mi.
   h. 18 ft. = (5.4) m

2. *Metric units of capacity* (Lesson 100).
   a. 5 kl = (5,000) l
   b. 3,500 ml = (3.5) l
   c. 14 dkl = (1,400) dl
   d. 12.5 cl = (125) ml

3. *Writing ratios* (Lesson 92).
   a. Compare 66 books in the Bible to 27 books in the New Testament.
       (66 to 27 = 22 to 9 *or* 22:9 *or* $\frac{22}{9}$)
   b. Compare 9 sixth grade students to 17 seventh grade students.
       (9 to 17 *or* 9:17 *or* $\frac{9}{17}$)

4. *Comparing decimals by annexing zeroes* (Lesson 75).
   a. 0.775 (>) 0.7749
   b. 0.81 (<) 0.8101
   c. 0.1 (>) 0.099

Introduction

Introduce the reading of blueprints with a review of finding distances by using map scales. Choose a few places to which your students can relate, such as cities near distant churches.

Class interest in this lesson will be increased if you present an actual blueprint of a house or of your school or church. If you bring such a blueprint, have the students use their rulers to interpret it.

Teaching Guide

1. **On a blueprint, the scale shows the ratio of any measurement on the blueprint to the actual length it represents.**

2. **The scale of a blueprint can be used to find the actual size of any item shown on the blueprint.** The following steps are used.
    (1) *Using a ruler, measure carefully the distance on the blueprint.*
    (2) *Divide the measurement found in step 1 by the first part of the scale.* Because the second part of the scale is 1, this quotient is the answer. Label it with the unit used in the second part of the scale.

    The following measurements can be used for further practice.

    Scale: 1/4 inch = 1 foot
    a. 3/4 in. = (3) ft.
    b. 3 1/4 in. = (13) ft.
    c. 1 1/2 in. = (6) ft.
    d. 2 1/4 in. = (9) ft.

    Scale: 1/8 inch = 1 foot
    e. 7/8 in. = (7) ft.
    f. 4 in. = (32) ft.
    g. 1 3/8 in. = (11) ft.
    h. 3 5/8 in. = (29) ft.

108. Reading a Blueprint

A blueprint is a scale drawing that a builder uses as his pattern for the building he is constructing. The scale $\frac{1}{8}$ inch = 1 foot means that $\frac{1}{8}$ inch on the blueprint represents 1 foot in the actual building.

Blueprint of a One-Story House With Basement   Scale: $\frac{1}{8}$ inch = 1 foot

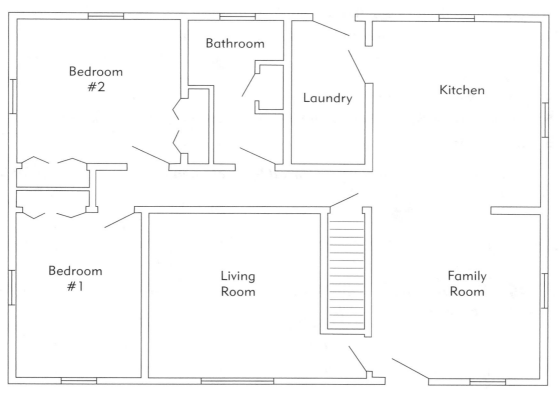

The following steps explain how to find actual lengths by using a blueprint.

1. Using a ruler, measure carefully the distance on the blueprint.
2. Divide the measurement found in Step 1 by the first part of the scale. Because the second part of the scale is 1, this quotient is the answer. Label it with the unit used in the second part of the scale.

Example A	**Example B**
Find the width of the outside of the house.	Find the length of the inside of the stairway.
Measured width = 4 in.	Measured length = $1\frac{1}{4}$ in.
$4 \div \frac{1}{8} = 32$ ft.	$1\frac{1}{4} \div \frac{1}{8} = 10$ ft.

CLASS PRACTICE

Give the actual length represented by each measurement on a blueprint if the scale is $\frac{1}{8}$ inch = 1 foot.

a. 3 in.   24 ft.   **b.** $\frac{1}{2}$ in.   4 ft.   **c.** $1\frac{1}{4}$ in.   10 ft.   **d.** $2\frac{1}{8}$ in.   17 ft.

WRITTEN EXERCISES

A.   Refer to the blueprint in the lesson to answer these questions. Write both the ruler measure and the distance it represents.

1. How wide is the inside of the stairway? $\frac{3}{8}$ in., 3 ft.

2. How long is the outside of the house? $5\frac{5}{8}$ in., 45 ft.

3. How wide is the inside of the kitchen? (*Width* is the smaller of the two dimensions.)
$1\frac{3}{4}$ in., 14 ft.

4. How wide is the picture window in the living room? $\frac{3}{4}$ in., 6 ft.

5. How long is the hallway? (Measure to the nearest $\frac{1}{8}$ inch.) $2\frac{7}{8}$ in., 23 ft.

6. How wide is the window in the bathroom? $\frac{3}{8}$ in., 3 ft.

B.   Give the actual length represented by each measurement on a blueprint if the scale is $\frac{1}{4}$ inch = 1 foot.

7. 3 in.   12 ft.   8. $\frac{1}{2}$ in.   2 ft.   9. $1\frac{1}{4}$ in.   5 ft.

10. $1\frac{3}{4}$ in.   7 ft.   11. $3\frac{3}{4}$ in.   15 ft.   12. $4\frac{1}{2}$ in.   18 ft.

C.   Give the actual length represented by each measurement on a blueprint if the scale is $\frac{1}{8}$ inch = 1 foot.

13. $1\frac{3}{4}$ in.   14 ft.   14. $\frac{5}{8}$ in.   5 ft.   15. $1\frac{7}{8}$ in.   15 ft.

16. $4\frac{1}{8}$ in.   33 ft.   17. $2\frac{1}{2}$ in.   20 ft.   18. $3\frac{3}{8}$ in.   27 ft.

D.   Solve these reading problems.

19. Bruce saw the blueprint for the church building his father was helping to build. The drawing of the building was $18\frac{3}{4}$ inches long, and the scale was $\frac{1}{4}$ inch = 1 foot. How long was the new church building?   75 feet

20. If the auditorium was $12\frac{1}{2}$ inches long on the blueprint, what was its actual length? (Scale: $\frac{1}{4}$ inch = 1 foot)   50 feet

21. Two cities on a map are $5\frac{1}{2}$ inches apart. If the scale is 1 inch = 90 miles, what is the actual distance between the cities?   495 miles

22. The scale of a map is 1 inch = 150 miles. If it shows two cities 18 inches apart, what is the actual distance between them?   2,700 miles

Note: Many blueprints are drawn on graph paper with 1/4-inch squares and a scale of 1/4 inch = 1 foot, or with 1/2-inch squares and a scale of 1/2 inch = 1 foot. Then the number of feet can be found simply by counting squares.

REVIEW EXERCISES

E. *Use the tables in Lessons 103 and 104 to change these measures as indicated.*

23. 14 mi. = <u>22.54</u> km   **24.** 8 cm = <u>3.12</u> in.   **25.** 15 ft. = <u>4.5</u> m

26. 20 kg = <u>44</u> lb.   **27.** 40 lb. = <u>18</u> kg   **28.** 25 l = <u>26.5</u> qt.

F. *Change these measures of capacity as indicated. (Lesson 100)*

29. 4 l = <u>4,000</u> ml   **30.** 4 kl = <u>4,000</u> l **31.** 1,500 ml = <u>1.5</u> l

G. *Write a ratio in lowest terms for each exercise. (Lesson 92)*

32. Compare 8 calves to 40 cows. $\frac{1}{5}$

33. Compare 78 students to 3 classrooms. $\frac{26}{1}$

H. *Copy each pair of decimals, compare them, and write > or < between them. (Lesson 75)*

34. 0.35 <u>></u> 0.349   **35.** 0.3006 <u><</u> 0.31   **36.** 0.48 <u>></u> 0.4799

109. Working With Bar Graphs

Reading Bar Graphs

Bar graphs compare the value of different things with each other. A solid bar is used for each item. The value of each item is indicated by the height of the bar in relation to a marked scale. But the values shown are approximate because it is usually not practical to draw bar graphs that show exact numbers.

To read a bar graph, follow the horizontal line nearest to the top of the bar to see what its value is on the scale at the left edge of the graph. When you read the number on the scale, take note of how the scale is labeled so that you understand the number correctly.

Graph 1

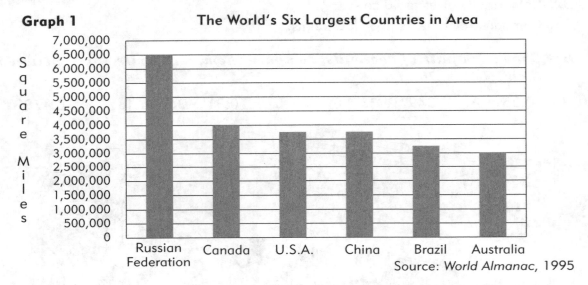

The World's Six Largest Countries in Area

Source: *World Almanac*, 1995

Graph 2

The World's Six Largest Countries in Population

Source: *World Almanac*, 1995

LESSON 109

Objectives

- To review reading bar graphs.
- To teach *drawing bar graphs.

Review

1. *Measurements on a blueprint* (Lesson 108).
   a. 3 1/2 inches when 1/4 inch = 1 foot (14 feet)
   b. 1 3/4 inches when 1/4 inch = 1 foot (7 feet)
   c. 2 1/4 inches when 1/8 inch = 1 foot (18 feet)
   d. 1 7/8 inches when 1/8 inch = 1 foot (15 feet)

2. *Distances on a map* (Lesson 107).
   a. 4 inches when 1 inch = 20 miles (80 miles)
   b. 3 1/2 inches when 1 inch = 30 miles (105 miles)
   c. 3 3/4 inches when 1 inch = 16 miles (60 miles)
   d. 2 1/2 inches when 1 inch = 24 miles (60 miles)

3. *Subtracting decimals* (Lesson 77).

   a.   3.1   b.   4.3
        − 1.68   − 2.674
        ─────   ──────
         (1.42)   (1.626)

   c.   7   d.   8
        − 5.3   − 4.751
        ─────   ──────
         (1.7)   (3.249)

4. *Finding the prime factors of composite numbers* (Lesson 46).
   a. 48 (2 × 2 × 2 × 2 × 3)
   b. 54 (2 × 3 × 3 × 3)
   c. 96 (2 × 2 × 2 × 2 × 2 × 3)
   d. 50 (2 × 5 × 5)

Introduction

Introduce bar graphs by calling attention to Graph 1. What information does the graph give? Which is the largest country in area? How do the rest of the countries compare in size?

Teaching Guide

1. Give practice with reading bar graphs. Ask the following questions about Graph 1 in the text to develop this part of the lesson. (Graphs 2 and 3 in the text are used for the written exercises.)
   a. Does this bar graph show approximate or exact information? It shows approximate information; it is accurate only to the nearest 500,000 square miles. Any amount between the lines on the scale must be estimated. (For the question below, the answers give both approximate and exact numbers.)
   b. How large is each of the following countries?

	As shown on graph	Actual area (square miles)
(1) Russian Federation	6,500,000	6,592,800
(2) Canada	4,000,000	3,849,674
(3) U.S.A.	3,750,000	3,787,318
(4) China	3,750,000	3,696,100
(5) Brazil	3,250,000	3,286,470
(6) Australia	3,000,000	2,966,200

2. Show how to make a bar graph according the steps in the lesson. Use the following information to construct a bar graph.

Five Longest Suspension Bridges in the United States

Verrazano Narrows, New York, N.Y.
    4,260 feet

Golden Gate, San Francisco, Calif.
    4,200 feet

Mackinac, Straits of Mackinac, Mich.
    3,800 feet

George Washington, N.Y. and N.J.
    3,500 feet

Tacoma Narrows, Washington
    2,800 feet

Source: *World Almanac*

An Ounce of Prevention

Plan ahead for the students' bar graphs. If they will be using graph paper with small squares, you may want them to label only every other horizontal line (step 3). If they use paper with larger squares, it may be better to label every horizontal line.

The numbers for the vertical scale should be written directly on the horizontal lines, not in the spaces, so that the graph is simpler to read. The labels for the bars should be centered beneath their respective bars.

Five Longest Suspension Bridges in the United States

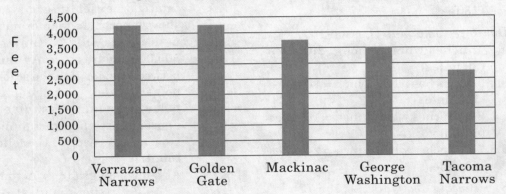

Source: *World Almanac*

> Using Graph 2, find the population of the U.S.A.
>
> Answer: The bar indicating the population of the U.S.A. shows 250 (halfway between 200 and 300). The label indicates that the numbers are millions. So the population of the U.S.A. is 250 million, or 250,000,000.

Drawing Bar Graphs

The best kind of paper for drawing bar graphs is graph paper. To draw a bar graph, use the following steps.

1. Look over the numbers to be shown on the graph, and pick out the largest one.

2. Decide on the vertical scale you will use. For example, if the largest number is 900, the scale should be numbered by hundreds from 0 to 1,000. If the largest number is 90,000, the numbers should go by ten thousands from 0 to 100,000.

3. Starting with zero, label the horizontal lines according to the scale that you chose in step 2. For example, if the numbers on the scale represent thousands, write *thousands*. If the numbers represent millions, write *millions*.

4. Round each of the numbers to the place indicated on the vertical scale. That is, if the label is *thousands*, round each number to the nearest thousand.

5. Decide where each bar will be, and mark it at the bottom of the graph. Each bar should be the same width, and the distance between the bars should be the same.

6. Write a label for each bar. Draw each bar to the correct height as indicated by your rounded numbers.

7. Write a title for the graph.

CLASS PRACTICE

Refer to Graph 1 to answer these questions.

a. What is the approximate size of the Russian Federation?   6,500,000 square miles

b. What is the approximate size of Canada?   4,000,000 square miles

c. What is the approximate area of Canada and the United States combined?
     7,750,000 square miles

d. About how many times larger is the Russian Federation than Australia? Answer to the nearest whole number.   2 times

WRITTEN EXERCISES

A. *Give the population of each country as shown on Graph 2.*

1. India   900 million
2. Indonesia   200 million
3. China   1,200 million
4. Brazil   150 million
5. Russian Federation   150 million

B.   Give the following facts as shown on Graph 3 below. If a bar is between two lines, write an estimate to the nearest whole number.

6. The mammal with the longest average life span shown   elephant

7. The mammals with the shortest average life span shown   lion, zebra

8. The average life span of a hippopotamus   40 years

9. The average life span of a chimpanzee   45 years

10. The average life span of a horse   25 years

11. The average life span of an elephant   60 years

12. The average life span of a zebra   23 years (or 22 years)

13. The average life span of a lion   23 years (or 22 years)

Graph 3   **Average Life Spans of the Longest-Living Mammals**

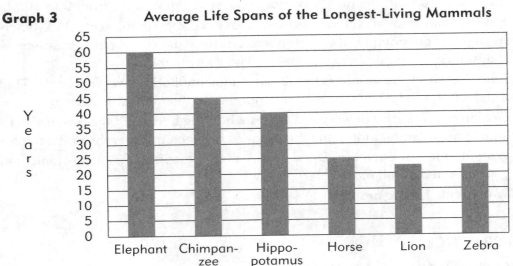

Source: *World Book Encyclopedia*

C.   On graph paper, draw a bar graph for each set of facts below. Number every other horizontal line on the vertical scale, make each bar 3 squares wide, and leave 2 blank squares between each pair of bars.

14. Draw a bar graph with the title *Maximum Life Span of the Longest-Living Fish*. The vertical scale should be numbered by fives and be labeled *Years*. Give the source of information at the bottom of the graph.   (Sample graph on facing page)

     Sturgeon . . . . .50 years
     Halibut . . . . .40 years
     Goldfish . . . . .25 years
     Pike . . . . .24 years
     Lungfish (African) . . . . . . .17 years

                    Source: *World Book Encyclopedia*

14.

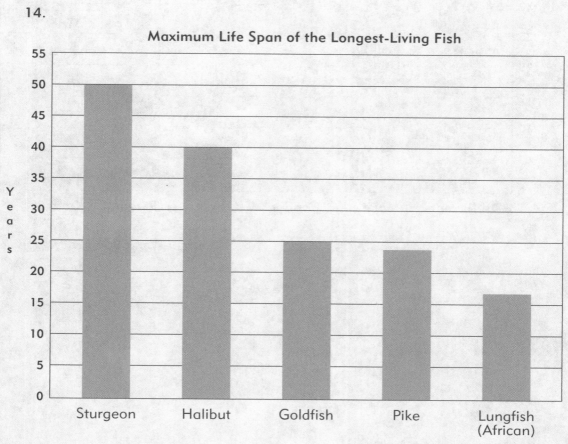

Maximum Life Span of the Longest-Living Fish

Source: *World Book Encyclopedia*

15.

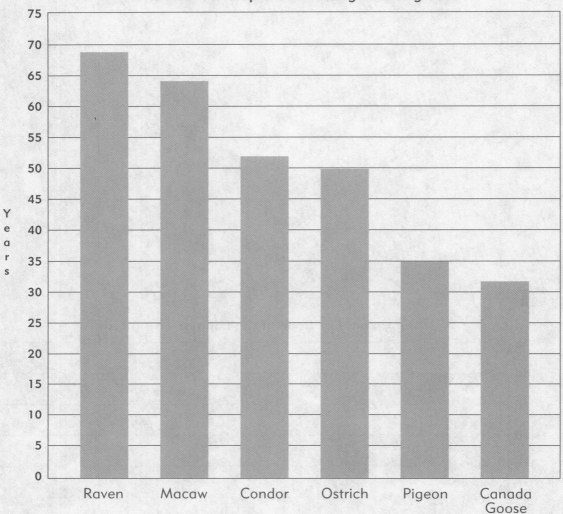

Maximum Life Span of the Longest-Living Birds

Source: *World Book Encyclopedia*

15. Draw a bar graph with the title *Maximum Life Span of the Longest-Living Birds*. The vertical scale should be numbered by fives and be labeled *Years*. Give the source of information at the bottom of the graph.   (Sample graph on facing page)

>   Raven . . . . .69 years
>   Macaw . . . . .64 years
>   Condor . . . . .52 years
>   Ostrich . . . . .50 years
>   Pigeon . . . . .35 years
>   Canada Goose . . . . .32 years
>
>   Source: *World Book Encyclopedia*

REVIEW EXERCISES

D. Solve these reading problems. *(Lessons 107, 108)*

16. Clarence measured the distance between two cities on a map and found it to be $4\frac{1}{4}$ inches. The map scale is $\frac{1}{4}$ inch = 20 miles. What is the distance between the two cities?   340 miles

17. Esther found that Syracuse and Rochester, New York, were $4\frac{7}{8}$ inches apart on a map. The map has a scale of $\frac{5}{8}$ inch = 10 miles. What is the distance between Syracuse and Rochester?   78 miles

18. The blueprint of the Risser home is drawn to a scale of $\frac{1}{4}$ inch = 1 foot. On the blueprint, the living room is 4 inches long. How long is the living room?   16 feet

19. The living room in the Risser home is $3\frac{1}{2}$ inches wide on the blueprint. If the scale is $\frac{1}{4}$ inch = 1 foot, how wide is the living room?   14 feet

E. Solve these subtraction problems. *(Lesson 77)*

20.	21.	22.	23.
3.21	5.3	4	6
− 1.119	− 2.709	− 2.71	− 2.003
2.091	2.591	1.29	3.997

F. Find the prime factors of these composite numbers. *(Lesson 46)*

24. 18	25. 40	26. 68	27. 92
18 = 2 × 3 × 3	40 = 2 × 2 × 2 × 5	68 = 2 × 2 × 17	92 = 2 × 2 × 23

110. Chapter 8 Review

A. Write the meaning of each metric prefix. *(Lesson 97)*

1. hecto- 100
2. centi- 0.01
3. kilo- 1,000
4. deka- 10
5. milli- 0.001
6. deci- 0.1

B. Measure these lines to the nearest centimeter. *(Lesson 97)*

7. ⎯⎯⎯⎯⎯⎯⎯⎯⎯   5 cm
8. ⎯⎯⎯⎯⎯⎯⎯⎯⎯⎯⎯⎯   8 cm
9. ⎯⎯⎯   2 cm
10. ⎯⎯⎯⎯⎯⎯⎯⎯⎯⎯⎯⎯⎯   10 cm

C. Change these metric measures as indicated. *(Lessons 98–101)*

11. 4 m = _400_ cm
12. 1,700 m = _1.7_ km
13. 44 cm = _440_ mm
14. 8,000 g = _8_ kg
15. 7.5 g = _7,500_ mg
16. 475 kg = _0.475_ m.t.
17. 2.3 l = _2,300_ ml
18. 460 ml = _0.46_ l
19. 1.2 kl = _1,200_ l
20. 11 km^2 = _1,100_ ha
21. 2 ha = _20,000_ m^2
22. 3.2 m^2 = _32,000_ cm^2

D. Change these measures as indicated. *(Lessons 103, 104)*

23. 15 in. = _38.1_ cm
24. 20 m = _65.6_ ft.
25. 13 mi. = _20.93_ km
26. 20 kg = _44_ lb.
27. 15 oz. = _424.5_ g
28. 20 lb. = _9_ kg
29. 8 l = _8.48_ qt.
30. 7 qt. = _6.65_ l
31. 15 ha = _37.5_ a.
32. 22 sq. mi. = _56.98_ km^2
33. 25 a. = _10_ ha
34. 30 km^2 = _11.7_ sq. mi.

E. Solve these reading problems on distance, rate, and time. *(Lessons 105, 106)*

35. The *Renaissance*, a passenger train, covers the 165 miles between Kingston and Dorval in 2 hours. What is its average speed?   82.5 miles per hour

36. The Sensenig family drove $2\frac{1}{2}$ hours to take their minister to a church service in another community. Father said their average speed had been 46 miles per hour. How many miles did they travel to the church?   115 miles

LESSON 110

Objective

- To review the concepts taught in Chapter 8.

Teaching Guide

This review covers Lessons 97–109.

47.

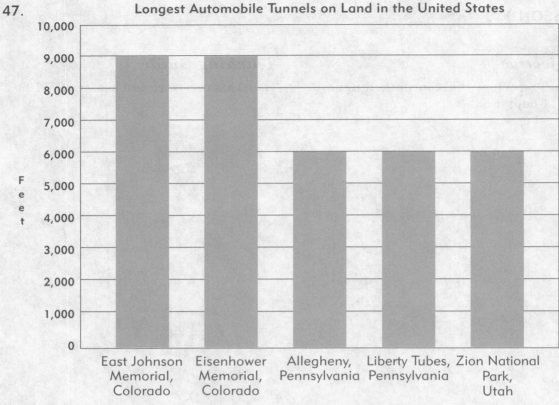

Longest Automobile Tunnels on Land in the United States

Source: *World Almanac*

48.

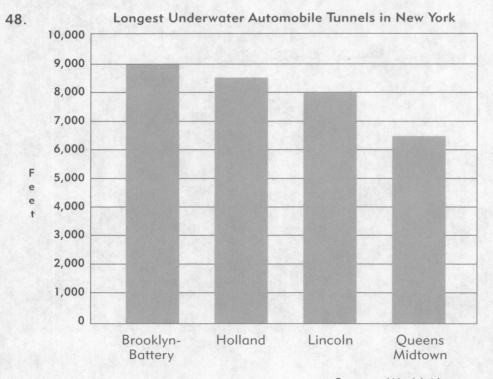

Longest Underwater Automobile Tunnels in New York

Source: *World Almanac*

37. Luke's family plans to visit him at Bible school, which is 175 miles from their home. How long will it take them to get there if they drive at an average speed of 50 miles per hour?

$3\frac{1}{2}$ hours

38. Dale often rides his bicycle to Sister Joan's home to mow her lawn. If he travels 12 miles per hour, it takes $\frac{1}{2}$ hour to get there. How far does he travel to Sister Joan's home?

6 miles

F. *If the scale of a map is 1 inch = 20 miles, how many miles do the following measurements represent? (Lesson 107)*

39. 4 in. 80 miles **40.** $1\frac{1}{2}$ in. 30 miles **41.** $2\frac{3}{4}$ in. 55 miles **42.** $3\frac{1}{2}$ in. 70 miles

G. *If the scale of a blueprint is $\frac{1}{8}$ inch = 1 foot, how many feet do the following measurements represent? (Lesson 108)*

43. 3 in.   24 feet **44.** $1\frac{1}{4}$ in. 10 feet **45.** $1\frac{3}{4}$ in. 14 feet **46.** $4\frac{1}{2}$ in. 36 feet

H. *Use graph paper to draw the bar graphs indicated. Number every other horizontal line on the vertical scale, make each bar 3 squares wide, and leave 2 blank squares between each pair of bars. (Lesson 109)*

(Sample graphs on facing page)

47. Draw a bar graph with the title *Longest Automobile Tunnels on Land in the United States*. The vertical scale should be numbered by thousands and be labeled *Feet*. Give the source of the information at the bottom of the graph.

East Johnson Memorial	Colorado	8,959 feet
Eisenhower Memorial	Colorado	8,941 feet
Allegheny	Pennsylvania	6,072 feet
Liberty Tubes	Pennsylvania	5,920 feet
Zion National Park	Utah	5,766 feet

Source: *World Almanac*

48. Draw a bar graph with the title *Longest Underwater Automobile Tunnels in New York City*. The vertical scale should be numbered by thousands and be labeled *Feet*. Give the source of the information at the bottom of the graph.

Brooklyn-Battery	9,117 feet
Holland	8,557 feet
Lincoln	8,216 feet
Queens Midtown	6,414 feet

Source: *World Almanac*

111. Chapter 8 Test

LESSON 111

Objective

- To test the students' mastery of the concepts in Chapter 8.

Teaching Guide

1. Correct Lesson 110.
2. Review any areas of special difficulty.
3. Administer the test.

Use of percents is a sensible way to practice stewardship and recognition of God's ownership. We need to give back to God a portion of the bountiful blessings He gives us.

Chapter 9

Working With Percents

Bring ye all the tithes into the storehouse, that there may be meat in mine house, and prove me now herewith, saith the LORD of hosts, if I will not open you the windows of heaven, and pour you out a blessing, that there shall not be room enough to receive it.

(Malachi 3:10)

112. Introduction to Percents

Did you ever wonder why two wrong in one assignment is a score of 95 percent, on another is 92 percent, and on still another is 80 percent? **Percent** means "per hundred" or "by the hundred." A percent is a fraction in which the numerator is the percent figure and the denominator is 100. Thus, a score of 92 percent means that 92 out of every 100 answers are correct. The percent sign (%) means "percent"; 92% means the same as 92 percent and 92 out of 100.

If a fraction has a denominator of 100, it can easily be changed to a percent. Write the numerator, and put a percent sign after it.

$$\frac{33}{100} = 33\%$$

To express a decimal as a percent, move the decimal point two places to the right. If the result is a whole number, drop the decimal point. Place a percent sign after the number.

$$0.48 = 48\%$$

To express a percent as a fraction, write the percent as the numerator and 100 as the denominator.

$$53\% = \frac{53}{100}$$

To express a percent as a decimal, write the percent as hundredths.

$$27\% = \frac{27}{100} = 0.27$$

CLASS PRACTICE

Write these fractions as percents.

a. $\frac{77}{100}$ 77%   b. $\frac{11}{100}$ 11%   c. $\frac{43}{100}$ 43%   d. $\frac{89}{100}$ 89%   e. $\frac{91}{100}$ 91%   f. $\frac{23}{100}$ 23%

Write these decimals as percents.

g. 0.14   h. 0.30   i. 0.09   j. 0.78   k. 0.93   l. 0.45
14%   30%   9%   78%   93%   45%

Write these percents as fractions and as decimals.

m. 67% $\frac{67}{100}$ n. 31% $\frac{31}{100}$ o. 27% $\frac{27}{100}$ p. 87% $\frac{87}{100}$ q. 99% $\frac{99}{100}$ r. 63% $\frac{63}{100}$
0.67   0.31   0.27   0.87   0.99   0.63

WRITTEN EXERCISES

A. *Write these fractions as percents.*

1. $\frac{29}{100}$ 29%   2. $\frac{37}{100}$ 37%   3. $\frac{91}{100}$ 91%   4. $\frac{73}{100}$ 73%   5. $\frac{47}{100}$ 47%   6. $\frac{83}{100}$ 83%

B. *Write these decimals as percents.*

7. 0.68   8. 0.85   9. 0.13   10. 0.90   11. 0.42   12. 0.12
68%   85%   13%   90%   42%   12%

LESSON 112

Objectives

- To review the meaning of percent.
- To teach changing fractions with denominators of 100 to percents and vice versa.
- To teach changing two-place decimals to percents and vice versa.

Review

1. *Reading a blueprint* (Lesson 108).
   Scale: 1/8 inch = 1 foot
   a. 2 in. = (16 ft.)
   b. $1\frac{3}{4}$ in. = (14 ft.)
   c. $5\frac{1}{2}$ in. = (44 ft.)
   d. $3\frac{1}{8}$ in. = (25 ft.)

2. *Reading a map* (Lesson 107).
   Scale: 1 inch = 48 miles
   a. 4 in. = (192 mi.)
   b. $1\frac{1}{2}$ in. = (72 mi.)
   c. $3\frac{1}{4}$ in. = (156 mi.)
   d. $2\frac{5}{8}$ in. = (126 mi.)

3. *Converting between English and metric measures* (Lessons 103, 104).
   a. 2 km = (1.24) mi.
   b. 14 lb. = (6.3) kg
   c. 20 qt. = (19) l
   d. 15 ha = (37.5) a.

4. *Multiplying decimals mentally* (Lesson 78). No class review is necessary.

5. *Finding the greatest common factor* (Lesson 47).
   a. 18, 24   (g.c.f. = 6)
   b. 32, 48   (g.c.f. = 16)
   c. 30, 75   (g.c.f. = 15)
   d. 40, 50   (g.c.f. = 10)

Introduction

Ask the pupils why a penny is called 1 cent. The word *cent* means "hundredth." One cent is 1/100 of a dollar.

Percent also has to do with hundredths. *Percent* means "per hundred" or "by the hundred." If a student receives a score of 95% on an assignment, that means 95/100 of the answers are correct. This is a way of saying that if there had been 100 answers, 95 of them would have been correct.

Make a grid of 100 blocks. One percent is 1 shaded out of 100 blocks. Ninety-five percent is 95 shaded blocks out of 100 blocks.

Teaching Guide

1. **Percent means "per hundred" or "by the hundred."** Percent is usually written by using the percent sign (%). Practice reading these numbers.
   a. 14%   (Fourteen percent)
   b. 92%   (Ninety-two percent)
   c. 99%   (Ninety-nine percent)
   d. 12%   (Twelve percent)
   e. 14 1/2%
      (Fourteen and one-half percent)
   f. 29 3/4%
      (Twenty-nine and three-fourths percent)

2. **To express a fraction with a denominator of 100 as a percent, write the numerator, and put a percent sign after it.**
   a. 12/100 = (12%)
   b. 26/100 = (26%)
   c. 99/100 = (99%)
   d. 21/100 = (21%)
   e. 1/100 = (1%)
   f. 8/100 = (8%)

3. **To express a decimal as a percent, move the decimal point two places to the right. If the result is a whole number, drop the decimal point. Place a percent sign after the number.**
   a. 0.19 = (19%)
   b. 0.99 = (99%)
   c. 0.34 = (34%)
   d. 0.43 = (43%)
   e. 0.01 = (1%)
   f. 0.08 = (8%)

4. **To express a percent as a fraction, write the percent as the numerator and 100 as the denominator.**
   a. 14% = (14/100)
   b. 26% = (26/100)
   c. 49% = (49/100)
   d. 98% = (98/100)
   e. 29% = (29/100)
   f. 68% = (68/100)

5. **To express a percent as a decimal, write the percent as hundredths.**
   a. 14% = (0.14)
   b. 26% = (0.26)
   c. 49% = (0.49)
   d. 98% = (0.98)
   e. 29% = (0.29)
   f. 68% = (0.68)

C. Write these percents as fractions.

13. 17% $\frac{17}{100}$ **14.** 23% $\frac{23}{100}$ **15.** 97% $\frac{97}{100}$ **16.** 89% $\frac{89}{100}$ **17.** 91% $\frac{91}{100}$ **18.** 11% $\frac{11}{100}$

D. Write these percents as decimals.

19. 19%	**20.** 26%	**21.** 33%	**22.** 16%	**23.** 98%	**24.** 90%
0.19	0.26	0.33	0.16	0.98	0.90

E. Solve these reading problems.

25. Daryl had 93 out of 100 words correct on his review spelling test. What was his score as a percent.
93%

26. About 21 out of every 100 people in the world live in China. What percent of the world's population lives in China?
21%

27. About 0.59 of the books of the Bible are in the Old Testament. Write 0.59 as a percent.
59%

28. Leonard's Bible has 1,143 pages. Of those pages, about 0.77 of them are in the Old Testament. Write 0.77 as a percent.
77%

29. If 0.77 of the pages in Leonard's 1,143-page Bible are in the Old Testament, how many pages does the Old Testament in his Bible contain? Round your answer to the nearest whole number.
880 pages

30. There are 25 students in grades 5 and 6. Of those students, 0.44 are in grade 6. How many sixth grade students are in the classroom?
11 students

REVIEW EXERCISES

F. Find the actual length represented by each measurement if the scale of a blueprint is $\frac{1}{4}$ inch = 1 foot. (Lesson 108)

31. 4 inches 16 ft. **32.** $\frac{3}{4}$ inches 3 ft. **33.** $3\frac{1}{2}$ inches 14 ft. **34.** $4\frac{3}{4}$ inches 19 ft.

G. Find the actual length represented by each measurement if the scale of a map is 1 inch = 24 miles. (Lesson 107)

35. 2 inches	**36.** $1\frac{1}{8}$ inches	**37.** $3\frac{7}{8}$ inches	**38.** $3\frac{1}{4}$ inches
48 mi.	27 mi.	93 mi.	78 mi.

H. Change these measures as indicated. (Lessons 103, 104)

39. 4 mi. = <u>6.44</u> km **40.** 48 kg = <u>105.6</u> lb.

41. 17 l = <u>18.02</u> qt. **42.** 24 a. = <u>9.6</u> ha

I. Multiply these decimals mentally. (Lesson 78)

43. 1.6 × 10   16 **44.** 3.62 × 100   362

45. 0.71 × 1,000   710 **46.** 0.0067 × 1,000   6.7

J. Find the greatest common factor of each set. (Lesson 47)

47. 12, 18   6 **48.** 15, 25   5 **49.** 24, 40   8 **50.** 27, 45   9

113. Expressing Decimals and Fractions as Percents

Decimals and fractions are often converted to percents to make them easier to compare. For example, if you have 29 out of 32 math problems correct one day and 36 out of 40 correct the next day, on which day did you do better? It is easier to compare your scores when you calculate that you had about 91% of your problems correct the first day and 90% correct the second day.

To change a decimal to a percent, use the following steps.

1. Move the decimal point two places to the right. Annex zeroes if necessary, and drop the decimal point if the result is a whole number.
2. Write the percent sign (%) after the number.

Example A
Express 0.61 as a percent.

$0.61 = 61\%$

Example B
Express 0.6 as a percent.

$0.60 = 60\%$

Some common fractions have denominators that are factors of 100. To change such a fraction to a percent, use the following steps.

1. Change the fraction to an equivalent fraction with a denominator of 100.
2. Write the numerator of the fraction as a whole number, and place the percent sign (%) after it.

Example C
Express $\frac{1}{2}$ as a percent.

$\frac{1}{2} = \frac{50}{100} = 50\%$

Example D
Express $\frac{17}{20}$ as a percent.

$\frac{17}{20} = \frac{85}{100} = 85\%$

CLASS PRACTICE

Express these decimals as percents.

a. 0.4   b. 0.34   c. 0.2   d. 0.07   e. 0.5   f. 0.09
  40%   34%   20%   7%   50%   9%

Express these fractions as percents. See how many you can change mentally.

g. $\frac{4}{5}$ 80%   h. $\frac{19}{20}$ 95%   i. $\frac{7}{25}$ 28%   j. $\frac{9}{10}$ 90%   k. $\frac{21}{25}$ 84%   l. $\frac{3}{20}$ 15%

WRITTEN EXERCISES

A. *Express these decimals as percents.*

1. 0.46   2. 0.89   3. 0.81   4. 0.63   5. 0.23   6. 0.84
   46%   89%   81%   63%   23%   84%

LESSON 113

Objectives

- To teach *changing decimals to percents, including those with only one decimal place.

- To teach changing fractions to percents.

- To work with familiar fraction–decimal equivalents.

Review

1. Give Lesson 113 Speed Test (Distance, Rate, and Time). You may want to wait until after class for this speed test because the same concept is reviewed in the lesson.

2. *Bar graphs* (Lesson 109). You will need graph paper for the students to prepare graphs. Graph paper with 1/4-inch squares is suitable.

   Briefly discuss how the bar graph will be drawn, pointing out the scale and the titles. If time allows, practice reading a bar graph from another textbook.

3. *Distance, rate, and time* (Lesson 105).

Rate	Time	Distance
a. 50 m.p.h.	(5 hr.)	250 miles
b. (48 m.p.h.)	3 hr.	144 miles
c. 45 m.p.h.	8 hr.	(360 miles)

4. *Lowest common multiples* (Lesson 48). The trial-and-error method can be used for problem *a*, and the factoring method for problem *b*.
   a. 12, 18 (l.c.m. = 36)
      $2 \times 18 = 36$
   b. 15, 25 (l.c.m. = 75)
      $15 = 3 \times 5$
      $25 = 5 \times 5$
      $3 \times 5 \times 5 = 75$

Introduction

Ask the students which problem is easier to add, 1/4 + 1/9 or 1/4 + 3/4. Why is 1/4 + 3/4 easier? (The fractions are like fractions.) Why would percents be easy fractions to work with? (They all have the denominator 100.)

Teaching Guide

1. **Any decimal can be changed to a percent.** The steps are as follows:
   (1) Move the decimal point two places to the right. Annex zeroes if necessary, and drop the decimal point if the result is a whole number.
   (2) Write the % sign after the number.

   Stress the procedure for changing one-place decimals to percents. See Example B and items *d–f* below.
   a. 0.42 = (42%)
   b. 0.59 = (59%)
   c. 0.98 = (98%)
   d. 0.4 = (40%)
   e. 0.3 = (30%)
   f. 0.9 = (90%)

2. **Any fraction can be changed to a percent.** If the denominator is a factor of 100, the steps are as follows:
   (1) Change the fraction to an equivalent fraction with a denominator of 100.
   (2) Write the numerator of the fraction as a whole number, and place the percent sign (%) after it.

   Stress doing the first step mentally if possible. Many of the fractions in the written work are fractions for which the pupils have memorized the decimal equivalents.
   a. $\frac{4}{5} = \frac{80}{100} = (80\%)$
   b. $\frac{9}{10} = \frac{90}{100} = (90\%)$
   c. $\frac{7}{20} = \frac{35}{100} = (35\%)$
   d. $\frac{13}{25} = \frac{52}{100} = (52\%)$

An Ounce of Prevention

1. Students may try to express 0.6 as 6%. Stress the need to annex a zero if there is only one place in the decimal.

2. Give specific instructions to the students on how to arrange their bar graphs, based on the format you established in Lesson 109.

34.

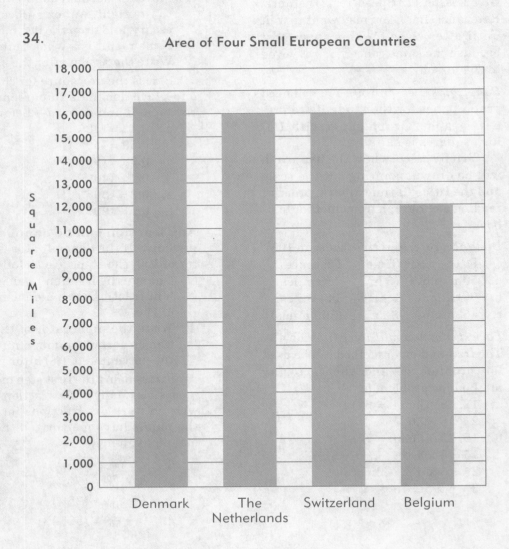

Area of Four Small European Countries

7. 0.05   **8.** 0.02   **9.** 0.1   **10.** 0.8   **11.** 0.7   **12.** 0.9
    5%   2%   10%   80%   70%   90%

B.   *Express these fractions as percents. See how many you can change mentally.*

13. $\frac{1}{5}$ 20% **14.** $\frac{3}{4}$ 75% **15.** $\frac{7}{20}$ 35% **16.** $\frac{13}{25}$ 52% **17.** $\frac{1}{4}$ 25%

18. $\frac{3}{5}$ 60% **19.** $\frac{1}{10}$ 10% **20.** $\frac{4}{5}$ 80% **21.** $\frac{3}{10}$ 30% **22.** $\frac{2}{5}$ 40%

23. $\frac{7}{10}$ 70% **24.** $\frac{9}{20}$ 45% **25.** $\frac{11}{20}$ 55% **26.** $\frac{17}{25}$ 68% **27.** $\frac{23}{25}$ 92%

C.   *Solve these reading problems. In problems 28–31, write each decimal or fraction as a percent.*

28. Switzerland is about 0.65 the size of West Virginia.   65%

29. About three-fourths of the area of Switzerland is covered by the Alps and the Jura Mountains.   75%

30. About 0.35 of the people of Switzerland live in rural areas or in communities with fewer than 10,000 people.   35%

31. Many of the Mennonites who settled in the eastern United States in the 1700s were originally from the canton of Bern, Switzerland. More than 0.14 of the population of Switzerland lives in Canton Bern.   14%

32. Thomas correctly answered 8 out of 10 questions on a social studies quiz. Write a fraction showing what part of the answers were correct. Then express that fraction as a percent. $\frac{8}{10}$ 80%

33. Delmar correctly spelled 18 out of 20 words on a spelling test. Write a fraction showing what part of the words he spelled correctly. Express that fraction as a percent. $\frac{18}{20}$ 90%

REVIEW EXERCISES

D.   *Draw a bar graph for the facts below. Make each bar three squares wide, with two blank squares between each pair of bars. (Lesson 109)*

34. The area of several European countries is shown below. Use the title *Area of Four Small European Countries*. Number the vertical scale by 1,000's, and use the label *square miles*.   (Sample graph on facing page)

Denmark . . . . .16,639 sq. mi.
The Netherlands . . .16,033 sq. mi.
Switzerland . . . . . . .15,943 sq. mi.
Belgium . . . . .11,787 sq. mi.

E.   *Solve these problems on distance, rate, and time. (Lesson 105)*

35. rate: 45 m.p.h.   time: 3 hr.   distance: 135 mi.
36. rate: 51 m.p.h.   time: 5 hr.   distance: 255 mi.

F.   *Find the lowest common multiple of each set. (Lesson 48)*

37. 12, 15   60   **38.** 14, 21   42   **39.** 15, 18   90   **40.** 21, 28   84

114. Expressing Fractions as Percents

Many fractions have denominators that are not factors of 100. Such a fraction is changed to a percent by division. Use the following steps.

1. Divide the numerator by the denominator to obtain a decimal. If the answer does not divide evenly to the hundredths' place, write the remainder as a fraction in lowest terms.

2. Change the decimal to a percent as you learned in the previous lesson.

Example A	**Example B**
Express $\frac{3}{8}$ as a percent.	Express $\frac{5}{6}$ as a percent.
$\dfrac{0.37\frac{4}{8}=0.37\frac{1}{2}}{8\overline{)3.00}}$	$\dfrac{0.83\frac{2}{6}=0.83\frac{1}{3}}{6\overline{)5.00}}$
$0.37\frac{1}{2}=37\frac{1}{2}\%$	$0.83\frac{1}{3}=83\frac{1}{3}\%$

Memorize the following fraction–percent equivalents. They are similar to the decimal equivalents that you have already learned.

$$\frac{1}{2}=50\%$$

$$\frac{1}{3}=33\tfrac{1}{3}\% \qquad \frac{2}{3}=66\tfrac{2}{3}\%$$

$$\frac{1}{4}=25\% \qquad \frac{3}{4}=75\%$$

$$\frac{1}{5}=20\% \qquad \frac{2}{5}=40\% \qquad \frac{3}{5}=60\% \qquad \frac{4}{5}=80\%$$

$$\frac{1}{10}=10\% \qquad \frac{3}{10}=30\% \qquad \frac{7}{10}=70\% \qquad \frac{9}{10}=90\%$$

CLASS PRACTICE

Find the percent equivalents, and express remainders as fractions in lowest terms. See how many you can do by memory.

a. $\frac{1}{3}$ b. $\frac{4}{5}$ c. $\frac{1}{6}$ d. $\frac{3}{10}$ e. $\frac{7}{16}$ f. $\frac{17}{20}$
    $33\frac{1}{3}\%$ 80% $16\frac{2}{3}\%$ 30% $43\frac{3}{4}\%$ 85%

WRITTEN EXERCISES

A. *Find the percent equivalents of these fractions. Express remainders as fractions in lowest terms.*

1. $\frac{7}{20}$ 2. $\frac{11}{20}$ 3. $\frac{1}{8}$ 4. $\frac{7}{8}$ 5. $\frac{1}{9}$ 6. $\frac{3}{7}$
   35% 55% $12\frac{1}{2}\%$ $87\frac{1}{2}\%$ $11\frac{1}{9}\%$ $42\frac{6}{7}\%$

7. $\frac{1}{12}$ 8. $\frac{5}{12}$ 9. $\frac{7}{12}$ 10. $\frac{1}{16}$ 11. $\frac{5}{16}$ 12. $\frac{17}{40}$
   $8\frac{1}{3}\%$ $41\frac{2}{3}\%$ $58\frac{1}{3}\%$ $6\frac{1}{4}\%$ $31\frac{1}{4}\%$ $42\frac{1}{2}\%$

LESSON 114

Objectives

- To have students *memorize fraction–percent equivalents.
- To teach *changing more difficult fractions to percents by division.

Review

1. *Metric linear measures* (Lesson 98).
   a. 4 km = (4,000) m
   b. 7 m = (700) cm
   c. 15 cm = (150) mm
   d. 250 mm = (25) cm
   e. 775 cm = (7.75) m
   f. 1,400 m = (1.4) km

2. *Measuring with a metric ruler* (Lesson 97). Have the students practice measuring various items in their desks.

3. *Fraction terms and reducing fractions* (Lesson 49).
   a. $\frac{\text{(numerator)}}{\text{(denominator)}}$ $\frac{16}{20} = (\frac{4}{5})$
   b. $\frac{\text{(numerator)}}{\text{(denominator)}}$ $\frac{36}{42} = (\frac{6}{7})$

Introduction

In Lesson 73, the students memorized some frequently used fraction–decimal equivalents. Review some equivalents and change them to percents.

a. $\frac{3}{4} = 0.75 = (75\%)$
b. $\frac{3}{10} = 0.3 = (30\%)$
c. $\frac{1}{5} = 0.2 = (20\%)$
d. $\frac{4}{5} = 0.8 = (80\%)$
e. $\frac{9}{10} = 0.9 = (90\%)$
f. $\frac{2}{3} = 0.66\frac{2}{3} = (66\frac{2}{3}\%)$

Call the students' attention to the table of fraction–percent equivalents in the lesson. Do the numbers seem familiar? If the pupils memorized the fraction–decimal equivalents well, they will have no trouble with these.

Teaching Guide

1. **Any fraction can be changed to a percent.** If the denominator is not a factor of 100, the steps are as follows:
   (1) Divide the numerator by the denominator to obtain a decimal. If the answer does not divide evenly to the hundredths' place, write the remainder as a fraction in lowest terms.
   (2) Change the decimal to a percent. Move the decimal point in the quotient two places to the right; drop it if the percent is either a whole or mixed number. Add the percent sign.
   a. $\frac{7}{9} = 7 \div 9 = 0.77\frac{7}{9} = (77\frac{7}{9}\%)$
   b. $\frac{11}{12} = 11 \div 12 = 0.91\frac{2}{3} = (91\frac{2}{3}\%)$
   c. $\frac{3}{40} = 3 \div 40 = 0.07\frac{1}{2} = (07\frac{1}{2}\%)$
   d. $\frac{8}{15} = 8 \div 15 = 0.53\frac{1}{3} = (53\frac{1}{3}\%)$

2. **The percent equivalents of commonly used fractions should be memorized.** Fraction–percent equivalents are useful for solving percent problems mentally. See the table in the lesson.

An Ounce of Prevention

Stress that the decimal point is to be dropped unless a decimal fraction is involved; otherwise, pupils may write answers such as 23.1/4%. In this lesson, all decimal points are dropped in changing decimals to percents.

Further Study

Percents are the third kind of fractions that are taught this year.

1. A *common fraction* is a fraction with a written numerator and denominator, such as 1/4, 2/3, and 7/6.

2. A *decimal fraction* is a fraction expressed with a decimal point, such as 0.8, 0.08, and 0.0667. Place value identifies the denominator.

3. A *percent* is a special kind of fraction with a denominator of 100.

B. **Write the percent equivalents of these fractions. See how many of them you can do by memory.**

13. $\frac{1}{4}$ 25% **14.** $\frac{3}{4}$ 75% **15.** $\frac{1}{5}$ 20% **16.** $\frac{2}{5}$ 40% **17.** $\frac{3}{5}$ 60%

18. $\frac{1}{2}$ 50% **19.** $\frac{1}{10}$ 10% **20.** $\frac{2}{3}$ $66\frac{2}{3}$% **21.** $\frac{7}{10}$ 70% **22.** $\frac{9}{10}$ 90%

C. **Solve these reading problems.**

23. When Moses sent 12 spies into the land of Canaan, 10 of the spies discouraged the people with their evil report. What percent of the spies brought back an evil report?
$83\frac{1}{3}$%

24. Moses wrote 5 of the 39 books in the Old Testament. What percent of the Old Testament books did Moses write? Round the answer to the nearest whole percent.
13%

25. Twelve of the 39 books in the Old Testament are books of history. What percent of the Old Testament books are about history? Round the answer to the nearest whole percent.
31%

26. One morning Stephen had 35 out of 40 math problems correct. What was his score as a percent? Round the answer to the nearest whole percent.
88%

27. The same morning Cynthia had 37 of the 40 math problems correct. What was her score as a percent? Round the answer to the nearest whole percent.
93%

28. Cynthia spelled 19 out of 20 spelling words correctly on her spelling test. What was her score as a percent?
95%

REVIEW EXERCISES

D. **Change these metric linear measures as indicated.** *(Lesson 98)*

29. 3 m = __300__ cm   **30.** 15 km = __15,000__ m   **31.** 4.5 cm = __45__ mm

E. **Measure these lines to the nearest centimeter.** *(Lesson 97)*

32. ——————————————— 5 cm

33. ———————————————————— 8 cm

F. **Reduce these fractions to lowest terms. Label each number in the first two answers.** *(Lesson 49)*

34. $\frac{9}{12}$ $\frac{3}{4}$ $\frac{\text{numerator}}{\text{denominator}}$ **35.** $\frac{8}{20}$ $\frac{2}{5}$ $\frac{\text{numerator}}{\text{denominator}}$ **36.** $\frac{16}{48}$ $\frac{1}{3}$ **37.** $\frac{30}{45}$ $\frac{2}{3}$ **38.** $\frac{15}{27}$ $\frac{5}{9}$ **39.** $\frac{20}{35}$ $\frac{4}{7}$

115. Expressing Percents as Decimals and Fractions

Percents are an excellent way to compare numbers. However, percents are not used to calculate. To use a percent in calculation, you must change it to a decimal or a common fraction.

To change a percent to a decimal, drop the percent sign and move the decimal point two places to the left. If there is no decimal point, it is assumed to be at the right of the number. In the first example below, notice that a tenth of a percent equals $\frac{1}{1,000}$ (0.001) in a decimal.

$$28.1\% = 28.1 = 0.281 \qquad\qquad 7\% = 07. = 0.07$$

Use the fraction form if you are solving a ratio problem. To change a percent to a fraction, write the percent as the numerator of the fraction and 100 as the denominator. Reduce the fraction to lowest terms.

$$28\% = \tfrac{28}{100} = \tfrac{7}{25} \qquad\qquad 62\% = \tfrac{62}{100} = \tfrac{31}{50}$$

CLASS PRACTICE

Write each percent as a decimal and a fraction in lowest terms. You should be able to do a and b from memory.

	Percent	Decimal	Fraction
a.	25%	0.25	$\frac{1}{4}$
b.	60%	0.6	$\frac{3}{5}$
c.	7%	0.07	$\frac{7}{100}$
d.	45%	0.45	$\frac{9}{20}$

WRITTEN EXERCISES

A. *Write each percent as a decimal and a fraction in lowest terms. You should be able to do numbers 1–4 from memory.*

	Percent	Decimal	Fraction		Percent	Decimal	Fraction
1.	50%	0.5	$\frac{1}{2}$	2.	75%	0.75	$\frac{3}{4}$
3.	80%	0.8	$\frac{4}{5}$	4.	40%	0.4	$\frac{2}{5}$
5.	48%	0.48	$\frac{12}{25}$	6.	95%	0.95	$\frac{19}{20}$
7.	5%	0.05	$\frac{1}{20}$	8.	8%	0.08	$\frac{2}{25}$

LESSON 115

Objectives

- To give practice with changing percents to decimals.

- To introduce *changing a percent containing a decimal into a decimal.

- To give practice with changing percents to fractions in lowest terms.

Review

1. *Changing fractions to percents* (Lesson 114).

   a. $\frac{7}{20}$ = (35%)

   b. $\frac{7}{12}$ = (58$\frac{1}{3}$%)

   c. $\frac{11}{40}$ = (27$\frac{1}{2}$%)

2. *Changing decimals to percents* (Lesson 113).

   a. 0.36 (36%)

   b. 0.87 (87%)

   c. 0.05 (5%)

3. *Working with maps* (Lesson 107).
   Scale: 1/4 inch = 12 miles

   a. $1\frac{3}{4}$ in. = (84) mi.

   b. $2\frac{1}{4}$ in. = (108) mi.

4. *Working with metric measures* (Lesson 99).

   a. 6,000 g = (6) kg

   b. 5 g = (5,000) mg

   c. 3 m.t. = (3,000) kg

5. *Changing between improper fractions and mixed numbers* (Lesson 50).

   a. $\frac{33}{4}$ = ($8\frac{1}{4}$)

   b. $\frac{46}{7}$ = ($6\frac{4}{7}$)

   c. $\frac{35}{9}$ = ($3\frac{8}{9}$)

   d. $5\frac{7}{8}$ = ($\frac{47}{8}$)

   e. $7\frac{3}{5}$ = ($\frac{38}{5}$)

   f. $6\frac{2}{9}$ = ($\frac{56}{9}$)

Introduction

Review the table of fraction–percent equivalents in Lesson 114. There is no corresponding written work in the lesson.

   a. $\frac{1}{2}$ = (50%)

   b. $\frac{1}{3}$ = (33$\frac{1}{3}$%)

   c. $\frac{2}{3}$ = (66$\frac{2}{3}$%)

   d. $\frac{1}{4}$ = (25%)

   e. $\frac{1}{5}$ = (20%)

   f. $\frac{3}{4}$ = (75%)

   g. $\frac{7}{10}$ = (70%)

   h. $\frac{3}{5}$ = (60%)

   i. $\frac{4}{5}$ = (80%)

Teaching Guide

1. **Any percent can be changed to a decimal.** Drop the percent sign, and move the decimal point two places to the left. If there is no decimal point, it is assumed to be at the right of the number. Tenths of a percent equal thousandths in a decimal (23.4% = 0.234).

   a. 45% = (0.45)

   b. 91% = (0.91)

   c. 99% = (0.99)

   d. 43.5% = (0.435)

   e. 87.8% = (0.878)

   f. 14.5% = (0.145)

   g. 6% = (0.06)

   h. 4% = (0.04)

   i. 3.5% = (0.035)

2. **Any percent can be changed to a fraction.** Write the percent as the numerator of the fraction and 100 as the denominator. Reduce the fraction to lowest terms if possible.

   a. 45% = $\frac{45}{100}$ = $\frac{9}{20}$

   b. 88% = $\frac{88}{100}$ = $\frac{22}{25}$

   c. $85\% = \frac{85}{100} = \frac{17}{20}$

   d. $64\% = \frac{64}{100} = \frac{16}{25}$

Note that a percent is a kind of ratio. The above procedure is used to express a percent as a ratio in fraction form.

B. Solve these reading problems. Express fractions and ratios in simplest form.

9. Randy's math grade was 85% one morning. Write 85% as a fraction. $\frac{17}{20}$

10. Daniel had 90% of his math problems done correctly. Write 90% as a ratio. $\frac{9}{10}$

11. Marvin read in the encyclopedia that about 73.7% of the United States population lives in urban areas. Write 73.7% as a decimal. 0.737

12. About 26% of the population of the United States lives in rural areas. Write 26% as a fraction. $\frac{13}{50}$

REVIEW EXERCISES

C. Change these fractions to percents. Express remainders as fractions. *(Lesson 114)*

13. $\frac{13}{20}$ 65%   14. $\frac{7}{8}$ $87\frac{1}{2}$%   15. $\frac{17}{40}$ $42\frac{1}{2}$%   16. $\frac{3}{7}$ $42\frac{6}{7}$%

D. Change these decimals to percents. Remember that thousandths equal tenths of a percent. *(Lesson 113)*

17. 0.68 68%   18. 0.83 83%   19. 0.4 40%   20. 0.9 90%

21. 0.04 4%   22. 0.07 7%   23. 0.765 76.5%   24. 0.035 3.5%

E. Solve these reading problems. *(Lesson 107)*

25. Two cities are $2\frac{3}{4}$ inches apart on a map with a scale of $\frac{1}{8}$ inch = 10 miles. What is the actual distance between the cities? 220 miles

26. A map has a scale of $\frac{1}{8}$ inch = 15 miles. If two cities are $3\frac{1}{8}$ inches apart on the map, how many miles apart are they? 375 miles

27. A map in Jason's Bible has a scale of $\frac{3}{4}$ inch = 20 miles. On the map, the distance between the town of Nazareth where Jesus grew into manhood and Jerusalem where He was crucified is $2\frac{1}{4}$ inches. How far apart were Nazareth and Jerusalem? 60 miles

28. On a large-scale map, the villages of Pleasant Gap and Cedar Hill are $6\frac{3}{4}$ inches apart. The scale of miles is $\frac{7}{8}$ inch = 2 miles. What is the actual distance between the two villages? $15\frac{3}{7}$ miles

F. Change these metric measures as indicated. *(Lesson 99)*

29. 4 kg = <u>4,000</u> g   30. 3,500 mg = <u>3.5</u> g   31. 350 kg = <u>0.35</u> m.t.

G. Change mixed numbers to improper fractions, and improper fractions to mixed numbers. *(Lesson 50)*

32. $3\frac{3}{5}$ $\frac{18}{5}$ 33. $5\frac{7}{9}$ $\frac{52}{9}$ 34. $\frac{17}{3}$ $5\frac{2}{3}$ 35. $\frac{36}{7}$ $5\frac{1}{7}$

116. Subtracting Percents From 100%

One hundred percent (100%) means the whole amount of anything you are considering. If you receive a score of 100% on your math assignment, it means all the problems are done correctly.

Percents can be added and subtracted just like inches or dollars. If you have 20% of the problems done incorrectly, your score is 100% – 20% = 80%. To subtract a percent from 100%, subtract the percent from 100 and label it as a percent.

Example A
Sally had 13% of her math problems done incorrectly. What was her score as a percent?

$$\begin{array}{r} 100\% \\ -\ 13\% \\ \hline 87\% \end{array}$$

Example B
The Sandy Ridge Christian Bookstore had a clearance sale in which the price of all books was 15% off the regular price. What percent was the sale price of the regular price?

$$\begin{array}{r} 100\% \\ -\ 15\% \\ \hline 85\% \end{array}$$

CLASS PRACTICE

Subtract these percents from 100%.

a. 82%	b. 97%	c. 11%	d. 49%	e. 46%	f. 73%
18%	3%	89%	51%	54%	27%

WRITTEN EXERCISES

A.   Subtract these percents from 100%.

1. 23%	2. 18%	3. 45%	4. 88%	5. 39%	6. 58%
77%	82%	55%	12%	61%	42%

7. 34%	8. 32%	9. 95%	10. 98%	11. 91%	12. 99%
66%	68%	5%	2%	9%	1%

B.   Solve these reading problems.

13. Rhoda's mother bought dress fabric that was on sale at 20% off the regular price. What percent of the regular price did Mother pay?   80%

14. Mary bought a new Bible at a price 25% less than the regular price. What percent of the regular price did Mary pay?   75%

15. For Anna Rose, Mother bought a light jacket that was made of polyester and cotton. If the jacket was 35% cotton, what percent was polyester?   65%

LESSON 116

Objective

- To teach *subtracting percents from 100%.

Review

1. *Changing percents to decimals and fractions* (Lesson 115). Have students do *d–g* by memory.
   a. 28% = (0.28)
   b. 1% = (0.01)
   c. 13.5% = (0.135)
   d. 25% = ($\frac{1}{4}$)
   e. 33$\frac{1}{3}$% = ($\frac{1}{3}$)
   f. 40% = ($\frac{2}{5}$)
   g. 75% = ($\frac{3}{4}$)
   h. 44% = ($\frac{11}{25}$)
   i. 22% = ($\frac{11}{50}$)
   j. 2% = ($\frac{1}{50}$)
   k. 99% = ($\frac{99}{100}$)

2. *Changing fractions and decimals to percents* (Lessons 112–114).
   a. 0.32 = (32%)
   b. 0.05 = (5%)
   c. 0.065 = (6.5%)
   d. $\frac{2}{9}$ = (22$\frac{2}{9}$%)
   e. $\frac{7}{15}$ = (46$\frac{2}{3}$%)
   f. $\frac{7}{16}$ = (43$\frac{3}{4}$%)

3. *Reading a blueprint* (Lesson 108). Scale: 1 inch = 4 feet
   a. 3 in. = (12 ft.)
   b. 2$\frac{1}{2}$ in. = (10 ft.)
   c. 3$\frac{1}{4}$ in. = (13 ft.)
   d. 5$\frac{3}{4}$ in. = (23 ft.)

4. *Metric measures of capacity* (Lesson 100).
   a. 640 ml = (0.64) l
   b. 1,300 l = (1.3) kl
   c. 15 kl = (15,000) l
   d. 0.25 l = (250) ml

Introduction

Help the pupils to understand the meaning of 100% by using the following sentences.

a. Denise had all her math problems done correctly. Denise had 100% of her math problems done correctly.

b. All the students in the classroom have Bibles in their desks. One hundred percent of the students in the classroom have Bibles in their desks.

c. All the boys went outside to shovel snow off the walks. One hundred percent of the boys went outside to shovel snow off the walks.

d. What percent is equal to the fraction 1/1? (100%) One hundred percent is equal to all the items being considered.

Teaching Guide

Percents can be added and subtracted like other numbers. Subtraction is used to find the percent remaining. The given percent is subtracted from 100%, and the answer is labeled as a percent.

a. 100%
    − 46%
    (54%)

b. 100%
    − 2%
    (98%)

c. 100%
    − 96%
    (4%)

d. 100%
    − 73%
    (27%)

e. Miriam had 9% of her geography answers wrong. What was her score as a percent? (91%)

The reading problems on sale prices reinforce the concept that the regular price is 100% of regular price. The percent off is subtracted from that.

f. Royers' Hardware Store is having a

fall clearance sale in which all garden tools are priced at 30% off the regular price. At what percent of the regular price are the garden tools being sold? (70%)

g.   In the spring, Rod and Staff Publishers often has a sale in which the regular prices of school textbooks are reduced by 10%. At what percent of the regular price are the textbooks being sold? (90%)

An Ounce of Prevention

This lesson is a bit more difficult than it may appear on the surface. The concept of subtracting from 100% involves more than simply doing the mechanical calculations. In Example B, for instance, pupils must comprehend that the regular price is 100% of the regular price, and they must subtract the percent off from 100% to find what percent of the regular price is being paid.

16. David had 11% of the questions on his Bible test wrong. What was his score as a percent?
89%

17. In Bible class, David learned that about 41% of the books of the Bible are in the New Testament. What percent of the books of the Bible are in the Old Testament? 59%

18. In social studies class, the sixth grade learned that 59% of the world's population lives on the continent of Asia. What percent of the world's population lives in the rest of the world?
41%

REVIEW EXERCISES

C. *Write each percent as a decimal and a fraction in lowest terms.* (*Lesson 115*)

	Percent	Decimal	Fraction
19.	36%	0.36	$\frac{9}{25}$
20.	45%	0.45	$\frac{9}{20}$

D. *Change these fractions to percents. Express remainders as fractions in lowest terms.* (*Lesson 114*)

21. $\frac{3}{5}$ 60%   22. $\frac{3}{8}$ $37\frac{1}{2}$%   23. $\frac{11}{25}$ 44%   24. $\frac{5}{7}$ $71\frac{3}{7}$%

E. *Change these decimals to percents.* (*Lesson 113*)

25. 0.45   26. 0.67   27. 0.8   28. 0.1   29. 0.125   30. 0.755
    45%   67%   80%   10%   12.5%   75.5%

F. *Solve these reading problems.* (*Lesson 108*)

31. Douglas's father went to a distant city to help rebuild houses that had been damaged by a tornado. The blueprint for one house was drawn to the scale of 1 inch = 2 feet. How long is the house if its length on the blueprint is $22\frac{1}{2}$ inches?
45 feet

32. On the blueprint, the width of the house in problem 31 is 16 inches. How wide is the house? (1 inch = 2 feet)
32 feet

33. The kitchen of the house in problem 31 is $7\frac{1}{2}$ inches long on the blueprint. What is its actual length? (1 inch = 2 feet)
15 feet

34. Douglas's father also helped to rebuild a warehouse. The scale of that blueprint was 1 inch = 8 feet. How long is the warehouse if its length on the blueprint is $13\frac{1}{2}$ inches?
108 feet

G. *Change these metric measures as indicated.* (*Lesson 100*)

35. 5 l = __5,000__ ml   36. 4,000 l = __4__ kl   37. 3,300 ml = __3.3__ l
38. 2.5 kl = __2,500__ l 39. 450 ml = __0.45__ l 40. 280 l = __0.28__ kl

173

117. Finding a Percentage of a Number

One of the most frequent uses of percents is to find a percentage of a number. Below is an example of such a problem.

> Mr. Turner owns a 320-acre farm in North Dakota. This year he planted 35% of the farm in wheat. How many acres of wheat did he plant?

Finding 35% of 320 actually means finding $\frac{35}{100}$ of 320 ($\frac{35}{100} \times 320$) or 0.35 of 320. The word *of* in the problem means "times," the same as in problems with fractions and decimals. To find a percentage of a number, change the percent to a decimal and multiply.

Example A	**Example B**
Find 35% of 320 acres.	Find 12% of 750.
35% of 320 = $\begin{array}{r} 320 \\ \times\, 0.35 \\ \hline 1600 \\ 960 \\ \hline 112.00 = 112 \end{array}$	12% of 750 = $\begin{array}{r} 750 \\ \times\, 0.12 \\ \hline 1500 \\ 750 \\ \hline 90.00\ = 90 \end{array}$
35% of 320 acres = 112 acres	12% of 750 = 90

> **To find a percentage of a number, change the percent to a decimal, and multiply the number by the decimal.**

CLASS PRACTICE

Express these percents as decimals.

a. 67%   b. 14%   c. 52%   d. 88%   e. 91%   f. 70%
   0.67   0.14   0.52   0.88   0.91   0.70

Find the following percentages. Remember that of means "times."

g. 50% of 72   h. 25% of 52   i. 12% of 35   j. 45% of 23
      36   13   4.2   10.35

k. 65% × 42   l. 20% × 61   m. 85% × 60   n. 24% × 95
      27.3   12.2   51   22.8

WRITTEN EXERCISES

A.   Express these percents as decimals.

1. 68%   2. 82%   3. 34%   4. 58%   5. 42%   6. 23%
   0.68   0.82   0.34   0.58   0.42   0.23

LESSON 117

Objective

- To teach *finding a percentage of a number. (Two-digit percents are used in this lesson, and one-digit percents in Lesson 118.)

Review

1. Give Lesson 117 Quiz (Expressing Percents as Decimals and Fractions).

2. *Subtracting percents from 100%* (Lesson 116).
   a. 100% − 56%   (44%)
   b. 100% − 32%   (68%)
   c. 100% − 97%   (3%)
   d. 100% − 6%   (94%)

3. *Metric units of area* (Lesson 101).
   a. 1 km² = (100) ha
   b. 1 m² = (10,000) cm²
   c. 5 km² = (500) ha
   d. 350 ha = (3.5) km²
   e. 5 m² = (50,000) cm²
   f. 30,000 cm² = (3) m²

4. *Adding fractions* (Lessons 52, 54).

   a. $\frac{1}{2}$
       $+ \frac{5}{14}$
       $(\frac{6}{7})$

   b. $\frac{3}{8}$
       $+ \frac{5}{6}$
       $(1\frac{5}{24})$

   c. $2\frac{3}{4}$
       $+ 2\frac{2}{3}$
       $(5\frac{5}{12})$

   d. $3\frac{3}{5}$
       $+ 4\frac{1}{4}$
       $(7\frac{17}{20})$

Introduction

Solve the two problems below in class. After you find each answer, ask the class to change the decimal multiplier into a percent. For the first one, ask the students, "Do you think 35% × 40 is equal to 0.35 × 40?"

a.   40
    × 0.35 (35%)
    (14.00 = 14)

b.   45
    × 0.60 (60%)
    (27.00 = 27)

Now read the following problem to the students, and see if they have any idea how to solve it.

Of the 72 students in the Benwood Mennonite School, 25% are in the sixth and seventh grades. How many students is that?

25% of 72 = 0.25 × 72

c.   72
    × 0.25
    (18.00)

Teaching Guide

To find a percentage of a number, change the percent to a decimal, and multiply. The word *of* in the problem means "times," the same as in problems with fractions and decimals.

Work with both vertical and horizontal problems in class. The students should set them up vertically to solve them.

   a. 45% of 80 = (36)
   b. 48% of 25 = (12)
   c. 28% of 75 = (21)
   d. 42% of 35 = (14.7)
   e. 36% of 45 = (16.2)
   f. 22% of 56 = (12.32)

g. 32% × 35 = (11.2)
h. 62% × 48 = (29.76)
i. 44% × 115 = (50.6)

An Ounce of Prevention

Occasionally a student thinks that a whole number multiplied by a percent yields a percent answer. This is likely a carry-over from a problem such as 6 × 6 feet = 36 feet, where one factor has a label and that label is written after the answer. Try to prevent this mistake by briefly discussing it in class. Students will further overcome this misunderstanding as they grasp the concept of multiplying by percents.

B. *Find the following percentages. Remember that* of means *"times."*

7. 50% of 64 32
8. 85% of 20 17
9. 14% of 50 7
10. 60% of 75 45

11. 84% of 25 21
12. 68% of 75 51
13. 40% of 35 14
14. 45% of 120 54

15. 48% × 125 60
16. 55% × 74 40.7
17. 35% × 48 16.8
18. 42% × 85 35.7

19. 65% × 32 20.8
20. 54% × 65 35.1
21. 38% × 23 8.74
22. 18% × 48 8.64

23. 95% × 45 42.75
24. 65% × 92 59.8
25. 65% × 32 20.8
26. 35% × 82 28.7

C. *Solve these reading problems.*

27. On a spelling test of 50 words, Brenda had a score of 88%. How many words did she spell correctly?　　　　　　44 words

28. There are 50 parking spaces in the parking lot at the Dover Mennonite Church. One Sunday morning, 82% of the parking spaces were full. How many parking spaces were used?　　　　　41 parking spaces

29. If 82% of the parking spaces at the Dover Church were filled, what percent of the parking spaces were not filled?　　　　　18%

30. Judith had 15% of the 40 problems in her math assignment done incorrectly. How many of her answers were wrong?　　　　　6 answers

31. If Judith had 15% of her math problems done incorrectly, what was her score as a percent?　　　　　85%

32. Calvin's father had 75 head of beef cattle and sold 44% of them. How many cattle did he sell?　　　　　33 cattle

REVIEW EXERCISES

D. *Subtract these percents from 100%. (Lesson 116)*

33. 34%　66%
34. 89%　11%
35. 92%　8%
36. 5%　95%

E. *Change these metric measures as indicated. (Lesson 101)*

37. 1 m² = __10,000__ cm²
38. 1 ha = __10,000__ m²
39. 1 km² = __100__ ha

40. 20 m² = __200,000__ cm²
41. 300 ha = __3__ km²
42. 8 km² = __800__ ha

F. *Solve these addition problems, and write the sums in simplest form.* *(Lessons 52, 54)*

43. $\frac{3}{4}$
　$+ \frac{5}{6}$
　$1\frac{7}{12}$

44. $\frac{3}{5}$
　$+ \frac{2}{3}$
　$1\frac{4}{15}$

45. $2\frac{1}{2}$
　$+ 3\frac{3}{4}$
　$6\frac{1}{4}$

46. $3\frac{5}{6}$
　$+ 2\frac{3}{5}$
　$6\frac{13}{30}$

118. Solving More Challenging Percent Problems

In Lesson 117, you learned to find a percentage of a number when the percent has two digits. Multiplying by a one-digit percent is performed by the same method. However, you must be sure to change the one-digit percent to a two-place decimal.

Example A

Find 8% of 25.

$8\% = 08 = 0.08$

$$8\% \text{ of } 25 = \begin{array}{r} 25 \\ \times\ 0.08 \\ \hline 2.00 \end{array} = 2$$

Example B

Find 2% of 45.

$2\% = 02 = 0.02$

$$2\% \text{ of } 45 = \begin{array}{r} 45 \\ \times\ 0.02 \\ \hline 0.90 \end{array} = 0.9$$

A percent can sometimes be multiplied more easily as a fraction than as a decimal. This is often true when the percent is equal to a frequently used fraction such as $\frac{1}{2}$ or $\frac{1}{4}$. In order to know when it is easier to multiply by a fraction, you will need to memorize well the percent–fraction equivalents listed in Lesson 114.

Example C

Find 25% of 40

Think: $25\% = \frac{1}{4}$

25% of 40 = $\frac{1}{4} \times 40 = 10$

Example D

Find $33\frac{1}{3}\%$ of 15.

Think: $33\frac{1}{3}\% = \frac{1}{3}$

$33\frac{1}{3}\%$ of 15 = $\frac{1}{3} \times 15 = 5$

CLASS PRACTICE

Express these percents as decimals.

a. 9%   b. 5%   c. 1%   d. 7%   e. 4%   f. 6%
   0.09   0.05   0.01   0.07   0.04   0.06

Find the percentages indicated. Be careful to change these one-digit percents to the correct decimals.

g. 2% × 82   h. 7% of 35   i. 1% of 132   j. 5% × 49
      1.64   2.45   1.32   2.45

Solve by changing the percents to frequently used fractions before multiplying. See how many of these you can do mentally.

k. 50% of 70   l. $33\frac{1}{3}\%$ of 36   m. 40% of 35   n. 75% of 28
         35   12   14   21

WRITTEN EXERCISES

A.   Express these percents as decimals.

1. 2%   2. 3%   3. 4%   4. 6%   5. 8%   6. 9%
      0.02   0.03   0.04   0.06   0.08   0.09

LESSON 118

Objectives

- To teach finding a percentage of a number, *including one-digit percents.

- To teach finding a percentage of a number *by changing the percent to a commonly used fraction.

Review

1. *Subtracting percents from 100%* (Lesson 116). Problems *a* and *b* reverse the subtrahend and the difference, and *c* and *d* do likewise.

   a. $100\% - 35\%$ (65%)
   b. $100\% - 65\%$ (35%)
   c. $100\% - 91\%$ (9%)
   d. $100\% - 9\%$ (91%)

2. *Changing percents to decimals and fractions* (Lesson 115).

Percent	Decimal	Fraction
a. 32%	(0.32)	$(\frac{8}{25})$
b. 5%	(0.05)	$(\frac{1}{20})$

Introduction

Practice changing percents to decimals. Be sure that the students are familiar with changing one-digit percents to decimals.

Teaching Guide

1. Give practice with multiplying by one-digit percents. Make sure the decimal equivalents are written correctly.

   a. $2\% \times 35 = 0.02 \times 35 = (0.7)$
   b. $5\% \times 42 = 0.05 \times 42 = (2.1)$
   c. $1\% \times 36 = 0.01 \times 36 = (0.36)$
   d. $1\% \times 98 = 0.01 \times 98 = (0.98)$
   e. $9\% \times 92 = 0.09 \times 92 = (8.28)$
   f. $7\% \times 48 = 0.07 \times 48 = (3.36)$
   g. $8\% \times 42 = 0.08 \times 42 = (3.36)$
   h. $3\% \times 58 = 0.03 \times 58 = (1.74)$
   i. $4\% \times 125 = 0.04 \times 125 = (5)$
   j. $8\% \times 350 = 0.08 \times 350 = (28)$
   k. $7\% \times 135 = 0.07 \times 135 = (9.45)$
   l. $6\% \times 225 = 0.06 \times 225 = (13.5)$

2. Give practice with changing percents to frequently used fractions before multiplying. If students become skilled in this method, they will begin using it almost automatically in everyday situations.

   a. 25% of 24 = 1/4 of 24 = (6)
   b. 33 1/3% of 21 = 1/3 of 21 = (7)
   c. 20% of 25 = 1/5 of 25 = (5)
   d. 60% of 25 = 3/5 of 25 = (15)
   e. 66 2/3% of 24 = 2/3 of 24 = (16)
   f. 75% of 16 = 3/4 of 16 = (12)
   g. 80% of 35 = 4/5 of 35 = (28)
   h. 75% of 48 = 3/4 of 48 = (36)

B. **Find the percentages indicated. Be careful to change these one-digit percents to the correct decimals.**

7. 4% of 75   8. 2% of 50   9. 8% of 65   10. 9% of 38
      3   1   5.2   3.42

11. 1% of 20   12. 1% of 300   13. 5% of 80   14. 3% of 150
       0.2   3   4   4.5

15. 7% of 53   16. 8% of 95   17. 6% of 93   18. 9% of 117
      3.71   7.6   5.58   10.53

C. **See if you can change these percents to fractions by memory. Refer to Lesson 114 if you need help.**

19. 20% $\frac{1}{5}$ 20. 75% $\frac{3}{4}$ 21. 90% $\frac{9}{10}$ 22. 80% $\frac{4}{5}$ 23. $66\frac{2}{3}$% $\frac{2}{3}$ 24. 60% $\frac{3}{5}$

D. **Solve by changing the percents to frequently used fractions before multiplying. See how many of these you can do mentally.**

25. 50% of 90   26. $33\frac{1}{3}$% of 45   27. 30% of 40   28. 25% of 44
       45   15   12   11

29. 90% of 80   30. 20% of 50   31. 75% of 28   32. 10% of 60
       72   10   21   6

E. **Solve these reading problems.**

33. Crystal had 5% of 40 math problems done incorrectly. How many of her answers were wrong?   2 answers

34. If 5% of Crystal's math answers were incorrect, what was her score as a percent? 95%

35. Father bought a copy of *Doctrines of the Bible* for $18.00. He paid New York sales tax of 7% of the price of the book. How much was the sales tax? $1.26

36. Andrew bought a copy of *Martyrs Mirror* for $42.00. The Kentucky sales tax amounted to 6% of the price of the book. How much was the sales tax? $2.52

37. One morning at school, 20% of the 20 students in grades 6 and 7 were absent because of illness. How many students were missing?   4 students

38. At the end of one school day, 75% of Brother Martin's 24 students had completed all their assignments for the next morning. How many students had finished their work?
                                                                       18 students

REVIEW EXERCISES

F. **Subtract these percents from 100%.** (*Lesson 116*)

39. 43%   57%   40. 42%   58%   41. 8%   92%   42. 97%   3%

G. **Write each percent as a decimal and a fraction in lowest terms.** (*Lesson 115*)

	Percent	Decimal	Fraction
43.	42%	0.42	$\frac{21}{50}$
44.	65%	0.65	$\frac{13}{20}$

119. Finding a Percent More or Less Than a Number

Changes in numbers are often given in percents, such as a 15% increase or a 3% decrease. Because the original number is always 100%, an increase in percentage is added to 100% and a decrease in percentage is subtracted from 100%. For example, a price that has increased by 15% is now 100% + 15%, or 115% of the original price. Likewise, a price that has decreased by 3% is now 100% – 3%, or 97% of the original price.

To increase or decrease a number by a given percent, use the following steps.

1. Find the percent by which you will multiply the original number. If the number is to be increased by a given percent, add that percent to 100%. If it is to be decreased, subtract the percent from 100%.

2. Change the new percent to a decimal by dropping the percent sign and moving the decimal point two places to the left.

3. Multiply the original number by the decimal found in step 2.

4. Check your work by casting out nines. Be sure your answer is reasonable. If the original number is to be increased, the answer will be a larger number. If the original number is to be decreased, the answer will be a smaller number.

Example A

What number is a 20% increase over 65?

100% + 20% = 120%

120% = 1.20 or 1.2

$$
\begin{array}{r}
65 \\
\times\ 1.2 \\
\hline
130 \\
65\ \ \ \\
\hline
78.0\ = 78
\end{array}
$$

Example B

An item regularly priced at $30.00 is on sale for 15% off. What is the sale price?

100% – 15% = 85%

85% = 0.85

$$
\begin{array}{r}
\$30 \\
\times\ 0.85 \\
\hline
150 \\
240\ \ \\
\hline
\$25.50\ = \$25.50
\end{array}
$$

CLASS PRACTICE

Add these percents.

a. 100% + 25%   b. 100% + 8%   c. 100% + 33%   d. 100% + 16%

125%   108%   133%   116%

Lesson 119

Objective

- To teach *finding a percent more or less than a number.

Review

1. Give Lesson 119 Speed Test (Finding a Percentage of a Number). This concept is reviewed in the lesson.

2. *Finding a percentage of a number* (Lessons 117, 118).
   a. 20% of 25 = 1/5 of 25 = (5)
   b. 40% of 35 = 2/5 of 35 = (14)
   c. 12% of 25 = (3)
   d. 5% of 62 = (3.1)

3. *Dividing fractions* (Lessons 65–67).
   a. $\frac{9}{10} \div \frac{3}{4} = (1\frac{1}{5})$
   b. $7 \div \frac{5}{6} = (8\frac{2}{5})$
   c. $3\frac{3}{4} \div \frac{7}{8} = (4\frac{2}{7})$
   d. $4\frac{1}{6} \div 1\frac{1}{2} = (2\frac{7}{9})$

4. *Converting between English and metric measures* (Lessons 103, 104).
   a. 3 mi. = (4.83) km
   b. 17 km = (10.54) mi.
   c. 12 ft. = (3.6) m
   d. 15 m = (49.2) ft.
   e. 15 lb. = (6.75) kg
   f. 15 kg = (33) lb.
   g. 3 qt. = (2.85) l
   h. 3 l = (3.18) qt.
   i. 15 a. = (6) ha
   j. 15 ha = (37.5) a.

Introduction

Ask the pupils to find 10% of $30.00. ($3.00) Then challenge them to find the cost of an item if the selling price was $30.00 and that price is reduced by 10%. ($30.00 - 3.00 = $27.00) Can they calculate the price if it was originally $30.00 and it is increased by 10%? ($30.00 + 3.00 = $33.00) Problems like these are what this lesson is about.

Teaching Guide

1. Give practice with subtracting percents from 100%. This is review work.
   a. 100% − 50% = (50%)
   b. 100% − 21% = (79%)
   c. 100% − 99% = (1%)
   d. 100% − 3% = (97%)

2. Give practice with adding percents to 100%. This follows the same pattern as subtracting percents from 100%.
   a. 100% + 15% = (115%)
   b. 100% + 20% = (120%)
   c. 100% + 35% = (135%)
   d. 100% + 2% = (102%)

3. **A number can be increased or decreased by a given percent.** The following steps are used.
   (1) Find the percent by which you will multiply the original number. If the number is to be increased by a given percent, add that percent to 100%. If it is to be decreased, subtract the percent from 100%.
   (2) Change the new percent to a decimal by dropping the percent sign and moving the decimal point two places to the left.
   (3) Multiply the original number by the decimal found in step 2.
   (4) Check your work by casting out nines. Be sure your answer is

reasonable. If the original number is to be increased, the answer will be a larger number. If the original number is to be decreased, the answer will be a smaller number.

a. What number is 12% less than 35?
    $100\% - 12\% = 88\%$
    88% of 35 = 0.88 × 35 = (30.8)

b. What number is 8% less than 28?
    $100\% - 8\% = 92\%$
    92% of 28 = 0.92 × 28 = (25.76)

c. What is the price of a $40.00 item if the price is reduced by 15%?
    $100\% - 15\% = 85\%$
    85% of $40.00 = 0.85 × $40.00 =
    ($34.00)

d. What number is 12% more than 35?
    $100\% + 12\% = 112\%$
    112% of 35 = 1.12 × 35 = (39.2)

e. What number is 8% more than 28?
    $100\% + 8\% = 108\%$
    108% of 28 = 1.08 × 28 = (30.24)

f. What is the price of a $40.00 item if the price is increased by 15%?
    $100\% + 15\% = 115\%$
    115% of $40.00 = 1.15 × $40.00 =
    ($46.00)

Find the new amounts after the increases or decreases shown.

e. 10% increase over 45   49.5

f. 50% more than 36   54

g. 25% decrease from 48   36

h. 45% less than 92   50.6

i. 20% more than 53   63.6

j. 15% decrease from 76   64.6

k. 40% less than 58   34.8

l. 65% increase over $14.00 $23.10

WRITTEN EXERCISES

A. Add these percents.

1. 100% + 15%   115%

2. 100% + 20%   120%

3. 100% + 35%   135%

4. 100% + 62%   162%

B. Find each new price after the increase shown.

	Original	Increase			Original	Increase	
5.	$20.00	10%	$22.00	6.	$10.00	5%	$10.50
7.	$18.00	15%	$20.70	8.	$25.00	10%	$27.50
9.	$40.00	15%	$46.00	10.	$80.00	6%	$84.80

C. Subtract these percents.

11. 100% − 95%   5%

12. 100% − 50%   50%

13. 100% − 8%   92%

14. 100% − 2%   98%

D. Find each new price after the decrease shown.

	Original	Decrease			Original	Decrease	
15.	$20.00	10%	$18.00	16.	$10.00	5%	$9.50
17.	$18.00	15%	$15.30	18.	$30.00	15%	$25.50
19.	$50.00	15%	$42.50	20.	$75.00	6%	$70.50

E. Find the new amounts after the increases or decreases shown.

21. 20% increase over $20.00 $24.00

22. 25% decrease from $28.00 $21.00

23. 35% less than 80   52

24. 15% more than 30   34.5

F.   Solve these reading problems.

25. The Lincoln Christian Bookstore had a year-end sale. If prices were reduced by 10%, what was the sale price of a Bible regularly priced at $17.00? $15.30

26. The price of *Home Fires at the Foot of the Rockies* was decreased by 15%. If the regular price was $8.00, what was the sale price? $6.80

27. The fifth grade at Lanesville Mennonite School has 15 students. There are 20% more students in sixth grade than in fifth grade. How many students are in the sixth grade?

18 students

28. United States postage for a 1-ounce letter, which had been $0.25, was increased by 16% in 1991. What was the new postage? $0.29

REVIEW EXERCISES

G.   Find the percentages indicated. *(Lessons 117, 118)*

29. 25% of 36   **30.** 95% of 60   **31.** 4% of 85   **32.** 7% of 69

9   57   3.4   4.83

H.   Solve these division problems. *(Lessons 65–67)*

33. $6 \div \frac{1}{2}$ 12   **34.** $\frac{5}{8} \div \frac{3}{4}$ $\frac{5}{6}$ **35.** $3\frac{3}{5} \div 1\frac{1}{10}$ $3\frac{3}{11}$ **36.** $4\frac{5}{8} \div 2\frac{1}{4}$ $2\frac{1}{18}$

I.   Change these measures as indicated. *(Lessons 103, 104)*

37. 12 ft. = __3.6__ m   **38.** 4 mi. = __6.44__ km

39. 25 lb. = __11.25__ kg   **40.** 30 *l* = __31.8__ qt.

LESSON 120

Objectives

- To teach *finding a discount by using the regular price and the rate of discount.

- To teach *finding a sale price by using the regular price and the discount.

Review

1. *Finding a percent more or less than a number* (Lesson 119).
   a. 15% increase over $12.00 ($13.80)
   b. 12% more than 22 (24.64)
   c. 15% decrease from $12.00 ($10.20)
   d. 12% less than 22 (19.36)

2. *Changing decimals to percents* (Lessons 112, 113).
   a. 0.82 = (82%)
   b. 0.49 = (49%)
   c. 0.08 = (8%)
   d. 0.13 = (13%)

3. *Changing fractions to percents* (Lessons 112–114).
   a. $\frac{13}{20}$ = (65%)
   b. $\frac{11}{12}$ = ($91\frac{2}{3}$%)
   c. $\frac{13}{16}$ = ($81\frac{1}{4}$%)
   d. $\frac{5}{18}$ = ($27\frac{7}{9}$%)

4. *Adding mixed numbers* (Lesson 55).

   a. $3\frac{3}{5}$ b. $3\frac{1}{3}$
       $4\frac{1}{4}$ $4\frac{3}{5}$
       $+2\frac{1}{2}$ $+5\frac{2}{3}$
       $(10\frac{7}{20})$ $(13\frac{3}{5})$

   c. $5\frac{5}{6}$ d. $5\frac{1}{8}$
       $2\frac{1}{4}$ $2\frac{5}{6}$
       $+3\frac{1}{3}$ $+4\frac{5}{12}$
       $(11\frac{5}{12})$ $(12\frac{3}{8})$

Introduction

Read the following problem, and solve it step by step to see if the students already understand the concept in this lesson.

David is buying a hammer that is on sale. The regular price of the hammer is $9.00, and the percent of discount is 25%.
a. How much will David save by purchasing the hammer at the sale price?
($9.00 × 0.25 = $2.25)
b. What is the sale price of the hammer?
($9.00 – $2.25 = $6.75)

If the students grasp the concept easily, the greater part of the class period should be spent in solving the problems in the Teaching Guide below. If they have difficulty, more time should be spent in teaching the individual points.

Teaching Guide

1. **A discount can be found by using the regular price and the rate of discount.** The steps are as follows:
   (1) Change the percent of discount to a decimal by moving the decimal point two places to the left.
   (2) Multiply the original price by the decimal.
   (3) If the product has more than two decimal places, round the answer to the nearest cent (hundredth of a dollar). The result is the amount of the discount.

2. **A sale price can be found by using the regular price and the discount.** To find the sale price, subtract the discount from the original price.
   a. Find the discount and the sale

120. Calculating Discount Prices

If the price of an item is reduced by a certain percent, the amount of the reduction is the **discount.** Sometimes it is necessary to know both the discount and the sale price. To find these, use the following steps.

1. Change the percent of discount to a decimal by moving the decimal point two places to the left.
2. Multiply the original price by the decimal.
3. If the product has more than two decimal places, round the answer to the nearest cent (hundredth of a dollar). This answer is the amount of the discount.
4. To find the sale price, subtract the discount from the original price.

Example A

A $15.00 item is on sale at 20% off. Find the discount and the sale price.

$$20\% = 0.20 \text{ or } 0.2$$

$$\begin{array}{r} \$15.00 \\ \times\ 0.2 \\ \hline \$3.00 \end{array} \text{ Discount}$$

$$\begin{array}{r} \$15.00 \\ -\ 3.00 \\ \hline \$12.00 \end{array} \text{ Sale Price}$$

Example B

An item regularly priced at $12.95 is on sale for 5% off. Find the discount and the sale price.

$$5\% = 0.05$$

$$\begin{array}{r} \$12.95 \\ \times\ 0.05 \\ \hline \$0.6475 \end{array} \text{ Discount}$$
$$= \$0.65 \text{ to nearest cent}$$

$$\begin{array}{r} \$12.95 \\ -\ 0.65 \\ \hline \$12.30 \end{array} \text{ Sale Price}$$

CLASS PRACTICE

Find both the discount and the sale price of each item.

	Regular Price	Percent of Discount		Regular Price	Percent of Discount		Regular Price	Percent of Discount
a.	$15.00	10%	b.	$30.00	8%	c.	$20.00	15%
	$1.50	$13.50		$2.40	$27.60		$3.00	$17.00
d.	$42.00	20%	e.	$50.00	5%	f.	$20.00	25%
	$8.40	$33.60		$2.50	$47.50		$5.00	$15.00

WRITTEN EXERCISES

A. *Find both the discount and the sale price of each item.*

	Regular Price	Percent of Discount		Regular Price	Percent of Discount		Regular Price	Percent of Discount
1.	$10.00	10%	2.	$22.00	10%	3.	$50.00	15%
	$1.00	$9.00		$2.20	$19.80		$7.50	$42.50

	Regular Price	Percent of Discount		Regular Price	Percent of Discount		Regular Price	Percent of Discount
4.	$30.00 $4.50	15% $25.50	5.	$30.00 $6.00	20% $24.00	6.	$25.00 $2.50	10% $22.50
7.	$20.00 $2.00	10% $18.00	8.	$15.00 $3.00	20% $12.00	9.	$40.00 $6.00	15% $34.00
10.	$100.00 $15.00	15% $85.00	11.	$50.00 $2.50	5% $47.50	12.	$60.00 $4.20	7% $55.80

B. Solve these reading problems.

13. The book *Traveling the Way* usually sells for $6.55. If the book is on sale at 15% off, find the discount and the sale price. $0.98 $5.57

14. The book *The Anguish of Love* usually sells for $6.70. If the book is on sale at 20% off, find the discount and the sale price. $1.34 $5.36

15. Warner's Hardware Store posted a sign that read "Autumn Clearance Sale—All garden tools reduced 30%." Find the discount and the sale price on a shovel with a regular price of $15.98. $4.79 $11.19

16. The regular price of a fertilizer spreader is $59.95. At 35% off, what is the discount and the sale price of this spreader? $20.98 $38.97

17. Faye's father bought a garden rake at a price of $11.00. How much is 6% sales tax on $11.00? What did Father pay for the rake, including sales tax? $0.66 $11.66

18. Marlin's father bought a pair of work gloves for $4.99 and a pair of boots for $11.99. He paid 7% sales tax. Find the sales tax for both items together. Round your answer to the nearest cent. $1.19

REVIEW EXERCISES

C. Find the new price after each increase or decrease. *(Lesson 119)*

19. 15% increase over $15.00 $17.25   **20.** 12% decrease from $18.00 $15.84

21. 18% decrease from $13.00 $10.66   **22.** 16% increase over $25.00 $29.00

D. Change these decimals to percents. *(Lessons 112, 113)*

23. 0.23 23%   24. 0.39 39%   25. 0.83 83%
26. 0.91 91%   27. 0.04 4%   28. 0.02 2%

E. Change these fractions to percents. Express any remainders as fractions in lowest terms. *(Lessons 112–114)*

29. $\frac{1}{8}$ $12\frac{1}{2}\%$ **30.** $\frac{5}{6}$ $83\frac{1}{3}\%$ **31.** $\frac{4}{15}$ $26\frac{2}{3}\%$ **32.** $\frac{3}{16}$ $18\frac{3}{4}\%$

F. Add these mixed numbers. *(Lesson 55)*

33.	34.	35.	36.
$1\frac{1}{4}$	$3\frac{5}{6}$	$4\frac{1}{6}$	$5\frac{3}{4}$
$3\frac{3}{8}$	$2\frac{1}{10}$	$3\frac{1}{2}$	$4\frac{1}{2}$
$+2\frac{1}{2}$	$+3\frac{3}{5}$	$+2\frac{1}{3}$	$+3\frac{3}{8}$
$7\frac{1}{8}$	$9\frac{8}{15}$	10	$13\frac{5}{8}$

price of an item that is on sale at 10% off the regular price of $20.50.
Discount: 10% of $20.50 = ($2.05)
Sale Price: $20.50 – $2.05 =
($18.45)

b. Find the discount and the sale price of an item that is on sale at 15% off the regular price of $15.95.
Discount: 15% of $15.95 = $2.3925
= ($2.39) to nearest cent
Sale Price: $15.95 – $2.39 =
($13.56)

c. Find the discount and the sale price of an item that is on sale at 8% off the regular price of $9.95.
Discount: 8% of $9.95 = $0.796 =
($0.80) to nearest cent
Sale Price: $9.95 – $0.80 = ($9.15)

	Regular Price	Rate of Discount	Discount	Sale Price
d.	$7.75	15%	($1.16)	($6.59)
e.	$98.75	12%	($11.85)	($86.90)
f.	$25.50	9%	($2.30)	($23.20)
g.	$55.75	18%	($10.04)	($45.71)

An Ounce of Prevention

Note that both the discount and the sale price are required for each answer from 1 to 16.

LESSON 121

Objective

- To apply percents by *finding sales commissions. (The concept of commission is new, but no new mathematical concepts are taught in this lesson.)

Review

1. *Finding the discount and the sale price* (Lesson 120).

	Regular Price	Rate of Discount	Discount	Sale Price
a.	$11.50	6%	($0.69)	($10.81)
b.	$18.00	10%	($1.80)	($16.20)
c.	$99.95	15%	($14.99)	($84.96)

2. *Finding a percent more or less than a number* (Lesson 119).
    a. 10% increase over $30.00 ($33.00)
    b. 25% decrease from $60.00 ($45.00)

3. *Reading a map* (Lesson 107).
    Scale: 1/4 in. = 8 miles
    a. 1 3/4 in. = (56 mi.)
    b. 2 1/2 in. = (80 mi.)
    c. 3 5/8 in. = (116 mi.)
    d. 5 1/8 in. = (164 mi.)

4. *Working with distance, rate, and time* (Lesson 105).

	Rate	Time	Distance
a.	51 m.p.h.	5 hr.	(255 mi.)
b.	(53.5 m.p.h.)	6 hr.	321 mi.
c.	52 m.p.h.	(3.5 hr.)	182 mi.

5. *Changing fractions to decimals* (Lesson 89). Divide to the hundredths' place, and express the remainder as a fraction in lowest terms.

    a. $\frac{7}{9} = 0.77\frac{7}{9}$

    b. $\frac{5}{12} = 0.41\frac{2}{3}$

Introduction

Some of your pupils probably are familiar with shipping livestock to market. They may even have raised small animals themselves, such as rabbits, and may have taken them to an auction. Draw upon this experience to help them grasp the concepts in this lesson.

Teaching Guide

A sales commission is computed by finding a percentage of a number. The procedure is the same as in Lessons 117 and 118.

1. Change the rate of commission to a decimal by dropping the percent sign and moving the decimal point two places to the left.

2. Multiply the amount of sales by the decimal you found in step 1.

3. Check by casting out nines.

4. If the product has more than two decimal places, round the answer to the nearest cent (hundredth of a dollar). The result is the amount of the commission.

	Sales	Rate	Commission
a.	$2,000	6%	($120.00)
b.	$357.88	8%	($28.63)
c.	$1,115.50	12%	($133.86)
d.	$2,577.91	5%	($128.90)

121. Finding Sales Commissions

Salesmen are often paid a percentage of the selling price of the products they sell. This percentage is called a **commission.** To find the amount of a salesman's commission, use the following steps.

1. Change the rate of commission to a decimal by dropping the percent sign and moving the decimal point two places to the left.
2. Multiply the amount of sales by the decimal you found in step 1.
3. Check by casting out nines.
4. If the product has more than two decimal places, round the answer to the nearest cent (hundredth of a dollar). This answer is the amount of the commission.

Example A		**Example B**	
Sales	$3,000.00	Sales	$3,456.80
Rate of Commission	8%	Rate of Commission	7%
8% = 0.08		7% = 0.07	

$$\begin{array}{r} \$3,000 \\ \times\ 0.08 \\ \hline \$240.00 \end{array} \text{ Commission}$$

$$\begin{array}{r} \$3,456.80 \\ \times\quad 0.07 \\ \hline \$241.9760 \end{array} \text{ Commission}$$
$$= \$241.98 \quad \text{to nearest cent}$$

CLASS PRACTICE

Find the amount of each commission.

	Sales	*Rate*			*Sales*	*Rate*	
a.	$800	8%	$64.00	b.	$2,100	11%	$231.00
c.	$580	3%	$17.40	d.	$1,400	4%	$56.00
e.	$620	2%	$12.40	f.	$2,200	9%	$198.00

WRITTEN EXERCISES

A. **Find the amount of each commission.**

	Sales	*Rate*			*Sales*	*Rate*	
1.	$2,000	10%	$200.00	2.	$2,400	9%	$216.00
3.	$3,800	5%	$190.00	4.	$800	11%	$88.00

	Sales	Rate			Sales	Rate	
5.	$950	7%	$66.50	**6.**	$1,400	5%	$70.00
7.	$410.00	5%	$20.50	**8.**	$2,200.00	4%	$88.00
9.	$1,850.00	7%	$129.50	**10.**	$1,200	9%	$108.00
11.	$450.00	12%	$54.00	**12.**	$310.00	6%	$18.60

B.   *Solve these reading problems.*

13. Mr. Johnston sells farm equipment at a 6% commission. If he sells a used tractor for $7,500.00, what is his commission? $450.00

14. At a livestock auction, Daniel sold three rabbits for $19.00. If the auction's rate of commission was 15%, what was the amount of commission? $2.85

15. An auctioneer conducted a sale for the Wenger family. The amount of the sale was $3,400.00. How much was the auctioneer's commission if it was 8% of the sales?
$272.00

16. The Landis family sold their house at public auction for $90,200. If the auctioneer charged a 3% commission, how much did he receive? $2,706.00

17. Duane used a map to find the distance to the town where his uncle had moved to help start an outreach church. The distance was $4\frac{1}{2}$ inches on a map with a scale of $\frac{1}{4}$ inch = 10 miles. How far away did his uncle live?   180 miles

18. Brenda was looking at a map of the county in which she lived. On the map, the distance between her home and Grandfather's home was $5\frac{3}{4}$ inches. The scale of miles was $\frac{1}{2}$ inch = 2 miles. What was the actual distance from Brenda's home to Grandfather's home?   23 miles

REVIEW EXERCISES

C. *Find both the discount and the sale price of each item. (Lesson 120)*

	Regular Price	Percent of Discount				Regular Price	Percent of Discount		
19.	$15.00	8%	$1.20	$13.80	**20.**	$25.00	12%	$3.00	$22.00
21.	$50.00	15%	$7.50	$42.50	**22.**	$70.00	20%	$14.00	$56.00

D. *Find the new amount after each increase or decrease. (Lesson 119)*

23. 10% less than 30   27   **24.** 15% more than 48   55.2

25. 25% increase over $60.00 $75.00   **26.** 5% decrease from $20.00 $19.00

E. *Find the distance represented by each measurement on a map with a scale of $\frac{1}{2}$ inch = 16 miles. (Lesson 107)*

27. 3 in.   96 mi.   **28.** $1\frac{1}{2}$ in.   48 mi.   **29.** $3\frac{1}{2}$ in.   112 mi.   **30.** $4\frac{3}{4}$ in.   152 mi.

F. *Solve these problems on distance, rate, and time. (Lesson 105)*

31. rate: 48 m.p.h.   time: 4 hr.   distance: 192 mi.

32. rate: 49 m.p.h.   time: 5 hr.   distance: 245 mi.

33. rate: 46 m.p.h.   time: 8 hr.   distance: 368 mi.

34. rate: 48 m.p.h.   time: $6\frac{1}{2}$ hr.   distance: 312 mi.

G. *Change each fraction to a decimal rounded to the nearest hundredth. (Lesson 89)*

35. $\frac{7}{8}$ 0.88   **36.** $\frac{9}{16}$ 0.56

122. Finding What Percent One Number Is of Another

When two numbers are compared, it is useful to know what percent one number is of the other. Consider 32 and 40 for one example. You know that 32 is more than one-half of 40. But if you know that 32 is 80% of 40, you have a much clearer understanding of the relationship between the two numbers. To find what percent one number is of another, follow the steps below.

1. Write the two numbers as a ratio in fraction form. Be sure to get the numerator and the denominator correct. *The number following **of** is always the denominator.* Reduce the fraction to lowest terms.
2. Divide the numerator by the denominator to change the fraction to a decimal.
3. Change the decimal to a percent by moving the decimal point two places to the right and adding a percent sign.

34 is what percent of 40?	$\frac{34}{40} = \frac{17}{20}$	$20\overline{)17.00}$ → $0.85 = 85\%$	34 is 85% of 40

CLASS PRACTICE

Find these percents.

a. 18 is __50__ % of 36   b. 70 is __35__ % of 200   c. 28 is __40__ % of 70

d. 27 is __75__ % of 36   e. 21 is __60__ % of 35   f. 7 is __28__ % of 25

WRITTEN EXERCISES

A.   *Find these percents.*

1. 25 is __50__ % of 50   2. 15 is __25__ % of 60   3. 40 is __20__ % of 200

4. 12 is __30__ % of 40   5. 12 is __20__ % of 60   6. 8 is __25__ % of 32

7. 9 is __30__ % of 30   8. 36 is __45__ % of 80   9. 9 is __60__ % of 15

10. 24 is __75__ % of 32   11. 14 is __20__ % of 70   12. 6 is __10__ % of 60

B.   *Solve these reading problems.*

13. In a sixth and seventh grade classroom, 14 of the 20 pupils are in grade 6. What percent of the pupils are in sixth grade?   70%

14. Dale has memorized 12 of the 16 Bible verses that he is assigned to memorize this month at school. What percent of his assigned Bible verses has he memorized?   75%

LESSON 122

Objective

• To teach *finding what percent one number is of another.

Review

1. Give Lesson 122 Quiz (Working With Percents).

2. *Finding commissions* (Lesson 121).

	Sales	Rate	Commission
a.	$800	8%	($64.00)
b.	$550	5%	($27.50)
c.	$2,650	9%	($238.50)

3. *Finding the discount and the sale price* (Lesson 120).

	Regular Price	Rate of Discount	Discount	Sale Price
a.	$15.00	10%	($1.50)	($13.50)
b.	$22.00	6%	($1.32)	($20.68)
c.	$25.95	15%	($3.89)	($22.06)

4. *Expressing percents as decimals and fractions* (Lesson 115). Reduce fractions to lowest terms.

   a. $28\% = (0.28) = (\frac{7}{25})$

   b. $55\% = (0.55) = (\frac{11}{20})$

5. *Reading blueprints* (Lesson 108). Scale: 1 inch = 4 feet
   a. 3 in. = (12 ft.)
   b. 2 1/2 in. = (10 ft.)
   c. 4 1/4 in. = (17 ft.)
   d. 3 1/8 in. = (12 1/2 ft.)

6. *Multiplying decimals mentally by changing them to fractions* (Lesson 90).
   a. 0.5 of 60 = (30)
   b. 0.33 1/3 of 36 = (12)
   c. 0.8 of 35 = (28)

Introduction

Finding what percent one number is of another is actually changing a ratio to a percent. Practice writing ratios to refresh the concept in the students' minds. It is not enough for them to always compare the first number in the problem to the second number (which is often true), nor is it enough to automatically write the smaller number first and the larger number second. The smaller number always comes first in this lesson, but that is certainly not always the case.

Write ratios to compare the following numbers.

a. 5 boys to 12 students: 5 to 12 *or* 5/12

b. 12 students to 7 girls: 12 to 7 *or* 12/7

c. There are 18 students in the classroom. Eight of them are in the sixth grade. Compare the number of sixth graders to the total number of students.

$$8 \text{ to } 18 \text{ } or \text{ } \tfrac{8}{18} = \tfrac{4}{9}$$

Teaching Guide

Division is used to find what percent one number is of another. The steps are as follows:

1. Write the two numbers as a ratio in fraction form. Be sure to get the numerator and the denominator correct. *The number following of is always the denominator.* Reduce the fraction to lowest terms.

   Reducing the fraction is not required to obtain the correct answer, but it is especially useful when the resulting fraction is one for which students have memorized the equivalent percent. Require them to reduce all fractions that can obviously be reduced, such as those with even terms (as 12/28) or with terms that are multiples of 5 (as 20/45).

2. Divide the numerator by the denominator to change the fraction to a decimal. (Division is not required if one knows the equivalent percent.)

3. Change the decimal to a percent by moving the decimal point two places to the right and adding a percent sign.

    a.   7 is what percent of 20?

    $\frac{7}{20} = 7 \div 20 = 0.35 = (35\%)$

    b.   15 is what percent of 50?

    $\frac{15}{50} = \frac{3}{10} = (30\%)$

    c.   26 is what percent of 40?

    $\frac{26}{40} = \frac{13}{20} = 13 \div 20 = 0.65 = (65\%)$

Note: When the fractions in this lesson are reduced to lowest terms, they all have denominators that are factors of 100. Therefore, they could all be changed to percents by the method taught in Lesson 113 rather than by division.

$$\frac{7}{20} = \frac{35}{100} = 35\%$$

$$\frac{26}{40} = \frac{13}{20} = \frac{65}{100} = 65\%$$

This method can be used for *any* fraction that equals a whole-number percent. However, the standard method for finding what percent one number is of another is to divide. The division method is taught in this lesson for that reason, and in Lesson 123 it is extended to fractions whose equivalent percents are not whole numbers.

15. Sylvia had 21 out of 25 answers correct on her Bible test. What was her score as a percent?

      84%

16. Stanley had 36 out of 40 problems done correctly on his math test. What was his score as a percent?

      90%

REVIEW EXERCISES

C. Find the sales commission in each of these problems. *(Lesson 121)*

	Sales	Rate			Sales	Rate	
17.	$500	14%	$70.00	**18.**	$950	8%	$76.00
19.	$1,650	6%	$99.00	**20.**	$2,340	9%	$210.60

D. Find both the discount and the sale price of each item. *(Lesson 120)*

	Regular Price	Percent of Discount				Regular Price	Percent of Discount		
21.	$20.50	10%	$2.05	$18.45	**22.**	$28.00	8%	$2.24	$25.76
23.	$59.95	6%	$3.60	$56.35	**24.**	$35.95	12%	$4.31	$31.64

E. Write each percent as a decimal and a fraction in lowest terms. *(Lesson 115)*

	Percent	Decimal	Fraction
25.	33%	0.33	$\frac{33}{100}$
26.	45%	0.45	$\frac{9}{20}$

F. Answer these problems on reading blueprints. *(Lesson 108)*

27. Father showed Dale a blueprint of the house he was building. The scale of the blueprint was 1 inch = 2 feet. What is the length of the house if it is $24\frac{1}{4}$ inches long on the blueprint?

      $48\frac{1}{2}$ feet

28. The living room is $8\frac{1}{4}$ inches long on the blueprint. At a scale of 1 inch = 2 feet, what will be the length of the living room?

      $16\frac{1}{2}$ feet

29. Father also showed Dale a blueprint of a barn. The scale of that one was 1 inch = 6 feet. If the barn is $16\frac{1}{2}$ inches long on the blueprint, what will be its actual length?

      99 feet

30. The width of the barn was 5 inches on the blueprint. At a scale of 1 inch = 6 feet, how wide will the actual barn be?

      30 feet

G. Solve these problems mentally by changing the decimals to fractions. *(Lesson 90)*

31. 0.5 of 80   40   **32.** 0.25 of 36   9   **33.** 0.75 of 32 24   **34.** 0.6 of 15   9

123. Finding What Percent One Number Is of Another

When you find what percent one number is of another, the answer is not always a whole percent. In that case, the remainder can be expressed as a fraction. Study the steps and examples below.

1. Write the two numbers as a ratio in fraction form, being sure to get the numerator and the denominator correct. (The number following of is the denominator.) Reduce the fraction to lowest terms.

2. Divide the numerator by the denominator to change the fraction into a decimal. Divide to the hundredths' place, and express any remainder as a fraction.

3. Change the decimal to a percent by moving the decimal point two places to the right and adding a percent sign.

Example A

9 is what percent of 60?

$$\frac{9}{60} = \frac{3}{20}$$

$$\begin{array}{r} 0.15 \\ 20\overline{)3.00} \end{array} = 15\%$$

9 is 15% of 60

Example B

10 is what percent of 16?

$$\frac{10}{16} = \frac{5}{8}$$

$$\begin{array}{r} 0.62\frac{1}{2} \\ 8\overline{)5.00} \end{array} = 62\frac{1}{2}\%$$

10 is $62\frac{1}{2}\%$ of 16

CLASS PRACTICE

Find the answers. All these are whole-number percents.

a. 18 is __60__ % 30

b. 5 is __4__ % 125

c. 9 is __6__ % 150

d. 6 is __15__ % 40

Find these percents. Some answers include fractions.

e. 6 is $33\frac{1}{3}$ % of 18

f. 15 is $62\frac{1}{2}$ % of 24

g. 24 is __40__ % of 60

h. 7 is $58\frac{1}{3}$ % of 12

WRITTEN EXERCISES

A.   Find the answers. All these are whole-number percents.

1. 3 is __75__ % of 4

2. 6 is __30__ % of 20

3. 27 is __75__ % of 36

4. 6 is __8__ % of 75

5. 12 is __15__ % of 80

6. 18 is __40__ % of 45

LESSON 123

Objectives

- To give more practice with finding what percent one number is of another.
- To teach *finding what percent one number is of another when the answer includes a fraction of a percent.

Review

1. *Finding commissions* (Lesson 121).

	Sales	Rate	Commission
a.	$30.00	35%	($10.50)
b.	$50.00	25%	($12.50)
c.	$14.75	15%	($2.21)

2. *Finding the discount and the sale price* (Lesson 120).

	Regular Price	Rate of Discount	Discount	Sale Price
a.	$12.00	10%	($1.20)	($10.80)
b.	$25.00	4%	($1.00)	($24.00)
c.	$36.95	12%	($4.43)	($35.52)

3. *Finding a percent more or less than a number* (Lesson 119).
   a. 10% increase over $32.00 ($35.20)
   b. 20% decrease from $22.50 ($18.00)
   c. 6% increase over $15.00 ($15.90)

Introduction

Practice changing fractions to non-terminating decimals. Divide to the hundredths' place, and express the remainder as a fraction in lowest terms. This is a review of the first concept in Lesson 89.

a. $\frac{1}{6} = 6\overline{)1.00}$ $0.16\frac{2}{3}$

b. $\frac{5}{6} = 6\overline{)5.00}$ $0.83\frac{1}{3}$

c. $\frac{5}{12} = 12\overline{)5.00}$ $0.41\frac{2}{3}$

d. $\frac{7}{9} = 9\overline{)7.00}$ $0.77\frac{7}{9}$

e. $\frac{2}{15} = 15\overline{)2.00}$ $0.13\frac{1}{3}$

f. $\frac{11}{15} = 15\overline{)11.00}$ $0.73\frac{1}{3}$

Teaching Guide

Division is used to find what percent one number is of another. The only thing new in this lesson is that division does not always come out evenly in the hundredths' place. The remainder is expressed as a fraction in lowest terms, exactly as in Lesson 89. Then the decimal is changed to a percent.

a. 30 is what percent of 75?
$\frac{30}{75} = \frac{2}{5} = (40\%)$

b. 18 is what percent of 40?
$\frac{18}{40} = \frac{9}{20} = 9 \div 20 = 0.45 = (45\%)$

c. 6 is what percent of 9?
$\frac{6}{9} = \frac{2}{3} = (66\frac{2}{3}\%)$

d. 7 is what percent of 8?
$\frac{7}{8} = 7 \div 8 = 0.87\frac{1}{2} = (87\frac{1}{2}\%)$

e. 16 is what percent of 30?
$\frac{16}{30} = \frac{8}{15} = 8 \div 15 = 0.53\frac{1}{3} = (53\frac{1}{3}\%)$

f. 8 is what percent of 18?
$\frac{8}{18} = \frac{4}{9} = 4 \div 9 = 0.44\frac{4}{9} = (44\frac{4}{9}\%)$

B. **Find the percents. Some answers include fractions.**

7. 3 is __$37\frac{1}{2}$__ % of 8   8. 1 is __$16\frac{2}{3}$__ % of 6   9. 12 is __30__ % of 40

10. 1 is __$33\frac{1}{3}$__ % of 3   11. 1 is __$8\frac{1}{3}$__ % of 12   12. 7 is __$16\frac{2}{3}$__ % of 42

C. **Solve these reading problems.**

13. One morning Beth had 32 out of 40 math problems correct. Write a ratio in fraction form to compare the number of problems correct to the total number of problems. Change the fraction to a percent. $\frac{32}{40}$ 80%

14. Ruth had 38 out of 40 math problems correct. Write a ratio in fraction form to compare the number of problems correct to the total number of problems. Then find Ruth's score as a percent. $\frac{38}{40}$ 95%

15. A block of cork weighs 15 pounds. A block of white pine the same size weighs 25 pounds. Cork is what percent as heavy as white pine?   60%

16. A block of white pine weighs 25 pounds. A block of maple the same size weighs 43 pounds. White pine is what percent as heavy as maple? $58\frac{6}{43}$%

17. The Miller family has a store where they sell used clothing on commission. What is their commission on a coat that sells for $15.00 if the rate of commission is 30%? $4.50

18. Father bought a suit for $45.00 at Millers' Used Clothing Store. What is the Millers' commission on the suit if the rate of commission is 20%? $9.00

REVIEW EXERCISES

D. **Find the amount of each commission.** *(Lesson 121)*

	Sales	Rate			Sales	Rate	
19.	$20.00	25%	$5.00	20.	$45.00	35%	$15.75
21.	$15.50	30%	$4.65	22.	$19.75	10%	$1.98

E. **Find both the discount and the sale price of each item.** *(Lesson 120)*

	Regular Price	Percent of Discount				Regular Price	Percent of Discount		
23.	$15.00	10%	$1.50	$13.50	24.	$32.00	5%	$1.60	$30.40
25.	$35.95	12%	$4.31	$31.64	26.	$42.00	15%	$6.30	$35.70

F. **Find the new amount after each increase or decrease.** *(Lesson 119)*

27. 10% increase over $25.00 $27.50   **28.** 20% decrease from $16.50 $13.20

29. 15% less than 48   40.8   **30.** 8% more than 25   27

124. Multiplying Mentally by Changing a Percent to a Fraction

You can greatly simplify some percentage problems by changing the percent to a fraction. If the fraction is one with which it is easy to calculate, you may even be able to solve the problem mentally. For example, to find 50% of a number, change 50% to $\frac{1}{2}$. To find $33\frac{1}{3}$% of a number, change $33\frac{1}{3}$% to $\frac{1}{3}$. Finding $\frac{1}{3}$ of a number is much easier than multiplying it by $0.33\frac{1}{3}$!

Example A

Find 25% of 240.

Think: 25% = $\frac{1}{4}$

$\frac{1}{4}$ of 240 = 240 ÷ 4 = 60

25% of 240 = 60

Example B

Find $66\frac{2}{3}$% of 270.

Think: $66\frac{2}{3}$% = $\frac{2}{3}$

$\frac{2}{3}$ of 270 = 270 ÷ 3 × 2 = 180

$66\frac{2}{3}$% of 270 = 180

CLASS PRACTICE

Solve these problems mentally by first changing the percents to fractions.

a. 25% of 16   4

b. 50% of 42   21

c. $66\frac{2}{3}$% of 21   14

d. 75% of 28   21

e. 80% of 35   28

f. 90% of 40   36

WRITTEN EXERCISES

A. Write fractions for the following percents. You should be able to do all of these by memory.

1. 10% $\frac{1}{10}$ 2. 20% $\frac{1}{5}$ 3. 25% $\frac{1}{4}$ 4. 30% $\frac{3}{10}$ 5. $33\frac{1}{3}$% $\frac{1}{3}$ 6. 40% $\frac{2}{5}$

7. 50% $\frac{1}{2}$ 8. 60% $\frac{3}{5}$ 9. 70% $\frac{7}{10}$ 10. 75% $\frac{3}{4}$ 11. $66\frac{2}{3}$% $\frac{2}{3}$ 12. 80% $\frac{4}{5}$

B. Solve these problems mentally by first changing the percents to fractions.

13. 25% of 28   7

14. 10% of 70   7

15. 50% of 40   20

16. 20% of 45   9

17. 75% of 36   27

18. $33\frac{1}{3}$% of 21   7

19. $66\frac{2}{3}$% of 27   18

20. 40% of 35   14

21. 80% of 15   12

22. 50% of 26   13

23. 60% of 45   27

24. 75% of 40   30

LESSON 124

Objective

- To give practice with finding percentages mentally by first changing percents to fractions.

Review

1. *Finding what percent one number is of another* (Lessons 122, 123).

   a. 5 is $(62\frac{1}{2}\%)$ of 8
   b. 2 is $(22\frac{2}{9}\%)$ of 9
   c. 4 is $(26\frac{2}{3}\%)$ of 15
   d. 5 is $(27\frac{7}{9}\%)$ of 18

2. *Finding the discount and the sale price* (Lesson 120).

	Regular Price	Rate of Discount	Discount	Sale Price
a.	$12.00	18%	($2.16)	($9.84)
b.	$25.00	12%	($3.00)	($22.00)
c.	$16.95	10%	($1.70)	($15.25)

3. *Subtracting percents from 100%* (Lesson 116).

   a. 61% (39%)
   b. 49% (51%)
   c. 44% (56%)
   d. 7% (93%)

4. *Writing ratios* (Lesson 92).

   a. Write a ratio comparing 8 pencils to 3 students. $(\frac{8}{3})$
   b. Write a ratio comparing 7 sixth grade students to 9 seventh grade students. $(\frac{7}{9})$

Introduction

In Lesson 90 the pupils learned to simplify multiplication by changing decimals to fractions. This lesson is similar except that it deals with percents changed to fractions before multiplying. A review of the concept in Lesson 90 is an excellent way to introduce this lesson, for the students will be using basically the same procedure.

   a. $0.5 \times 80 = 1/2$ of $80 = (40)$
   b. 0.25 of $80 = 1/4$ of $80 = (20)$
   c. $0.2 \times 30 = 1/5$ of $30 = (6)$
   d. 0.75 of $40 = 3/4$ of $40 = (30)$
   e. 0.8 of $50 = 4/5$ of $50 = (40)$
   f. 0.7 of $60 = 7/10$ of $60 = (42)$

Teaching Guide

Finding a percentage can sometimes be done mentally if the decimal is changed to a fraction. This is especially true when the fraction is a simple one like 1/2 or 1/4, or when the decimal is nonterminating, such as 0.33 1/3.

To find a percentage mentally, use the following steps.

   a. Change the percent to a simple fraction.
   b. Divide the other factor by the denominator of the fraction, and multiply the result by the numerator of the fraction.

Review the following fraction–percent equivalents, which the class is memorizing.

   a. 1/2 = (50%)
   b. 1/3 = (33 1/3%)
   c. 1/4 = (25%)
   d. 1/5 = (20%)
   e. 1/10 = (10%)
   f. 3/10 = (30%)
   g. 2/5 = (40%)

h.   3/5 = (60%)
i.   3/4 = (75%)
j.   9/10 = (90%)
k.   2/3 = (66 2/3%)
l.   4/5 = (80%)
m.   50% of 60 = 1/2 × 60 = 60 ÷ 2 × 1 = (30)
n.   20% of 25 = 1/5 × 25 = 25 ÷ 5 × 1 = (5)
o.   40% of 55 = 2/5 × 55 = 55 ÷ 5 × 2 = (22)
p.   75% of 48 = 3/4 × 48 = 48 ÷ 4 × 3 = (36)
q. $66\frac{2}{3}$% of 36 = 2/3 × 36 = 36 ÷ 3 × 2 = (24)
r.   80% of 40 = 4/5 × 40 = 40 ÷ 5 × 4 = (32)

C. *Solve these reading problems. Solve problems 25–28 mentally.*

25. In the 10 minutes between math class and Bible class, Sharon finished 25% of the 36 math problems that were assigned. How many problems did she solve?

9 problems

26. In Bible class, Sharon correctly answered 90% of the 20 questions. How many of her answers were correct?

18 answers

27. One evening Brent milked 20% of his father's 55 dairy cows. How many cows did he milk?

11 cows

28. Father milked 60% of the 55 cows. How many cows did he milk?

33 cows

29. Twenty-six of the 50 states in the United States are east of the Mississippi River. What percent of the 50 states is that?

52%

30. Two of the 50 states, Louisiana and Minnesota, have territory both east and west of the Mississippi. What percent is 2 of 50?

4%

REVIEW EXERCISES

D. *Find these percents.* (Lessons 122, 123)

31. 1 is $12\frac{1}{2}$ % of 8

32. 2 is $28\frac{4}{7}$ % of 7

33. 5 is $35\frac{5}{7}$ % of 14

34. 5 is $31\frac{1}{4}$ % of 16

E. *Find both the discount and the sale price of each item.* (Lesson 120)

	Regular Price	Percent of Discount				Regular Price	Percent of Discount		
35.	$20.00	15%	$3.00	$17.00	**36.**	$45.00	8%	$3.60	$41.40
37.	$26.50	12%	$3.18	$23.32	**38.**	$35.00	20%	$7.00	$28.00

F. *Subtract these percents from 100%.* (Lesson 116)

39. 51% 49% **40.** 69% 31% **41.** 14% 86% **42.** 5% 95%

G. *Write ratios for these reading problems.* (Lesson 92)

43. Write a ratio comparing 1 lost sheep to 99 other sheep. $\frac{1}{99}$

44. Write a ratio comparing 100 sheep to 1 shepherd. $\frac{100}{1}$

45. Write a ratio comparing 1 lost piece of silver to 10 pieces of silver. $\frac{1}{10}$

46. Write a ratio comparing the prodigal son to his loving father. $\frac{1}{1}$

125. Chapter 9 Review

A.   *Express these decimals as percents.* (Lesson 113)

1. 0.48   48%   2. 0.59   59%   3. 0.02   2%   4. 0.025   2.5%

B.   *Express these fractions as percents. Write any remainders as fractions.* (Lesson (114)

5. $\frac{3}{20}$ 15%   6. $\frac{9}{25}$ 36%   7. $\frac{7}{15}$ $46\frac{2}{3}$%   8. $\frac{6}{7}$ $85\frac{5}{7}$%

C.   *Write each percent as a decimal and a fraction in lowest terms.* (Lesson 115)

	Percent	Decimal	Fraction
9.	22%	0.22	$\frac{11}{50}$
10.	95%	0.95	$\frac{19}{20}$
11.	32%	0.32	$\frac{8}{25}$
12.	99%	0.99	$\frac{99}{100}$

D.   *Add or subtract these percents.* (Lessons 116, 119)

13. 100% – 44%   14. 100% – 7%   15. 100% + 15%   16. 100% + 7%
      56%   93%   115%   107%

E.   *Find these percentages.* (Lessons 117, 118)

17. 24% of 50   18. 45% of 30   19. 17% of 75   20. 42% of 65
      12   13.5   12.75   27.3

21. 5% of 90   22. 8% of 35   23. 1% of 95   24. 2% of 86
      4.5   2.8   0.95   1.72

F.   *Find the amount after each increase or decrease.* (Lesson 119)

25. 10% more than 15   16.5   26. 5% less than 18   17.1

27. 15% decrease from $28.75 $24.44   28. 12% increase over $37.95 $42.50

LESSON 125

Objective

- To review the material taught in Chapter 9.

Teaching Guide

This review covers Lessons 112–124.

G. *Find both the discount and the sale price of each item.* (*Lesson 120*)

	Regular Price	Percent of Discount				Regular Price	Percent of Discount		
29.	$18.00	15%	$2.70	$15.30	**30.**	$23.00	10%	$2.30	$20.70
31.	$36.75	5%	$1.84	$34.91	**32.**	$46.95	20%	$9.39	$37.56

H. *Find the commission in each problem.* (*Lesson 121*)

	Sales	Rate			Sales	Rate	
33.	$600	15%	$90.00	**34.**	$800	8%	$64.00
35.	$1,400	12%	$168.00	**36.**	$1,659	11%	$182.49

I. *Find these percents. Some of them include fractions.* (*Lessons 122, 123*)

37. 4 is $\underline{33\frac{1}{3}}$ % of 12   **38.** 6 is $\underline{25}$ % of 24

39. 5 is $\underline{62\frac{1}{2}}$ % of 8   **40.** 9 is $\underline{56\frac{1}{4}}$ % of 16

J. *Solve these problems mentally by first changing the percents to fractions.* (*Lesson 124*)

41. 25% of 44 11   **42.** 20% of 40 8   **43.** 75% of 32 24   **44.** $66\frac{2}{3}$% of 18 12

K. *Solve these reading problems.*

45. Father shipped a cull cow to the sales stable. The cow sold for $515.00, and the sales commission was 7%. What was the amount of the commission? $36.05

46. Father sells seed corn at a 12% commission. If he sells $125.00 worth of seed, what is his commission? $15.00

47. Father had 15 bags of seed corn in stock. One day he sold 4 bags. Four bags is what percent of 15 bags? $26\frac{2}{3}$%

48. Father also had 8 bags of soybean seed in stock. One week he sold 3 bags. What percent of the soybean seed did he sell? $37\frac{1}{2}$%

49. Darell read on a package of sweet corn seed that 95% of the seeds should germinate. If he plants 90 seeds in a row, how many of them can he expect to germinate? Round your answer to the nearest whole number.   86 seeds

50. Father had some leftover seed near the end of the planting season. He put this seed on sale at a discount of 10%. If a customer bought $195.00 worth of this seed, what was his discount? How much did he pay? $19.50 $175.50

126. Chapter 9 Test

LESSON 126

Objective

- To test the students' mastery of the concepts in Chapter 9.

Teaching Guide

1. Correct Lesson 125.
2. Review any areas of special difficulty.
3. Administer the test.

One farthing represents about $1\frac{1}{2}$ cents. If God concerns Himself with such tiny portions of His creation, we ought not be careless with our pennies.

The birds pictured are house sparrows.

Chapter 10

Working With Money

Are not two sparrows sold for a farthing? and one of them shall not fall on the ground without your Father. Fear ye not therefore, ye are of more value than many sparrows.

(Matthew 10:29, 31)

127. Counting Change

When a person buys something at a store, he often does not give the exact amount of money he owes. Then the clerk must give the buyer the right amount of change to equal the difference between the amount owed and the amount paid.

Change is usually given in the smallest possible number of bills and coins. For example, a dime is given instead of two nickels or ten pennies, and a 10-dollar bill is given instead of two 5-dollar bills.

It is fairly simple to give the right change with the fewest pieces of money. Begin with the amount of the bill, and count up to the amount paid as you give the change. The amount of change is correct when you reach the amount that the customer paid.

A customer's bill was $2.32, and he paid $10.00. Find the correct amount of change, using the smallest possible number of coins and bills.

What to Do

1. Starting with the amount of the bill, count up to the nearest multiple of 25¢ as you give coins.

2. Count up to the nearest dollar as you give quarters.

3. Count up to the nearest multiple of $5 as you give 1-dollar bills.

4. Give 5-dollar, 10-dollar, and 20-dollar bills as needed to count the rest of the way to the amount given by the customer.

What to Say

"$2.32 out of $10.00"

1. (3 pennies) "$2.35"
   (1 nickel) "$2.40"
   (1 dime)   "$2.50"

2. (1 quarter) "$2.75"
   (1 quarter) "$3.00"

3. (1 dollar) "$4.00"
   (1 dollar) "$5.00"

4. (5 dollars) "$10.00"

CLASS PRACTICE

Calculate the correct change.

	Amount of Sale	Amount Given	1¢	5¢	10¢	25¢	$1	$5	Total Change
a.	$0.77	$5.00	3		2		4		$4.23
b.	$3.03	$10.00	2		2	3	1	1	$6.97

Count the correct change back to the customer. Start with the amount of the sale.

	Amount of Sale	Amount Given	
c.	$0.37	$1.00	$0.37 out of $1.00, $0.40, $0.50, $0.75, $1.00
d.	$1.28	$5.00	$1.28 out of $5.00, $1.30, $1.40, $1.50, $1.75 $2.00, $3.00, $4.00, $5.00
e.	$2.61	$10.00	$2.61 out of $10.00, $2.65, $2.75, $3.00, $4.00, $5.00, $10.00
f.	$3.78	$20.00	$3.78 out of $20.00, $3.80, $3.90, $4.00, $5.00, $10.00, $20.00

LESSON 127

Objectives

- To review calculating the amount of change to return to a customer.
- To teach giving the least number of coins possible.
- To teach returning change to a customer by starting with the amount of the bill and counting up to the amount paid.

Review

1. *Finding what percent one number is of another* (Lessons 122, 123).
   a. 6 is (25%) of 24
   b. 9 is (18%) of 50
   c. 15 is (60%) of 25
   d. 12 is (30%) of 40

2. *Finding a price after an increase or decrease* (Lesson 119).
   a. 10% increase over $12.00 ($13.20)
   b. 15% more than 16 (18.4)
   c. 8% decrease from $16.00 ($14.72)
   d. 18% less than 15 (12.3)

3. *Using proportions to solve reading problems* (Lesson 94).
   a. Delores did 8 out of every 10 math problems correctly one morning. There were 35 math problems in all. How many of them did she do correctly?
   8 correct out of 10
   n correct out of 35
   $\frac{8}{10} = \frac{n}{35}$
   $8 \times 35 \div 10 = 28$
   b. David had 7 out of every 8 math problems correct one morning. He did 28 math problems correctly. How many problems were in the lesson?
   7 correct out of 8
   28 correct out of n
   $\frac{7}{8} = \frac{28}{n}$
   $8 \times 28 \div 7 = 32$

Introduction

Have enough coins available to count change at least up to $1.00. This requires 4 pennies, 1 nickel, 2 dimes, and 3 quarters. Including 4 dollar bills will enable you to return any amount of change up to $5.00.

Ask the students if they have ever noticed the procedure that a clerk uses in counting change back to a customer. Have one of the students tell what the clerk is doing as seen through his own eyes. Use his answers as a springboard for class discussion.

Teaching Guide

1. **The correct amount of change equals the difference between the amount owed and the amount paid.**

2. **Change is usually given in the smallest possible number of bills and coins.** To do this, use the following steps.
   (1) Begin by saying the amount of the bill and the amount given, such as "$2.32 out of $10.00."
   (2) Starting with the amount of the bill, count to the next higher multiple of 25¢ as you give coins.
   (3) Count to the next higher dollar as you give quarters.
   (4) Count to the next higher multiple of $5 as you give 1-dollar bills.
   (5) Give 5-dollar, 10-dollar, and 20-dollar bills as needed to count the rest of the way to the amount given by the customer.

	Amount of Sale	Amount Given	1¢	5¢	10¢	25¢	$1	$5	Total Change
a.	$0.71	$1.00	4			1			$0.29
b.	$0.23	$1.00	2			3			$0.77
c.	$1.26	$2.00	4		2	2			$0.74
d.	$2.34	$5.00	1	1	1	2	2		$2.66
e.	$3.09	$5.00	1	1	1	3	1		$1.91
f.	$4.38	$10.00	2		1	2		1	$5.62
g.	$11.62	$20.00	3		1	1	3	1	$8.38

Further Study

You may wish to point out how the customer can help to reduce the number of bills and coins that must be returned in change. For example, in line *a* above, the customer could pay $1.01 and receive only 1 quarter and 1 nickel in change (in contrast to the 5 coins needed otherwise). In line *e* he could pay $5.09 and receive only two 1-dollar bills, or he could pay $5.10 and receive $2.01. This method does make it more difficult to return change by counting it out; but since many cash registers compute the change automatically, it generally simplifies change making.

WRITTEN EXERCISES

A. *Copy and fill in the following chart. An example is done for you.*

	Amount of Sale	Amount Given	1¢	5¢	10¢	25¢	$1	$5	Total Change
Example	$12.12	$20.00	3		1	3	2	1	$7.88
1.	$0.75	$1.00				1			$0.25
2.	$0.37	$1.00	3		1	2			$0.63
3.	$0.63	$5.00	2		1	1	4		$4.37
4.	$2.25	$3.00				3			$0.75
5.	$2.52	$5.00	3		2	1	2		$2.48
6.	$4.30	$5.00			2	2			$0.70
7.	$4.82	$10.00	3	1	1			1	$5.18
8.	$3.91	$10.00	4	1			1	1	$6.09
9.	$7.41	$8.00	4	1		2			$0.59
10.	$7.62	$10.00	3		1	1	2		$2.38
11.	$11.95	$15.00		1			3		$3.05
12.	$18.43	$20.00	2	1		2	1		$1.57

B. *Write what you would say as you count the change to the customer. An example is done for you.*

Amount of Sale   Amount Given
   $12.12 $20.00

(*Answer*) $12.12 out of $20.00
$12.15, $12.25, $12.50, $12.75, $13.00, $14.00, $15.00, $20.00

	Amount of Sale	Amount Given	
13.	$0.65	$1.00	$0.65 out of $1.00, $0.75, $1.00
14.	$0.32	$1.00	$0.32 out of $1.00, $0.35, $0.40, $0.50, $0.75, $1.00
15.	$1.12	$2.00	$1.12 out of $2.00, $1.15, $1.25, $1.50, $1.75, $2.00
16.	$3.78	$5.00	$3.78 out of $5.00, $3.80, $3.90, $4.00, $5.00
17.	$2.65	$5.00	$2.65 out of $5.00, $2.75, $3.00, $4.00, $5.00
18.	$1.42	$5.00	$1.42 out of $5.00, $1.45, $1.50, $1.75, $2.00, $3.00, $4.00, $5.00
19.	$5.70	$10.00	$5.70 out of $10.00, $5.75, $6.00, $7.00, $8.00, $9.00, $10.00
20.	$2.34	$10.00	$2.34 out of $10.00, $2.35, $2.40, $2.50, $2.75, $3.00, $4.00, $5.00, $10.00

C.   Solve these reading problems.

21. Jeffrey bought the book *Martinko* for $4.35. He gave the clerk a 5-dollar bill. How much change should Jeffrey receive? $0.65

22. Jonas bought a copy of the book *Marita*. His total bill was $8.70. How much change should he receive from a 10-dollar bill? $1.30

23. Father bought a snow shovel at the hardware store for $8.95. He gave the clerk a 10-dollar bill. How much change should the clerk give Father? How many pieces of money will the clerk give if it is the smallest number possible? $1.05,   2 pieces

24. Mother bought dress fabric that cost $13.46. She gave the clerk $20.00. How much change should the clerk give Mother? How many pieces of money will the clerk give if it is the smallest number possible? $6.54,   8 pieces

REVIEW EXERCISES

D.   Find these percents. Some answers include fractions. *(Lessons 122, 123)*

25. 5 is ___20___% 25

26. 8 is ___16___% 50

27. 10 is __$71\frac{3}{7}$__% 14

28. 18 is __$22\frac{1}{2}$__% 80

E.   Find the amount after each increase or decrease. *(Lesson 119)*

29. 15% more than 18   20.7

30. 10% increase over $16.00 $17.60

31. 12% less than 15   13.2

32. 14% decrease from $19.00 $16.34

F.   Use a proportion to solve each reading problem. Show your proportion in your work. *(Lesson 94)*

33. Pedro and Jose hoed 20 rows of corn in 8 hours. At that rate, how long should it take them to hoe 30 rows? $\frac{20}{8} = \frac{30}{n}$ $n = 12$ hours

34. Carlos walked 5 miles to church in 2 hours. At that rate, how long would it take him to walk 8 miles? $\frac{5}{2} = \frac{8}{n}$ $n = 3\frac{1}{5}$ hours

LESSON 128

Objective

- To teach *working with multicolumn expense records and using their self-checking arrangement.

Review

1. *Calculating the discount and the sale price* (Lesson 120).

	Original Price	Discount Rate	Discount	Sale Price
a.	$35.00	15%	($5.25)	($29.75)
b.	$42.00	14%	($5.88)	($36.12)

2. *Calculating and counting change* (Lesson 127).

	Amount of Sale	Amount Given	1¢	5¢	10¢	25¢	$1	$5	Total Change
a.	$3.52	$5.00	3		2	1	1		$1.48
b.	$2.66	$10.00	4	1		1	2	1	$7.34

For $3.52 out of $5.00, the customer could pay $5.02 and receive $1.50 in change.

	Amount of Sale	Amount Given	What to Say
a.	$0.22	$1.00	($0.22 out of $1.00, $0.25, $0.50, $0.75, $1.00)
b.	$2.48	$5.00	($2.48 out of $5.00, $2.50, $2.75, $3.00; $4.00, $5.00)
c.	$3.15	$10.00	($3.15 out of $10.00, $3.25, $3.50, $3.75, $4.00, $5.00, $10.00)

128. Keeping an Expense Record

An **expense record** is a record of money spent for various purposes. Such a record is often kept on forms with a number of columns. The separate columns are useful for grouping similar expenses together.

Expense records are useful for several purposes. Families can use them to estimate future spending. Farmers and businessmen need records like these to file their yearly income tax returns. But in order to be truly valuable, these records must be kept accurately.

A multicolumn expense record is shown below. There is a simple method for checking addition on such a record. A total is found for each row (horizontally) and for each column (vertically). Then all the totals are added together to obtain a **grand total.** On the record below, the grand total is $1,126.84. Adding both ways must yield the same grand total, or there is a mistake in addition.

Record of Cash Expenses

Weeks	*Groceries*	*Clothing*	*Automobile*	*Other*	*Totals*
Jan. 1–7	$65 72	$12 95	$25 18	$83 50	$187 35
Jan. 8–14	45 38	55 78	185 35	38 77	325 28
Jan. 15–21	70 25	8 58	28 77	58 01	165 61
Jan. 22–28	155 38	11 62	32 56	99 09	298 65
Jan. 29–31	35 15	0 00	27 98	86 82	149 95
Totals	$371 88	$88 93	$299 84	$366 19	$1,126 84

Check

Grand total by weeks		Grand total by groups	
Jan. 1–7	$187.35	Groceries	$371.88
Jan. 8–14	325.28	Clothing	88.93
Jan. 15–21	165.61	Automobile	299.84
Jan. 22–28	298.65	Other	366.19
Jan. 29–31	149.95		$1,126.84
	$1,126.84		

"Let all things be done decently and in order" (1 Corinthians 14:40).

CLASS PRACTICE

Find the missing totals on this expense record.

Periods	Feed		Electric		Medication		Misc.		Totals	
Jan. 1–15	$148	57	$0	00	$6	95	$7	98	a. $163	50
Jan. 16–31	121	68	58	45	23	43	13	22	b. 216	78
Totals	c. $270	25	d. $58	45	e. $30	38	f. $21	20	g. $380	28

WRITTEN EXERCISES

A.   *Following is a cash expense record that the Garman family filled out for the small bookstore in their home. Find the missing totals. Check your work by making sure the grand total (number 10) is equal to the total for numbers 1–5 and also the total for numbers 6–9.*

Record of Cash Expenses

Weeks	Books		Wall Mottoes		Stationery		Other Expenses		Totals	
Jan. 1–7	$48	77	$18	43	$10	23	$41	18	1.$118	61
Jan. 8–14	12	65	82	61	15	67	22	19	2. 133	12
Jan. 15–21	215	18	0	00	75	63	15	78	3. 306	59
Jan. 22–28	28	95	23	28	0	00	31	28	4. 83	51
Jan. 29–31	117	81	28	63	12	37	53	68	5. 212	49
Totals	6. $423	36	7.$152	95	8.$113	90	9.$164	11	10.$854	32

B.   *Following is the cash expense record of Garmans' Bookstore for February. Copy and fill in the record, using the information at the top of the next page. Find all the totals. Check your work by making sure the grand total (number 20) is equal to the total for numbers 11–15 as well as numbers 16–19.*

Record of Cash Expenses

Weeks	Books		Wall Mottoes		Stationery		Other Expenses		Totals	
Feb. 1–4	$48	53	$16	95	$25	78	$19	95	11.$111	21
Feb. 5–11	76	52	0	00	8	95	79	83	12. 165	30
Feb. 12–18	92	87	9	98	17	93	14	35	13. 135	13
Feb. 19–25	83	48	69	32	14	51	59	41	14. 226	72
Feb. 26–28	16	53	0	00	15	65	0	00	15. 32	18
Totals	16.$317	93	17. $96	25	18. $82	82	19.$173	54	20.$670	54

Introduction

The table below shows the number of students who had a score of 100% in social studies class in the last two weeks. Challenge the students to prove that all the additions are correct.

Week	Mon.	Wed.	Fri.	Totals
First	2	4	3	9
Second	4	1	2	7
Totals	6	5	5	16

Teaching Guide

1. Discuss the practical uses of a multicolumn expense record. Some of the students' parents probably use similar forms for their farm or business records. This method is used in the popular one-write check accounting systems for small businesses and farmers (in which a carbon copy of each check amount goes on record at the time the check is written). If you have access to any of these, show them to the class.

2. Discuss the built-in method of checking by adding the totals horizontally and vertically. If the grand total is not the same both ways, one must go back and recalculate until both sums are equal. Practice completing the following multicolumn expense record in class as a preview of their assignment. Note that the decimal point does not need to be written on this type of form. The fine line represents the decimal point.

Record of Cash Expenses

Weeks	Books		Wall Mottoes		Stationery		Other Expenses		Totals	
Mar. 1–4	$35	57	$21	75	$14	69	$29	36	a.($101	37)
Mar. 5–11	199	25	63	14	14	38	5	48	b. (282	25)
Mar. 12–18	38	24	0	00	8	40	27	61	c. (74	25)
Mar. 19–25	78	91	0	00	0	00	15	97	d. (94	88)
Mar. 26–31	77	49	0	00	0	00	19	95	e. (97	44)
Totals	f. ($429	46)	g. ($84	89)	h. ($37	47)	i. ($98	37)	j.($650	19)

Check

Grand total by weeks

Mar. 1–4	$101.37
Mar. 5–11	282.25
Mar. 12–18	74.25
Mar. 19–25	94.88
Mar. 26–31	97.44
	$650.19

Grand total by groups

Books	$429.46
Mottoes	84.89
Stationery	37.47
Other	98.37
	$650.19

Allow sufficient time for the students to fill in and prove their expense records, as this work may be quite time-consuming. Grade the assignment as usual—one point for each exercise number.

Do not assign odd or even numbers in the expense records.

An Ounce of Prevention

1. Caution your students to use special care in completing their cash expense records. The most common error in this type of record is probably that of miscopying the original amount onto the expense record. If the prescribed checking method is used, the students should not have any addition errors.

2. Consider giving the students the answer for number 10. This will help them to prove the first expense record and grasp the concept of what they are doing.

Further Study

The form shown in this lesson is among the simplest of many record-keeping forms that businesses use. The students will become more familiar with these forms if they take a course on record keeping in the upper grades.

February 1–4:	Books, $48.53; wall mottoes, $16.95; stationery, $25.78; other expenses, $19.95
February 5–11:	Books, $76.52; wall mottoes, $0.00; stationery, $8.95; other expenses, $79.83
February 12–18:	Books, $92.87; wall mottoes, $9.98; stationery, $17.93; other expenses, $14.35
February 19–25:	Books, $83.48; wall mottoes, $69.32; stationery, $14.51; other expenses, $59.41
February 26–28:	Books, $16.53; wall mottoes, $0.00; stationery, $15.65; other expenses, $0.00

C. Solve these reading problems.

21. During the month of January, Garmans' Bookstore offered a discount of 15% on all books in stock. The regular price for *Thrilling Escapes by Night* was $8.95. What was the discount? What was the sale price? $1.34 $7.61

22. During the January sale, the Garmans sold mottoes at a discount of 12%. What is the discount and the sale price of a motto regularly priced at $11.45? $1.37 $10.08

23. One customer at Garmans' had a total bill of $12.48. She gave Mother a $20 bill. How much change did Mother give? $7.52

24. Another customer at the bookstore had a total bill of $9.32. She gave Mother a $20 bill. How much change did Mother give the customer? What was the smallest number of bills and coins that Mother could give? $10.68   8 pieces

REVIEW EXERCISES

D. Copy and fill in the following chart. *(Lesson 127)*

	Amount of Sale	Amount Given	1¢	5¢	10¢	25¢	$1	$5	Total Change
25.	$3.49	$5.00	1			2	1		$1.51
26.	$3.21	$10.00	4			3	1	1	$6.79
27.	$6.28	$10.00	2		2	2	3		$3.72
28.	$10.18	$20.00	2	1		3	4	1	$9.82

E. Write what you would say as you count the change to the customer. *(Lesson 127)*

	Amount of Sale	Amount Given	
29.	$0.58	$1.00	$0.58 out of $1.00, $0.60, $0.65, $0.75, $1.00
30.	$0.22	$1.00	$0.22 out of $1.00, $0.25, $0.50, $0.75, $1.00
31.	$1.54	$2.00	$1.54 out of $2.00, $1.55, $1.65, $1.75, $2.00
32.	$2.82	$5.00	$2.82 out of $5.00, $2.85, $2.90, $3.00, $4.00, $5.00

129. Income, Expense, and Profit

The Bible tells people to work so that they have money to help others in need. Some do this by operating a farm or a business.

The owners of a business must find out whether the business is earning money. To do this, they must first know how much money the business has received and how much it has paid out. Money received is **income,** and money paid out is **expenses.** The difference between income and expenses is the **net profit,** or simply the **profit.** The profit is the amount of money that the business has earned.

The formula for finding profit can be stated as follows:

$$\text{profit} = \text{income} - \text{expenses}$$

Example A

Brother Sanford repaired a roof and charged $75.00 for the job. If he spent $15.00 for materials, what was his profit?

profit = income − expenses
profit = $75.00 − $15.00
   = $60.00

Example B

Sister Edith bakes bread in her home. One week her bread sales were $45.00. Her expenses such as flour, other materials, and electricity were $12.50. What was her profit?

profit = income − expenses
profit = $45.00 − $12.50
   = $32.50

CLASS PRACTICE

Calculate the profit in each case.

	Income	Expenses	Profit		Income	Expenses	Profit
a.	$15.95	$7.52	$8.43	b.	$27.91	$13.03	$14.88
c.	$115.44	$38.84	$76.60	d.	$202.52	$88.31	$114.21

	Income	Materials	Electricity & Telephone	Small Tools	Total Expenses	Profit
e.	$137.16	$48.88	$7.99	$4.32	$61.19	$75.97
f.	$315.44	$155.73	$19.79	$22.54	$198.06	$117.38

WRITTEN EXERCISES

A.   Find each profit by subtracting the expenses from the income.

	Income	Expenses	Profit		Income	Expenses	Profit
1.	$78.56	$38.47	$40.09	2.	$82.52	$12.79	$69.73
3.	$128.39	$45.91	$82.48	4.	$186.41	$79.81	$106.60
5.	$431.89	$412.93	$18.96	6.	$185.81	$98.36	$87.45

LESSON 129

Objective

- To review finding profit by subtracting expenses from income.

Review

1. Give Lesson 129 Speed Test (Counting Change).

2. *Finding sales commissions* (Lesson 121).
   a. Sales, $250; Rate, 8%; Commission, ($20.00)
   b. Sales, $480; Rate, 12%; Commission, ($57.60)
   c. Sales, $396; Rate, 15%; Commission, ($59.40)

3. *Changing percents to decimals and fractions* (Lessons 112–114).

Percent	Decimal	Fraction
a. 89%	(0.89)	($\frac{89}{100}$)
b. 84%	(0.84)	($\frac{21}{25}$)

Introduction

Read the following problem to the class.

David's father is in the farm-supply business. He bought one bag of fertilizer for $7.50 and later sold it for $8.50. How much money did David's father make on the bag of fertilizer? ($1.00)

Now ask the students, "What is a word that describes the money that David's father made on the fertilizer?" (The word is *profit*.)

Teaching Guide

1. Introduce the three terms that are used in the lesson.
   a. Income—Money received by a business
   b. Expenses—Money spent by a business
   c. Profit—Money earned by a business (the difference between the money received and the money spent)

2. **Profit is computed by this formula: profit = income – expenses.** Make this practical by applying the formula to enterprises in your pupils' families. For example, if any of their fathers are carpenters, income is the amount they receive for a job; and expenses are the lumber, tools, and other supplies that must be purchased.

   Give practice with finding the profit when the expenses are already totaled.

	Income	Expenses	Profit
a.	$47.57	$15.69	($31.88)
b.	$86.47	$29.46	($57.01)
c.	$111.74	$59.65	($52.09)
d.	$167.93	$91.36	($76.57)
e.	$379.36	$312.36	($67.00)
f.	$435.82	$217.85	($217.97)

Also give practice with finding the profit when the total expenses must be found. First total the expenses; then subtract that total from the income.

Further Study

This lesson deals with only the most elementary concepts of profit. It does not deal with gross profit and net profit as calculated by retail and manufacturing firms. These aspects will be introduced at higher levels of this math series.

	Income	Materials	Electricity & Telephone	Small Tools	Total Expenses	Profit
a.	$115.26	$28.92	$3.48	$7.99	($40.39)	($74.87)
b.	$415.16	$131.68	$11.63	$10.82	($154.13)	($261.03)
c.	$397.47	$301.43	$15.99	$6.01	($323.43)	($74.04)

	Income	Expenses	Profit			Income	Expenses	Profit
7.	$281.73	$178.71	$103.02		8.	$642.91	$548.31	$94.60
9.	$437.88	$397.81	$40.07		10.	$284.78	$166.83	$117.95
11.	$981.25	$678.32	$302.93		12.	$782.89	$778.65	$4.24

B. **Add the expenses in each line to find the amount for the Total Expenses column. Then subtract the total expenses from the income to find the profit. You will have two answers for each line.**

	Income	Materials	Electricity & Telephone	Small Tools	Total Expenses	Profit
13.	$145.72	$35.52	$6.21	$1.21	$42.94	$102.78
14.	$385.81	$115.71	$15.81	$11.41	$142.93	$242.88
15.	$498.32	$287.32	$17.32	$5.81	$310.45	$187.87
16.	$271.91	$97.21	$18.71	$9.91	$125.83	$146.08
17.	$914.90	$514.27	$25.81	$75.91	$615.99	$298.91
18.	$275.18	$138.69	$5.21	$7.32	$151.22	$123.96

C. **Solve these reading problems.**

19. Father and Wesley build bookshelves during the winter months. Father calculates that the cost of each bookshelf is $15.25. They sell for $38.95 apiece. What is the profit on each bookshelf? $23.70

20. Father and Wesley also build lampstands. The cost of one stand is $12.68, and the selling price is $29.95. How much profit do they make on each lampstand they sell?
$17.27

21. The Landis family operates a small produce stand along the highway. One week their total sales amounted to $87.32. Father calculated that their total expenses for raising and picking the produce were $18.79. What was their profit? $68.53

22. During the berry season last summer, the Landis family had produce sales amounting to $342.91. If their total expenses were $113.25, what was their profit? $229.66

REVIEW EXERCISES

D. **Find the sales commission in each problem.** (Lesson 121)

	Sales	Rate			Sales	Rate	
23.	$375.00	8%	$30.00	24.	$490.00	9%	$44.10
25.	$235.82	7%	$16.51	26.	$432.12	12%	$51.85

E. **Complete the following chart. Write each fraction in lowest terms.** (Lessons 112–114)

	Percent	Decimal	Fraction
27.	29%	0.29	$\frac{29}{100}$
28.	6%	0.06	$\frac{3}{50}$

130. Calculating Unit Prices

It is easy to compare prices when items are of equal size. For example, if a gallon of milk costs $1.89 in one store and $2.19 in another store, it is easy to tell which is the better buy. But suppose you are shopping for laundry detergent. A 15-pound box of detergent is on sale for $10.95, and a 25-pound box of the same kind is priced at $19.95. How can you tell which is the better buy?

To compare prices when items are of different sizes, you must find the **unit price** of each item. The unit price is the price for one unit of the item—one ounce, one pound, one quart, and so forth. The steps for finding a unit price are described below.

1. Divide the cost of each item by the number of units in that item. If necessary, divide to the thousandths' place and round to the nearest cent.	A 15-pound box of laundry detergent is on sale for $10.95, and a 25-pound box of the same kind is priced at $19.95. Which is the better buy? *15-pound box* *25-pound box* $\dfrac{\$0.73}{15)\$10.95}$ $\dfrac{\$0.798}{25)\$19.95} = \$0.80$
2. Compare the two unit prices. The item with the lower unit price is the better buy.	$0.73 < $0.80 The 15-pound box is the better buy.

CLASS PRACTICE

Find the unit price of each item, to the nearest cent.

a.	15 oz. cereal for $2.49	$0.17	b. 2 qt. milk for $1.45	$0.73
c.	5 lb. flour for $1.69	$0.34	d. 100 lb. feed for $9.78	$0.10

WRITTEN EXERCISES

A.Find the unit price of each item, to the nearest cent.

1.	20 oz. cereal for $2.95	$0.15	2.	24 oz. cereal for $3.95	$0.16
3.	5 lb. sugar for $1.89	$0.38	4.	24 oz. yogurt for $1.00	$0.04
5.	2 qt. ice cream for $2.25	$1.13	6.	7.5 oz. baby food for $1.00	$0.13
7.	10 lb. flour for $1.45	$0.15	8.	46 oz. tomato juice for $0.99	$0.02
9.	10.5 oz. soup for $0.69	$0.07	10.	46 oz. fruit punch for $0.89	$0.02
11.	50 lb. sheep feed for $5.37	$0.11	12.	8 oz. baking soda for $0.33	$0.04
13.	3 lb. shortening for $1.49	$0.50	14.	2 lb. brown sugar for $1.15	$0.58
15.	10 reams paper for $32.33	$3.23	16.	12 ruled note pads for $6.99	$0.58

LESSON 130

Objective

- To teach *comparing prices by calculating unit prices.

Review

1. *Finding profit* (Lesson 129).

	Income	Materials	Electricity & Telephone	Small Tools	Total Expenses	Profit
a.	$103.29	$35.22	$3.20	$5.05	($43.47)	($59.82)
b.	$268.85	$101.44	$10.75	$12.83	($125.02)	($143.83)
c.	$388.59	$205.53	$19.86	$5.65	($231.04)	($157.55)

2. *Dividing fractions* (Lessons 65-67).

   a. $5 \div \frac{1}{9} = (45)$

   b. $\frac{7}{9} \div \frac{1}{3} = (2\frac{1}{3})$

   c. $8 \div \frac{3}{5} = (13\frac{1}{3})$

   d. $4\frac{1}{4} \div 1\frac{1}{2} = (2\frac{5}{6})$

3. *Writing large numbers* (Lesson 1).

   a. 3,050,000
      (Three million, fifty thousand)

   b. 1,898,000
      (One million, eight hundred
      ninety-eight thousand)

   c. 2,300,000,000
      (Two billion, three hundred mil-
      lion)

   d. 4,050,000,000,000
      (Four trillion, fifty billion)

Introduction

Read the following problem, and ask the students how they would solve it.

Mary was shopping with her mother. One of the things on Mother's list was laundry detergent. They saw that the 15-pound box was on sale for $10.95, and the 25-pound box that Mother usually bought was marked $19.95. Which box of detergent is the better buy? (This problem is solved in the lesson.)

Teaching Guide

To calculate a unit price, divide the cost of the item by the number of units in that item. Divide to the thousandths' place, if necessary, and round the quotient to the nearest cent. If two items are being compared, the product with the lower unit price is the cheaper item.

Be sure to review the concept of dividing money and rounding the quotient to the nearest cent.

a.   15 oz. cereal for $2.29,
         or 20 oz. for $2.85
$2.29 \div 15$ = about $0.153
              = ($0.15 per ounce)
$2.85 \div 20$ = about $0.143
              = ($0.14 per ounce)
The better buy is 20 ounces for $2.85.

b.   2 qt. ice cream for $1.69,
         or 5 qt. for $3.79
$1.69 \div 2$ = $0.845
              = (about $0.85 per quart)
$3.79 \div 5$ = $0.758
              = (about $0.76 per quart)
The better buy is 5 quarts for $3.79.

c.   5 lb. sugar for $1.79,
         or 25 lb. for $9.25
$1.79 \div 5$ = $0.358
              = (about $0.36 per pound)
$9.25 \div 25$ = ($0.37 per pound)
The better buy is 5 pounds for $1.79.

(The price of the smaller amount is sometimes lower because that size sells faster. It is not always cheaper to buy the larger amount.)

d.   100-lb. bag of feed for $9.92,
         or 2,000 lb. feed in bulk for $170.40
$9.92 \div 100$ = $0.0992
              = (about $0.10 per pound)
$170.40 \div 2,000$ = $0.085
              = (about $0.09 per pound)
The better buy is 2,000 lb. for $170.40.

(For something like feed, it is almost always cheaper to buy in bulk rather than in bags. Bagging the product adds to its price.)

B. *Solve these reading problems.*

17. Mother wants to buy eggs at the store. The prices are $0.95 for 1 dozen and $1.30 for $1\frac{1}{2}$ dozen. Which price is better? $1.30 per $1\frac{1}{2}$ dozen ($0.87 vs. $0.95)

18. Father was buying copier paper for the school. A local bookstore sells 10 reams of paper for $33.50. A mail-order catalog offers 30 reams for $104.70. Which is the better buy?   10 reams for $33.50 ($3.35 vs. $3.49)

19. Father bought 150 pounds of feed at a local feed mill for $16.11. Another feed mill sells a similar type of feed for $9.50 per 100 pounds. Which is the better buy?
                    $9.50 per 100 pounds ($0.10 vs. $0.11)

20. Furnams' Grocery has a certain brand of cheese on special for $1.89 per pound. Peiffer's Grocery has the same brand of cheese on special at $9.95 for a 5-pound block. Which is the better price? $1.89 per pound ($1.89 vs. $1.99)

21. Gehmans' Bookstore buys the book *Evangelists in Chains* from the publisher for $5.52. Other expenses of the bookstore amount to $1.75 for each book sold. The Gehmans sell the book for $8.95. What are the total expenses for the book? What is the profit?
                    $7.27 $1.68

22. Darlene's mother makes quilts during the winter. She pays $65.00 for the materials to make one quilt. The quilt is sold for $225.00. How much profit does Darlene's mother make? $160.00

> *Moreover it is required in stewards, that a man be found faithful.*
> *(1 Corinthians 4:2)*

REVIEW EXERCISES

C. *Find the total expenses and the profit. (Lesson 129)*

	Income	*Materials*	*Electricity & Telephone*	*Small Tools*	*Total Expenses*	*Profit*
23.	$179.53	$46.91	$7.15	$3.98	$58.04	$121.49
24.	$315.96	$145.58	$13.87	$14.95	$174.40	$141.56
25.	$377.62	$291.48	$14.65	$7.15	$313.28	$64.34

D. *Solve these division problems. (Lessons 65–67)*

26. $7 \div \frac{1}{8}$ 56   **27.** $\frac{3}{5} \div \frac{1}{4}$ $2\frac{2}{5}$ **28.** $5 \div \frac{2}{3}$ $7\frac{1}{2}$ **29.** $5\frac{1}{2} \div 2\frac{1}{4}$ $2\frac{4}{9}$

E. *Write these numbers, using words. (Lesson 1)*

30. 5,200,000   Five million, two hundred thousand

31. 4,717,000   Four million, seven hundred seventeen thousand

32. 3,500,000,000   Three billion, five hundred million

33. 4,000,000,000,000   Four trillion

131. Calculating Interest

In the parable of the talents in Matthew 25, the slothful servant was condemned because he had not been a good steward of his master's money. The master said that the servant could have lent the money to others and received usury, or interest, on it.

Interest is money paid for the privilege of borrowing money. The individual who borrows money pays interest, and the person who lends money receives interest. To find the amount of interest, the following three facts must be known.

1. **Principal**—How much money is borrowed
2. **Rate**—What percent of interest is paid
3. **Time**—How long the money is borrowed (stated in years)

To find the amount of interest, multiply the principal by the rate of interest, and multiply that product by the time for which the money is borrowed. This rule is expressed in the following formula.

$$\text{interest} = \text{principal} \times \text{rate} \times \text{time, or } i = p \times r \times t$$

Example A
Find the interest on $200 at 9% for 1 year.
interest = principal × rate × time
interest = $200 × 0.09 × 1 = $18.00

Example B
Find the interest on $300 at 8% for 3 years.
interest = principal × rate × time
interest = $300 × 0.08 × 3 = $72.00

When the time is 1 year, it is not necessary to multiply by the time, because multiplying by 1 does not change the answer.

CLASS PRACTICE

Find the interest in each case.

	Principal	Rate	Time			Principal	Rate	Time	
a.	$600	10%	2 yr.	$120.00	b.	$500	8%	4 yr.	$160.00
c.	$900	7%	6 yr.	$378.00	d.	$2,200	11%	3 yr.	$726.00

WRITTEN EXERCISES

A. Find the interest on each sum of money if it is borrowed for 1 year.

1. $400 at 8%
   $32.00
2. $300 at 9%
   $27.00
3. $1,000 at 8%
   $80.00
4. $900 at 12%
   $108.00

5. $800 at 7%
   $56.00
6. $700 at 9%
   $63.00
7. $1,500 at 12%
   $180.00
8. $850 at 11%
   $93.50

LESSON 131

Objective

- To teach *calculating simple interest, using full years and whole-number interest rates.

Review

1. *Calculating unit prices* (Lesson 130).
   a. 1 qt. milk for $0.65,
      or 4 quarts for $2.20
      ($0.65 per quart; $0.55 per quart)
   b. 14 oz. noodles for $0.65,
      or 18 oz. for $0.79
      (14 oz.: about $0.046 per ounce =
      $0.05 to nearest cent;
      18 oz.: about $0.044 per ounce =
      $0.04 to nearest cent)

2. *Calculating profit* (Lesson 129). The following table represents some greenhouse expenses.

Introduction

Ask the students if they know where banks get their money. A complete answer would be quite involved, but for the present purpose it is sufficient to say that banks get money from people who deposit money in banks.

What do banks do with the money on deposit? (They lend it out.) What term is used for the "rent" that people pay on borrowed money? (The term is *interest*.)

	Income	Seeds & Plants	Fuel & Electric	Supplies	Total Expenses	Profit
a.	$197.59	$88.43	$80.49	$15.56	($184.48)	($13.11)
b.	$305.39	$42.84	$35.95	$26.91	($105.70)	($199.69)
c.	$278.42	$15.63	$12.35	$38.63	($66.61)	($211.81)

3. *Finding what percent one number is of another* (Lessons 122, 123).
   a. 4 is (33 1/3%) of 12
   b. 3 is (20%) of 15
   c. 5 is (41 2/3%) of 12
   d. 16 is (26 2/3%) of 60

Teaching Guide

1. **Interest is money paid for the use of borrowed money.** When one person uses another person's money to make a profit, it is only fair that he pays the lender for the use of his money. However, when a person must borrow money to meet an unexpected need, a Christian should be willing to lend the money without charging interest.

    Point out that when a person puts money into a savings accounts, he is actually lending the money to the bank. The bank pays interest for the use of the money.

2. **The amount of interest is based on three factors.** They are as follows:
    (1) Principal—How much money is borrowed
    (2) Rate—What percent of interest is paid
    (3) Time—How long the money is borrowed (stated in years)

3. **Interest is computed by this formula: interest = principal × rate × time.** (In some cases it is simpler to begin by multiplying principal × rate. In other cases it is simpler to begin by multiplying principal × time.)

Principal	Rate	Time	Interest
a. $600	9%	1 year	($54.00)
b. $800	8%	1 year	($64.00)
c. $750	10%	1 year	($75.00)
d. $900	9%	2 years	($162.00)
e. $950	8%	2 years	($152.00)
f. $1,400	9%	3 years	($378.00)
g. $850	10%	5 years	($425.00)
h. $950	9%	4 years	($342.00)
i. $500	12%	6 years	($360.00)
j. $800	18%	3 years	($432.00)

(*Note:* The rate of 18%, or 1 1/2% per month, is typical for credit cards and other charge accounts.)

Further Study

Simple interest is interest that is not added to the principal, as when a bank pays interest to a depositor rather than adding it to his account balance. Compound interest is interest that is added to the principal, as when a bank adds interest to the balance in a savings account. Only simple interest is taught at this level.

17. $252.00
18. $240.00
19. $270.00
20. $117.00
21. $720.00
22. $1,050.00
23. $396.00
24. $1,620.00

B. Find the interest on each sum of money if it is borrowed for 2 years.

9. $500 at 8%   10. $400 at 9%   11. $750 at 8%   12. $1,000 at 9%
          $80.00 $72.00 $120.00 $180.00

13. $600 at 7%   14. $900 at 12%   15. $3,000 at 12% 16. $2,500 at 11%
          $84.00 $216.00 $720.00 $550.00

C. Find the interest on each sum of money at the rate and time indicated.
(Answers on facing page)

	Principal	Rate	Time		Principal	Rate	Time
17.	$700	9%	4 yr.	18.	$600	8%	5 yr.
19.	$900	10%	3 yr.	20.	$1,300	9%	1 yr.
21.	$3,000	12%	2 yr.	22.	$2,500	7%	6 yr.
23.	$1,200	11%	3 yr.	24.	$4,500	9%	4 yr.

D. Solve these reading problems.

25. Banks pay interest on savings accounts. Stanley had $150 in a savings account, and the bank paid 5% interest. How much interest did Stanley receive in 1 year? $7.50

26. How much interest will $500 earn in 1 year if it is kept in a savings account at 6% interest? $30.00

27. Money can also be placed in an account for which the bank issues a certificate of deposit. How much interest would a bank pay on $1,500 that is placed in such an account for 2 years at 7%? $210.00

28. If a person has a certificate of deposit for $2,000 at 7%, how much interest will he earn in 5 years? $700.00

REVIEW EXERCISES

E. Solve these problems on unit prices. *(Lesson 130)*

29. The price for a 50-pound bag of rabbit feed is $8.95. What is the unit price of the feed?
                                                                               $0.18

30. A 50-pound bag of rabbit feed costs $9.25. A different brand of rabbit feed costs $5.49 for a 25-pound bag. Which feed is cheaper per pound?
                                          50-pound bag for $9.25   ($0.19 vs. $0.22)

F. Solve these problems on profit. *(Lesson 129)*

31. Douglas and his father built a doghouse that sold for $42.00. The cost of materials was $8.46. How much profit did they make? $33.54

32. Mother helped Marianne make a motto that sold for $7.95. The materials for the motto cost $0.95. What was their profit? $7.00

G. Find these percents. Some answers include fractions. *(Lessons 122, 123)*

33. 9 is __20__ % of 45   34. 7 is __50__ % of 14

35. 9 is $33\frac{1}{3}$ % of 27   36. 12 is $13\frac{1}{3}$ % of 90

132. Calculating Interest for Part of a Year

You have learned how to find interest on money that is borrowed at a given rate for a given number of years. But loans are sometimes made for only several months instead of a whole year. In such a case, interest must be calculated for part of a year.

The same formula is used to find interest for part of a year as for full years:

interest = principal × rate × time

The time, you remember, is stated in years. Therefore, if a loan is for a certain number of months, the time must be expressed as part of a year. This is done by writing a fraction in which the numerator is the number of months and the denominator is 12. (There are 12 months in a year.) The fraction is then written in lowest terms.

Example A

Find the interest on $500 at 9% for 3 months.

interest = principal × rate × time

time = $\frac{3}{12}$ = $\frac{1}{4}$ of a year

interest = $500 × 0.09 × $\frac{1}{4}$ = $11.25

Example B

Find the interest on $400 at 8% for 5 months.

interest = principal × rate × time

time = $\frac{5}{12}$ of a year

interest = $400 × 0.08 × $\frac{5}{12}$

= 13.33\frac{1}{3}$ = $13.33 to the nearest cent

Example C

Find the interest on $600 at 9% for 8 months.

interest = principal × rate × time

time = $\frac{8}{12}$ = $\frac{2}{3}$ of a year

interest = $600 × 0.09 × $\frac{2}{3}$ = $36.00

CLASS PRACTICE

Find the interest for each part of a year as shown.

Principal	Rate	Time		Principal	Rate	Time	
a. $2,000	10%	$\frac{1}{2}$ yr.	$100.00	b. $800	8%	$\frac{1}{3}$ yr.	$21.33
c. $1,000	8%	3 mo.	$20.00	d. $2,200	9%	9 mo.	$148.50

LESSON 132

Objective

- To teach *calculating interest for part of a year by expressing months as a fraction of a year. (Only months—not days—are used in expressing part years in Grade 6.)

Review

1. *Finding unit prices* (Lesson 130).
   a. 32 oz. lawn weed killer for $8.49 = ($0.27 per oz.)
   b. 4 pairs boys' socks for $5.69 = ($1.42 per pair)

2. *Metric units of linear measure and capacity* (Lessons 99, 100).
   a. 6,500 m = (6.5) km
   b. 140 ml = (0.14) l
   c. 8 kl = (8,000) l
   d. 15 mm = (1.5) cm

3. *Rounding numbers* (Lesson 3).
   a. 368 to nearest ten   (370)
   b. 4,820 to nearest thousand   (5,000)
   c. 7,778,431 to nearest million (8,000,000)
   d. 24,987,456 to nearest ten million (20,000,000)

Introduction

Review the interest formula by finding the interest on $300 at 8% for 1 year and for 2 years.

$300 × 0.08 × 1 = ($24.00)
$300 × 0.08 × 2 = ($48.00)

Now challenge the students with this question: How would you find the interest on $300 at 8% for 1/2 year? ($300 × 0.08 × 1/2 = $12.00) Then ask, "How would you find the interest on $300 at 8% interest for 6 months?" They should recognize that 6 months is one-half of a year and that this answer is also $12.00.

Teaching Guide

The same formula is used to find interest for part of a year as for full years: interest = principal × rate × time. Since the time is only part of a year, it is written as a fraction. Give practice with writing any number of months as a fraction of a year.

1 month = $\frac{1}{12}$ year

2 months = $\frac{1}{6}$ year

3 months = $\frac{1}{4}$ year

4 months = $\frac{1}{3}$ year

5 months = $\frac{5}{12}$ year

6 months = $\frac{1}{2}$ year

7 months = $\frac{7}{12}$ year

8 months = $\frac{2}{3}$ year

9 months = $\frac{3}{4}$ year

10 months = $\frac{5}{6}$ year

11 months = $\frac{11}{12}$ year

a. $400 at 8% for 3 mo.
= $400 × 0.08 × 1/4 = ($8.00)

b. $600 at 9% for 1 mo.
= $600 × 0.09 × 1/12 = ($4.50)

c. $500 at 10% for 2 mo.
= $500 × 0.1 × 1/6 = ($8.33)

d. $800 at 12% for 5 mo.
= $800 × 0.12 × 5/12 = ($40.00)

e. $900 at 11% for 6 mo.
= $900 × 0.11 × 1/2 = ($49.50)

f. $700 at 9% for 7 mo.
= $700 × 0.09 × 7/12 = ($36.75)

g. $2,100 at 8% for 8 mo.
= $2,100 × 0.08 × 2/3 = ($112.00)

h. $1,200 at 9% for 9 mo.
= $1,200 × 0.09 × 3/4 = ($81.00)

i. $2,400 at 11% for 10 mo.
= $2,400 × 0.11 × 5/6 = ($220.00)

j. $1,500 at 10% for 11 mo.
= $1,500 × 0.1 × 11/12 = ($137.50)

1. $18.67   2. $28.00
3. $20.25   4. $12.00
5. $200.00   6. $105.00
7. $108.00   8. $240.00

9. $35.00   10. $27.00
11. $12.00   12. $32.00
13. $60.00   14. $50.00
15. $90.00   16. $236.25

WRITTEN EXERCISES

(Answers on facing page)

A. Find the interest for each part of a year as shown.

	Principal	Rate	Time			Principal	Rate	Time
1.	$700	8%	$\frac{1}{3}$ yr.	**2.**		$700	8%	$\frac{1}{2}$ yr.
3.	$900	9%	$\frac{1}{4}$ yr.	**4.**		$800	9%	$\frac{1}{6}$ yr.
5.	$3,000	10%	$\frac{2}{3}$ yr.	**6.**		$2,000	7%	$\frac{3}{4}$ yr.
7.	$1,200	12%	$\frac{3}{4}$ yr.	**8.**		$4,000	9%	$\frac{2}{3}$ yr.

B. Change each number of months to a fraction of a year, and calculate the interest. (Answers on facing page)

	Principal	Rate	Time			Principal	Rate	Time
9.	$700	10%	6 mo.	**10.**		$600	9%	6 mo.
11.	$300	12%	4 mo.	**12.**		$1,200	8%	4 mo.
13.	$3,000	8%	3 mo.	**14.**		$2,500	8%	3 mo.
15.	$1,200	10%	9 mo.	**16.**		$4,500	7%	9 mo.

C. Solve these reading problems.

17. Father borrowed $2,000 at 8% interest to buy feeder steers. He repaid the loan after 6 months. What was the interest on the loan? $80.00

18. Uncle Marvin had $1,500 in a savings account for 6 months at 5% interest. How much interest did he earn? $37.50

19. Darvin has $125 in a savings account that earns 5% interest. How much interest does Darvin earn in 3 months? $1.56

20. Mr. Bowman borrowed $5,000 at 9% interest to start a small business. He repaid the money in 9 months. How much interest did he pay? $337.50

21. One morning Jay had 11% of his Bible questions answered incorrectly. What score did Jay receive on that lesson? 89%

22. Marcus read in the encyclopedia that about 32% of the land area of the United States is forested. What percent of the land in the United States is not forested? 68%

REVIEW EXERCISES

D. Find the unit price for each item, to the nearest cent. (*Lesson 130*)

23. 15 oz. shampoo for $3.49 $0.23   **24.** 48 oz. antiseptic for $5.89 $0.12

25. 22 oz. laundry stain remover for $2.99   **26.** 15 oz. paint and varnish remover for $3.59
$0.14 $0.24

E. Change these measures as indicated. (*Lessons 99, 100*)

27. 5 km = <u>5,000</u> m   **28.** 350 ml = <u>0.35</u> *l*   **29.** 125 mm = <u>12.5</u> cm

F. Round these numbers as indicated. (*Lesson 3*)

6,000,000

30. 458 (nearest ten)   460   **31.** 5,639,101 (nearest million)

32. 1,630 (nearest thousand)   2,000   **33.** 46,001,000 (nearest ten million)

50,000,000

133. Review of Interest

$$\text{interest} = \text{principal} \times \text{rate} \times \text{time, or } i = p \times r \times t$$

CLASS PRACTICE

Find the interest in each case.

	Principal	Rate	Time			Principal	Rate	Time	
a.	$400	7%	2 yr.	$56.00	b.	$750	10%	5 yr.	$375.00
c.	$600	9%	$\frac{2}{3}$ yr.	$36.00	d.	$1,200	8%	$\frac{3}{4}$ yr.	$72.00
e.	$600	7%	4 mo.	$14.00	f.	$1,500	10%	8 mo.	$100.00

WRITTEN EXERCISES

(Answers on facing page)

A.   Find the interest from the loan information given.

	Principal	Rate	Time			Principal	Rate	Time
1.	$200	9%	2 yr.	2.		$250	10%	3 yr.
3.	$700	8%	3 yr.	4.		$450	12%	4 yr.
5.	$850	10%	5 yr.	6.		$1,200	9%	5 yr.

B.   Find the interest for the parts of a year given.   (Answers on facing page)

	Principal	Rate	Time			Principal	Rate	Time
7.	$300	9%	$\frac{1}{2}$ yr.	8.		$500	12%	$\frac{1}{2}$ yr.
9.	$1,250	12%	$\frac{1}{4}$ yr.	10.		$950	9%	$\frac{1}{4}$ yr.
11.	$1,000	10%	$\frac{3}{4}$ yr.	12.		$2,500	12%	$\frac{3}{4}$ yr.

C.   Change each number of months to a fraction of a year, and calculate the interest.   (Answers on facing page)

	Principal	Rate	Time			Principal	Rate	Time
13.	$300	12%	6 mo.	14.		$450	8%	6 mo.
15.	$550	9%	4 mo.	16.		$750	10%	3 mo.
17.	$1,500	2%	9 mo.	18.		$6,250	9%	11 mo.

LESSON 133

Objective

- To give further practice with computing simple interest.

Review

1. *Finding profit* (Lesson 129). The following table represents some sewing expenses.

	Income	*Fabric*	*Supplies*	*Miscel-laneous*	*Total Expenses*	*Profit*
a.	$215.00	$48.63	$9.56	$12.48	($70.67)	($144.33)
b.	$230.00	$45.78	$11.65	$9.68	($67.11)	($162.89)

2. *Finding what percent one number is of another* (Lessons 122, 123).
    a. 4 is (16 2/3%) of 24
    b. 6 is (25%) of 24
    c. 15 is (37 1/2%) of 40
    d. 9 is (20%) of 45

3. *Metric units of area* (Lesson 101).
    a. 7 km² = (700) ha
    b. 250 ha = (2.5) km²
    c. 7 ha = (70,000) m²
    d. 70,000 cm² = (7) m²

4. *Roman numerals* (Lesson 4).
    These use all the Roman symbols.
        a. MDCLXXXVI = (1,686)
        b. 3,667 = (MMMDCLXVII)
    These review the subtraction principle.
        c. CMXLIV = (944)
        d. 999 = (CMXCIX)

1. $36.00
2. $75.00
3. $168.00
4. $216.00
5. $425.00
6. $540.00

7. $13.50
8. $30.00
9. $37.50
10. $21.38
11. $75.00
12. $225.00

13. $18.00
14. $18.00
15. $16.50
16. $18.75
17. $22.50
18. $515.63

Introduction

Review the formula for finding interest: interest = principal × rate × time. Remind the class that the time is a fraction if it is less than one year.

Teaching Guide

This lesson reviews interest as taught in Lessons 131 and 132. Use the following problems to drill the concepts so that students have a solid understanding of how to calculate interest.

Finding interest for whole years.

Principal	Rate	Time	Interest
a. $300	8%	2 yr.	($48.00)
b. $450	9%	3 yr.	($121.50)
c. $625	9%	5 yr.	($281.25)

Finding interest for part of a year.

Principal	Rate	Time	Interest
d. $450	10%	1/4 yr.	($11.25)
e. $1,350	9%	1/2 yr.	($60.75)
f. $2,500	12%	5/12 yr.	($125.00)

Finding interest for months.

Principal	Rate	Time	Interest
g. $600	11%	6 mo.	($33.00)
h. $750	8%	3 mo.	($15.00)
i. $1,750	9%	8 mo.	($105.00)

D.   *Solve these reading problems.*

19. Dale had a balance of $150 in his savings account. At a rate of 5%, how much interest will he earn in 6 months? $3.75

20. Father borrowed $5,000 at 6% interest when he built an implement shed. He repaid the loan in 6 months. How much was the interest? $150.00

21. Grandfather lent $8,000 to build a new church building. He did not charge any interest. How much interest could he have earned if he had placed the money in a bank at 6% interest for 2 years? $960.00

22. The Steiner family had a truck garden in which they raised produce. Their total expenses were $325.52, and their produce sales amounted to $1,130.82. What was their profit? $805.30

23. Father helped Linda to open a savings account of $50 with money she earned in the family's truck-garden project. She had the money in the savings account for the last 3 months of the year at 5% interest. How much interest did she earn? $0.63

24. Harold had $75 in the bank for a whole year. He earned $3.75 interest. What rate of interest did he earn? (Think: $3.75 is what percent of $75?)   5%

REVIEW EXERCISES

E.   *Find the total expenses and the profit in each problem below.* (Lesson 129)

	Income	Fabric	Supplies	Miscel-laneous	Total Expenses	Profit
25.	$235.00	$51.32	$1.69	$11.63	$64.64	$170.36
26.	$249.00	$53.38	$5.67	$12.15	$71.20	$177.80

F.   *Find these percents. Some of the answers include fractions.* (Lessons 122, 123)

27. 3 is __12__ % of 25   **28.** 5 is __20__ % of 25
29. 8 is __$66\frac{2}{3}$__ % of 12   **30.** 17 is __$42\frac{1}{2}$__ % of 40

G.   *Change the following measures as indicated.* (Lesson 101)

31. 5 km² = __500__ ha   **32.** 2 ha = __0.02__ km²

H.   *Write the Roman numerals as Arabic numerals, and the Arabic numerals as Roman numerals.* (Lesson 4)

33. CCCXXVI   **34.** CMXLIX   **35.** 147   **36.** 91
326   949   CXLVII   XCI

134. Reading Problems: Solving Multistep Problems

Some reading problems can be solved in only one step. Consider the following example.

> Brian is putting 3 bushels of apples into peck baskets. How many peck baskets can he fill?

Only one step is required to solve this problem: 3 bushels times 4 pecks in a bushel equals 12 peck baskets.

Many math problems in life do not have a simple, one-step solution like the example above. Often two or more steps are required to find the answer. To solve a multistep reading problem, use the following steps.

1. Read the problem carefully. Note the facts that are given and the question that is asked.

2. Notice the clue words that indicate whether addition, subtraction, multiplication, or division should be used. Lesson 28 discusses clue words or phrases that suggest the operation needed.

3. Solve the problem one step at a time.

4. Check your answer to see if it is reasonable.

Brian is putting 3 bushels of apples into peck baskets. How much will Brian's father receive for them at $1.95 per peck?

This problem requires two steps.

Step 1: Find the number of pecks in 3 bushels.
3 bushels × 4 = 12 pecks

Step 2: Find the total selling price for that number of pecks.
12 pecks × $1.95 = $23.40
Brian's father will receive $23.40 for 3 bushels.

Check: $1.95 = about $2.00
3 × 4 = 12, and 12 × $2.00 = $24.00
The answer is reasonable.

CLASS PRACTICE

Solve these multistep reading problems.

a. Mother bought 2 gallons of milk for $2.27 per gallon and 3 dozen eggs for $0.87 per dozen. What was the total cost of these things? $7.15

b. One evening at summer Bible school the attendance was 105. There were 15 in the preschool class, 63 in grades 1–10, and 11 in the youth class. How many were in the adult class?   16 adults

LESSON 134

Objective

- To give practice with solving multistep problems.

Review

1. Give Lesson 134 Quiz (Computing Interest).
2. *Calculating interest for months* (Lessons 131, 132).

Principal	Rate	Time	Interest
a. $500	8%	4 months	($13.33)
b. $650	10%	5 months	($27.08)

3. *Finding unit prices* (Lesson 130).
   a. 64 oz. orange juice for $1.69 = ($0.03 per ounce)
   b. 12 oz. instant oatmeal for $1.99 = ($0.17 per ounce)

4. *Column addition* (Lesson 5). No class review is necessary.

Introduction

Read this simple two-step problem to the students.

> Mother bought a gallon of milk for $2.25 and a loaf of bread for $0.89. She gave the clerk a 5-dollar bill. How much change did she receive?

Ask what the students would do to solve the problem. They will probably identify the steps as addition and subtraction.

Step 1: $2.25 + $0.89 = $3.14
Step 2: $5.00 − $3.14 = $1.86

Many problems in everyday life require several steps.

Teaching Guide

Give practice with multistep reading problems by reading the following problems slowly and clearly to the class. Then solve them by using the steps listed in the lesson.

a. The Witmer family is planning to drive to Galeton, a distance of 375 miles. Their car travels about 25 miles per gallon of diesel fuel. What will be the cost of fuel if the price is $1.15 per gallon? (A sketch will be helpful to see through this problem.)

   Step 1: Find how many gallons of fuel will be needed.
   375 mi. ÷ 25 m.p.g. = 15 gal.
   Step 2: Find the cost of the fuel.
   15 gal. × $1.15 = ($17.25)
   Check: 375 ÷ 25 = 15,
   and 15 × $1 = $15
   The answer is reasonable.

b. When the Witmer family traveled 375 miles, they drove the first 240 miles in 5 hours. What must their average speed be for the rest of the trip in order to make the trip in 8 hours?

Step 1: Find how far they still need to travel.

375 mi. – 240 mi. = 135 mi.

Step 2: Find how many hours of traveling time are left.

8 hr. – 5 hr. = (3 hr.)

Step 3: Find the average speed required to cover the remaining distance in the allotted time.

135 mi. ÷ 3 hr. = (45 m.p.h.)

Check: 400 – 250 = 150; 8 – 5 = 3; and 150 ÷ 3 = 50

The answer is reasonable.

An Ounce of Prevention

Multistep reading problems are particularly difficult for some students because they have never learned to read through a reading problem and analyze it. Emphasize following a step-by-step method like the one taught in this lesson.

c. Robert put 375 gallons of water into the sprayer. One cubic foot of water weighs 62.4 pounds, and there are 7.5 gallons per cubic foot. What was the weight of the water in the tank?   3,120 pounds

WRITTEN EXERCISES

A. ***Solve these multistep reading problems. The first two problems have the steps listed for you.***

1. Merle bought and raised a veal calf. He paid $115.00 for the calf and $125.00 for veal feed. He sold the calf for $305.00. What was his profit? $65.00
   Step 1: Find the total expenses.
   Step 2: Subtract the expenses from the income.

2. Father had $225 in a savings account for a full year at 5% interest. If the bank calculates the interest at the end of the year, and adds it to his savings account, how much money will be in the account at the end of the year? $236.25
   Step 1: Find the interest for 1 year.
   Step 2: Add the interest to the principal.

3. A tank-truck driver left the bulk plant with 750 gallons of fuel oil. He delivered 327 gallons to one customer and 286 gallons to another. How much fuel oil was left in the truck?   137 gallons

4. The Mountain View Christian School is in session $3\frac{1}{4}$ hours each morning and $2\frac{1}{4}$ hours each afternoon for 5 days a week. How many hours is the school in session in one week? $27\frac{1}{2}$ hours

5. Andrew's family traveled three days to visit their grandparents. They drove 315 miles on the first day, 340 miles on the second day, and 362 miles on the third day. What was the average number of miles per day that they traveled?   339 miles

6. One time when Father filled up the car with gasoline, the odometer showed 45,405.7 miles. At the next fill-up it showed 45,690.5 miles, and the car had used 12.8 gallons of gasoline. How many miles per gallon had the car traveled? $22\frac{1}{4}$ miles per gallon

7. Rose bought 3 dozen eggs. She gave the clerk a $5 bill and received $2.33 change. What was the price per dozen for the eggs? $0.89

8. From a 12-foot board, Luke cut one piece that measured 3 feet 7 inches and one piece that measured 4 feet 2 inches. How much of the 12-foot board was left?

    4 feet 3 inches

9. Brother Ivan and his wife flew to Guatemala to visit their son, who was in mission service. While they were away, they parked their car at the airport at the rate of $4.00 per day. They left on October 15 and returned on October 29. What did it cost to park their car at the airport? (When counting days, do not count the 15th as a day.)

    $56.00

10. Matthew has 3 rabbits. If each rabbit eats $\frac{1}{4}$ pound of feed a day, how long will it take the rabbits to eat 25 pounds of rabbit feed? $33\frac{1}{3}$ days

REVIEW EXERCISES

B.   Calculate the interest. *(Lessons 131, 132)*

	Principal	Rate	Time	
11.	$600	9%	1 yr.	$54.00
12.	$800	8%	2 yr.	$128.00
13.	$550	12%	6 mo.	$33.00
14.	$1,000	11%	3 mo.	$27.50

C.   Find the unit price for each item, to the nearest cent. *(Lesson 130)*

15.   16 oz. Epsom salts for 59¢ $0.04   16.   4.5 oz. toothpaste for $1.89 $0.42

D.   Solve these addition problems. Check by adding up. *(Lesson 5)*

17.	18.	19.	20.
23,919	42,981	$2,891.85	$8,518.25
45,084	28,828	+ 5,981.73	+ 9,919.99
32,919	33,111	$8,873.58	$18,438.24
+ 18,938	+ 15,321		
120,860	120,241		

LESSON 135

Objective

- To review the material taught in Chapter 10.

Teaching Guide

This review covers Lessons 127–134. Note that the entire cash expense record must be assigned in order to complete numbers 17–25.

13. $0.43 out of $1.00, $0.45, $0.50, $0.75, $1.00

14. $1.27 out of $5.00, $1.30, $1.40, $1.50, $1.75, $2.00, $3.00, $4.00, $5.00

15. $8.35 out of $10.00, $8.40, $8.50, $8.75, $9.00, $10.00

16. $3.76 out of $10.00, $3.80, $3.90, $4.00, $5.00, $10.00

135. Chapter 10 Review

A. *Solve these problems.*

1. $\frac{3}{5} \times \frac{1}{6}$ $\frac{1}{10}$ 2. $3\frac{3}{4} \times 2\frac{1}{8}$ $7\frac{31}{32}$ 3. $\frac{2}{3} \div \frac{1}{4}$ $2\frac{2}{3}$ 4. $4\frac{5}{8} \div 1\frac{1}{2}$ $3\frac{1}{12}$

5.
$$\begin{array}{r} 3.56 \\ \times\,0.28 \\ \hline 0.9968 \end{array}$$

6.
$$\begin{array}{r} 7.17 \\ \times\,4.5 \\ \hline 32.265 \end{array}$$

7. $5.2\overline{)65.52}$ 12.6

8. $0.48\overline{)24}$ 50

B. *Copy and fill in the following chart.* *(Lesson 127)*

	Amount of Sale	Amount Given	1¢	5¢	10¢	25¢	$1	$5	Total Change
9.	$0.78	$1.00	2		2				$0.22
10.	$1.45	$5.00		1			2	3	$3.55
11.	$5.51	$10.00	4		2	1	4		$4.49
12.	$6.37	$10.00	3		1		2	3	$3.63

C. *Write what you would say as you count the change to the customer.*
(Lesson 127)

	Amount of Sale	Amount Given	(Answers on facing page)
13.	$0.43	$1.00	
14.	$1.27	$5.00	
15.	$8.35	$10.00	
16.	$3.76	$10.00	

D. *Find the missing totals. Check your work.* *(Lesson 128)*

Record of Cash Expenses

Weeks	Fabrics	Patterns	Crafts	Other	Totals
Week 1	$358 68	$25 65	$75 96	$65 98	17. $526 27
Week 2	234 65	69 91	65 78	54 87	18. 425 21
Week 3	499 98	65 57	85 75	42 36	19. 693 66
Week 4	305 76	15 75	88 01	69 95	20. 479 47
Totals	21. $1,399 07	22. $176 88	23. $315 50	24. $233 16	25. $2,124 61

E.   Find the profit by subtracting expenses from the income. *(Lesson 129)*

	Income	Expenses	Profit			Income	Expenses	Profit
26.	$85.34	$29.18	$56.16	**27.**		$95.34	$15.99	$79.35
28.	$156.96	$53.39	$103.57	**29.**		$199.41	$83.39	$116.02
30.	$315.85	$186.63	$129.22	**31.**		$689.15	$507.96	$181.19

F.   Find the unit price for each item, to the nearest cent. *(Lesson 130)*

32. 8 oz. cream cheese for $1.09 $0.14   **33.** 12 oz. cheese for $2.29 $0.19

34. 10 ft. roller chain for $17.23 $1.72   **35.** 55 gal. oil for $221.05 $4.02

G.   Calculate the interest. *(Lessons 131, 132)*

36. $400 at 8% for 1 year $32.00   **37.** $500 at 9% for 3 years $135.00

38. $1,200 at 8% for 3 years $288.00   **39.** $2,000 at 9% for 4 years $720.00

40. $1,000 at 10% for $\frac{1}{4}$ year $25.00   **41.** $800 at 7% for $\frac{1}{3}$ year $18.67

42. $550 at 12% for 6 months $33.00   **43.** $700 at 11% for 9 months $57.75

H.   Solve these multistep reading problems. *(Lesson 134)*

44. At the grocery store, Aunt Edith bought 1 gallon of milk for $2.28 and 2 loaves of bread for $0.89 each. She gave the clerk a five-dollar bill. How much change did Aunt Edith receive? $0.94

45. Uncle David bought the following items at the hardware store: a screwdriver for $2.25, a pack of screws for $1.59, and a pack of washers for $0.69. Sales tax was 6%. How much was the sales tax? $0.27

46. Material that usually sold for $2.79 a yard was reduced by $0.55 a yard. Mother bought 3 yards of this material, and the sales tax was $0.40. What was Mother's total bill? $7.12

47. Father shipped 5 hogs to market one day. The hogs weighed an average of 224 pounds each, and they sold for $0.42 per pound. What was the total selling price for the hogs? $470.40

48. The Millers sold the following items at their roadside stand one day:
      15 heads of lettuce at $0.45 each
      25 dozen ears of sweet corn at $1.25 per dozen
      12 dozen eggs at $0.85 per dozen
What was the total amount of their sales that day? $48.20

49. The Weber family bought the following items at a Christian bookstore: *Egermeier's Bible Story Book*, $17.55; *Eyes for Benny*, $7.45; and a chain-reference Bible for $38.50. Sales tax was 6%. What was their total bill? $67.31

136. Chapter 10 Test

LESSON 136

Objective

- To test the students' mastery of the concepts in Chapter 10.

Teaching Guide

1. Correct Lesson 135.
2. Review any areas of special difficulty.
3. Administer the test.

Setting up the tabernacle according to God's directions involved geometry. God gave specific measures of length and breadth for curtains, boards, and court. Precision in following directions is the course of blessing.

Chapter 11

Geometry:
Perimeter and Area

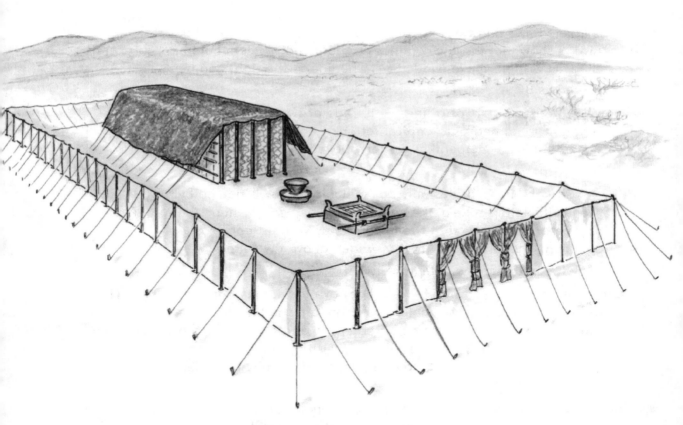

And Moses did look upon all the work, and, behold, they had done it as
the Lord commanded, even so had they done it: and Moses blessed them.
(Exodus 39:43)

137. Introduction to Geometry

Geometry is a branch of mathematics that deals with lines, angles, planes, and solids. The word *geometry* comes from two Greek words which mean "earth or land" and "to measure"; so the literal meaning of *geometry* is "to measure land."

A list of geometric terms and their definitions is given below. You should become familiar with these terms because they are used frequently in the next two chapters. To the right of each definition is the symbol used to represent that geometric concept.

Point—A location represented by a dot. A point is labeled with a capital letter.

A
·

Line—A straight line that extends without end in two directions. A line is labeled by using two capital letters at two points on the line. Arrows show that the line continues without end. The symbol for "line" is written above two letters. The line to the right can be named as $\overleftrightarrow{BC}$.

Line segment—A part of a line, with ends at two points. A line segment is named by a capital letter at each endpoint. The symbol for "line segment" is written above two letters, like this: $\overline{DE}$.

D   E

Ray—A straight line that has only one endpoint. A ray is named by two capital letters: one at the endpoint and one at a point on the ray. An arrow shows that the line extends without end in one direction. The symbol for "ray" is written above two letters, with the letter of the endpoint first: $\overrightarrow{FG}$.

Angle—A figure formed by two rays that have the same endpoint, which is the **vertex** of the angle. Angles are often named by using three letters, one for a point on each ray and a third for the vertex. (The letter for the vertex is always in the middle). The symbol for "angle" is ∠. The angle to the right may be called ∠HIJ or ∠JIH.

Right angle—An angle that is formed by perpendicular lines (like the lines at the corner of a square). The symbol ⌐ inside an angle shows that it is a right angle.

Intersecting lines—Two lines that intersect or cross at a point. In the diagram to the right, the intersecting lines cross at point K.

Parallel lines—Two lines that are always the same distance apart, no matter how far they are extended in either direction.

LESSON 137

Objectives

- To review the following geometric terms: point, line, line segment, perpendicular lines, intersecting lines, circle.

- To teach the following geometric terms: parallel lines, angle, *ray, plane, polygon.

- To review the names of the following polygons: triangle, rectangle, square, parallelogram, pentagon, hexagon, octagon.

Review

1. *Calculating interest for months* (Lesson 132).
   a. $300 8% 6 mo. ($12.00)
   b. $500 9% 3 mo. ($11.25)
   c. $800 7% 4 mo. ($18.67)
   d. $700 8% 5 mo. ($23.33)

2. *Calculating income, expenses, and profit* (Lesson 129).

	Income	Expenses	Profit
a.	$83.28	$16.49	($66.79)
b.	$156.91	$71.28	($85.63)
c.	$701.84	$649.21	($52.63)

3. *Calculating discounts and sales commissions* (Lesson 120, 121).

	Regular Price	Discount Rate	Discount	Sale Price
a.	$48.00	15%	($7.20)	($40.80)
b.	$62.50	12%	($7.50)	($55.00)

	Sales	Rate	Commission
c.	$250.00	6%	($15.00)
d.	$375.00	5%	($18.75)

4. *Changing between English and metric units* (Lessons 103, 104).
   a. 12 m = (39.36) ft.
   b. 25 ha = (62.5) a.
   c. 25 sq. mi. = (64.75) km²
   d. 4 in. = (10.16) cm

Introduction

Mention that various new terms will be introduced in this lesson. Go on to discuss the meanings of the terms as presented in the text.

Teaching Guide

Discuss each of the following concepts, and show how it is notated. Have the students give examples of them; a few possible objects are listed.

1. **A point is a fixed location such as a dot.** Technically, a point has no length or width; it is simply a location. For the sake of simplicity, however, the point is considered a dot even though a dot does have a bit of width.
   The illustration below shows point A.

   A

   Examples:
   a period at the end of a sentence
   the point of a pin

2. **A geometric line is a line that extends infinitely in two directions. A line segment has definite endpoints.** All *lines* used for practical purposes are actually line segments. Illustrations of line BC ($\overleftrightarrow{BC}$) and line segment DE ($\overline{DE}$) are shown below.

   Examples:
   one of the edges of a desk
   a corner of the room
   a ruling on a sheet of notebook paper

3. **A ray is a line with only one endpoint.** It extends infinitely in only one direction.
Ray FG ($\overrightarrow{FG}$) is illustrated below.

Example:
a ray from the sun

4. **An angle is formed by two rays with the same endpoint.** The vertex of an angle is the endpoint of the two rays. In naming an angle, the letter for the vertex must be in the middle. Angle HIJ or JIH ($\angle$ HIJ or $\angle$ JIH) is illustrated below.

Examples:
a corner of the room
the hands of a clock
the peak of a roof

Note: The sides of angle HIJ end with arrows to show that they are rays. It is also correct to make angles with line segments (without arrows).

5. **A right angle is an angle formed by perpendicular lines (like the lines at the corner of a square).** The symbol ⌐ inside an angle shows that it is a right angle. Right angle KLM is illustrated below.

Examples:
a corner of the room
the edge of a box
the hands of a clock at 3:00 or 9:00

6. **Intersecting lines are lines that cross at a point.** When two lines intersect, they form four angles. The illustration and the example of perpendicular lines below also apply to intersecting lines.

7. **Parallel lines are lines that never meet.** Parallel lines RS and TU are illustrated below.

R ←———→ S
T ←———→ U

Examples (with line segments):
rulings on notebook paper
railroad tracks

8. **Perpendicular lines are lines at a right angle to each other.** Perpendicular lines VW and XY are shown below.

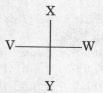

Example:
the marginal rule on notebook paper in relation to the horizontal lines

9. **A plane is a flat surface that extends in all directions but has no thickness.**
Examples (of partial planes):
a desk top
a wall
the floor
the ceiling

10. **A circle is a closed curve in which all points are the same distance from the center.**
Examples:
a button
a wheel
a clock face

Perpendicular lines—Lines that are at a right angle to each other. The lines shown for
right angle and *intersecting lines* are perpendicular.

Plane—A flat surface that extends in all directions but has no thickness. Your desk top
is an example of part of a plane.

Circle—A closed curve in which all points are the same distance from the center.

Polygon—Any closed figure that can be drawn with line segments. The following terms
are the names of various polygons.
Triangle—Any three-sided polygon.
Parallelogram—Any four-sided polygon whose opposite sides are parallel. (The corners
are usually not right angles.)
Rectangle—A four-sided polygon whose corners are right angles.
Square—A rectangle whose sides are of equal lengths.
Pentagon—Any five-sided polygon.
Hexagon—Any six-sided polygon.
Octagon—Any eight-sided polygon.

CLASS PRACTICE

Draw the following items.   (See page T–332 for answers.)

a. line
b. line segment
c. right angle
d. triangle
e. parallel lines
f. polygon
g. pentagon
h. rectangle
i. angle
j. line AB
k. ray CD
l. perpendicular line FG and HI

WRITTEN EXERCISES

A. ***Match the letters of the figures to these names.***

1. line   e.
2. parallel lines   d.
3. perpendicular lines   f.
4. right angle   a.
5. ray   c.
6. line segment   b.

B. ***Match the letters of the polygons to these descriptions.***

7. hexagon   f.
8. pentagon   g.
9. triangle   e.
10. circle   a.
11. octagon   d.
12. rectangle, but not a square   c.
13. square   b.

C. **Draw the symbol for each term.**

14. angle ∠ **15.** line ⟷ **16.** line segment — **17.** ray →

D. **Draw the following items.**

18. rectangle ▭ **19.** angle ⟋→ **20.** perpendicular lines

21. parallel lines ⟷ **22.** triangle △ **23.** right angle

E. **Draw and label the following items.**

24. line AB ⟨A B⟩ **25.** line segment CD C D **26.** angle EFG

27. ray HI H I **28.** parallel lines JK and LM J K / L M **29.** point N

REVIEW EXERCISES

F. **Solve these reading problems.** *(Lessons 120, 121, 129, 132)*

30. Matthew had $600 in a savings account for 6 months at 5% interest. How much interest did he earn? $15.00

31. Father loaned $4,000 to Brother David to help him pay a hospital bill. He did not charge any interest. How much interest could he have earned if he had kept the money in the bank for 9 months at 6% interest? $180.00

32. Daryl raised two hogs as a project of his own. He had $173.74 in expenses. The hogs sold for $199.36. How much profit did he make on them? $25.62

33. Ellen painted some Bible verses on mottoes for a winter project. She had $8.73 in expenses and sold $25.24 in mottoes. How much profit did she make? $16.51

34. Father sells farm supplies at a 6% sales commission. How much commission does he earn if he sells $65.00 worth of supplies? $3.90

35. Mother bought a coat that was on sale for 15% off the regular price of $48.00. What was the discount? How much did Mother pay for the coat? $7.20 $40.80

G. **Change these measures as indicated.** *(Lessons 103, 104)*

36. 44 ft. = __13.2__ m **37.** 175 lb. = __78.75__ kg

38. 28 l = __29.68__ qt. **38.** 17 km = __10.54__ mi.

H. **Find the lowest common multiple of each set.** *(Lesson 48)*

40. 12, 16 48 **41.** 15, 25 75 **42.** 12, 22 132 **43.** 8, 14 56

11. A polygon is any closed figure that can be drawn with line segments. It may have any number of edges, and the line segments may be of equal or unequal lengths. Following are names and examples of various polygons.

a. triangle (gable end of a house, yield sign)

b. parallelogram (any diamond-shaped object)

c. rectangle (floor, ceiling, chalkboard, door, window)

d. square (box, floor or ceiling tile, road sign)

e. pentagon (Pentagon building, school sign)

f. hexagon (some building tiles, cells in a honeycomb)

g. octagon (stop sign)

(Answers for **CLASS PRACTICE**)

a.   b. ─────── c.

d.   e.  f. (Any closed figure drawn with line segments.)

g.   h. ▭ i.

j.   k. ───C───D──➤ l.

LESSON 138

Objectives

- To review finding the perimeter of any polygon.
- To review finding the perimeter of a square.

Review

1. *Geometric figures* (Lesson 137). Draw the following geometric figures on the board and have the students identify them.

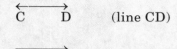

C   D   (line CD)

E   F   (ray EF)

G   H   (line segment GH)

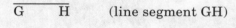

J   I   K   (angle IJK)

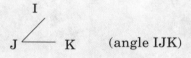

L

M   N   (right angle LMN)

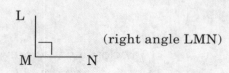

O ⟷ P   (parallel lines
Q ⟷ R   OP and QR)

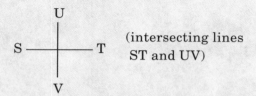

U

S   T   (intersecting lines
          ST and UV)

V

2. *Finding unit prices* (Lesson 130).
   a. 8 oz. baby cereal for $1.59 = ($0.20 per oz.)
   b. 50 booklets for $7.50 = ($0.15 each)

3. *Horizontal addition and subtraction* (Lessons 6, 9).
   a. 398 + 267 = (665)
   b. 429 + 196 = (625)
   c. 488 – 156 = (332)
   d. 635 – 468 = (167)

Introduction

Have the students find the distance around their tablets. How did they get their answers? They probably added all four dimensions. If they added two times the length and two times the width, they also have a good start on Lesson 139.

Teaching Guide

1. **The perimeter is the distance around an object.**

2. **To find the perimeter of any polygon, add the lengths of all the sides.** Find the perimeters of various polygons in the classroom. The measurements below can be used for further practice.
   a. 4 in., 5 in., 8 in., 3 in., 7 in. (27 in.)
   b. 14 ft., 12 ft., 14 ft., 12 ft. (52 ft.)
   c. 18 cm, 16 cm, 14 cm (48 cm)
   d. 6 yd., 8 yd., 9 yd., 7 yd. (30 yd.)
   e. 85 ft., 63 ft., 88 ft., 67 ft. (303 ft.)
   f. 8.2 m, 7.9 m, 6.8 m, 8.8 m (31.7 m)

3. **To find the perimeter of a square, use the formula $p = 4s$.** That is, multiply the length of one side by 4. Warn the pupils that before they multiply, they must make sure that what appears to be a square is really a square.

   Call attention to the standard practice of writing literal numbers directly beside each other to indicate multiplication. By the same principle,

138. Working With Perimeter

The **perimeter** of an object is the distance around it. The perimeter is equal to the combined length of all the sides of a polygon. To find the perimeter of any polygon, add the lengths of all the sides. Label the answer with the same units as those used to measure the sides.

Because a square has four equal sides, a special formula is used to find its perimeter. To find the perimeter of a square, multiply the length of one side by 4. The formula is as follows:

perimeter = 4 × length of 1 side, or $p = 4s$

In the abbreviated formula above, notice that the multiplication sign is omitted. This is the standard way of indicating multiplication when letters are used to stand for numbers.

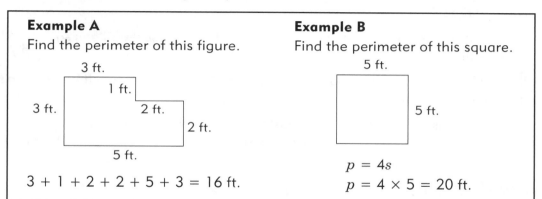

Example A
Find the perimeter of this figure.

3 ft.
1 ft.
3 ft.
2 ft.
2 ft.
5 ft.

$3 + 1 + 2 + 2 + 5 + 3 = 16$ ft.

Example B
Find the perimeter of this square.

5 ft.
5 ft.

$p = 4s$
$p = 4 \times 5 = 20$ ft.

CLASS PRACTICE

Find the perimeter of each square with the sides given below, using the formula $p = 4s$.

a. 12 inches   48 in.
b. 7 feet   28 ft.
c. 21 cm   84 cm
d. $16\frac{3}{4}$ yards   67 yd.
e. 9 m   36 m
f. 10.8 m   43.2 m

WRITTEN EXERCISES

A.   Find the perimeter of each polygon.

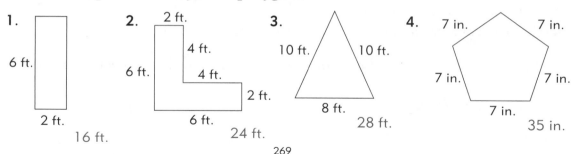

1.
6 ft.
2 ft.
16 ft.

2.
2 ft.
4 ft.
6 ft.
4 ft.
2 ft.
6 ft.
24 ft.

3.
10 ft.
10 ft.
8 ft.
28 ft.

4.
7 in.   7 in.
7 in.   7 in.
7 in.
35 in.

B. Find the perimeter of each square with the sides given below, using the formula $p = 4s$.

5. 15 inches 60 in.   6. 12 feet 48 ft.   7. 8 m 32 m   8. 14 cm 56 cm

9. 23 miles 92 mi.   10. 9 inches 36 in.   11. 13 km 52 km   12. 19 m 76 m

13. $6\frac{1}{2}$ in. 26 in.   14. $3\frac{3}{4}$ ft. 15 ft.   15. 4.5 m 18 m   16. 17.1 cm 68.4 cm

C. Solve these reading problems.

17. The Webers live in an L-shaped house. The lengths of the six sides are 44 feet, 42 feet, 20 feet, 12 feet, 22 feet, and 32 feet. What is the perimeter of the house?
172 feet

18. The Webers' property has five sides with the following measurements: 120 feet, 300 feet, 225 feet, 90 feet, and 495 feet. What is the perimeter of their property?
1,230 feet

19. The Moyers live on a square plot of land, with each side measuring 325 feet. What is the perimeter of their property?
1,300 feet

20. One classroom in the Roaring Falls Christian School measures 30 feet square. What is its perimeter?
120 feet

21. Brother Brubaker traveled 168 miles to preach at a distant church. If he traveled the distance in $3\frac{1}{2}$ hours, what was his average speed?
48 miles per hour

22. Nevin rode his bicycle to Mrs. Thomas's home to help rake her lawn. How fast did he travel if he covered the 3 miles in $\frac{1}{3}$ hour?
9 miles per hour

REVIEW EXERCISES

D. Draw the following items. Label numbers 23–26 with the letters given.
(Lesson 137)   (Answers on facing page)

23. line AB   24. angle CDE

25. ray FG   26. parallel lines HI and JK

27. square   28. rectangle

29. right angle   30. triangle

E. Find each unit price to the nearest cent. *(Lesson 130)*

31. 25 lb. bird seed for $7.98 $0.32   32. 12 pencils for $1.99 $0.17

33. $2\frac{1}{2}$ doz. eggs for $1.90 (price per dozen) $0.76

34. 35 acres of land for $45,000 (to nearest dollar) $1,286.00

F. Solve these problems horizontally, and write only the answers. *(Lessons 6, 9)*

35. 421 + 369   36. 369 + 278   37. 478 − 189   38. 808 − 462
        790   647   289   346

the formula for distance, rate, and time can be written as $d = rt$, and the formula for interest as $i = prt$.

Give practice with actual perimeters by measuring various squares in the room, such as floor tiles or ceiling tiles. The measurements below can be used for further practice.

a. s = 16 ft., p = (64 ft.)
b. s = 28 in., p = (112 in.)
c. s = 3 ft. 2 in., p = (12 ft. 8 in.)
d. s = 4 yd. 2 ft., p = (18 yd. 2 ft.)
e. s = 6.4 m, p = (25.6 m)
f. s = 8.8 km, p = (35.2 km)

23.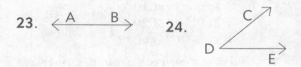

24.

25.

26.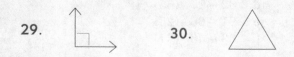

27.

28.

29.

30.

LESSON 139

Objectives

- To teach finding the perimeter of a rectangle *by using the formula $p = 2l + 2w$. (Previous experience: Adding 2 times the length and 2 times the width without using a formula.)

- To teach finding the perimeter of a triangle *by using the formula $p = a + b + c$. (Previous experience: adding the three sides without using a formula.)

Review

1. *Geometric figures* (Lesson 137).

   a. line DE

   b. line segment FG

   $$\overline{F \qquad G}$$

   c. ray HI

   $$\overrightarrow{H \qquad I}$$

   d. angle JKL

   e. right angle MNO

   M
   ⌐
   N   O

   f. parallel lines PQ and RS

   P $\longleftrightarrow$ Q
   R $\longleftrightarrow$ S

   g. intersecting lines TU and VW

   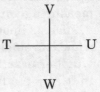

   h. perpendicular lines WX and YZ

   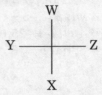

2. *Finding what percent one number is of another* (Lessons 122, 123).

   a. 8 is (25%) of 32
   b. 4 is (40%) of 10
   c. 7 is (35%) of 20
   d. 3 is (9 3/8%) of 32

3. *Changing between decimals and fractions* (Lessons 73, 74).

   a. $\frac{21}{25}$ = (0.84)
   b. $\frac{11}{20}$ = (0.55)
   c. $\frac{3}{16}$ = (0.18 $\frac{3}{4}$)
   d. 0.59 = ($\frac{59}{100}$)
   e. 0.78 = ($\frac{39}{50}$)
   f. 0.82 = ($\frac{41}{50}$)

4. *Mental addition and subtraction* (Lessons 7, 10).

   a. 38 + 44 (82)
   b. 58 + 72 (130)
   c. 39 + 77 (116)
   d. 82 – 17 (65)
   e. 91 – 66 (25)
   f. 83 – 46 (37)

139. Finding the Perimeter of Rectangles and Triangles

A rectangle has four right angles and two opposite sides of equal length. The longer set of sides is the length of the rectangle, and the shorter set of sides is its width. The length of a rectangle is represented by the letter l, and the width by the letter w.

Look at Example A below. You could find the perimeter of the rectangle by adding all the sides like this: $l + w + l + w$, or $12 + 4 + 12 + 4$. But since the length is added twice and the width is added twice, there is a quicker way to find the perimeter. The formula is as follows:

perimeter = (2 × length) + (2 × width), or $p = 2l + 2w$

To use this formula, multiply the length by 2 and the width by 2, and add the products together. Label the answer with the same units as those used for the length and the width.

To find the perimeter of a triangle, add the lengths of the three sides. Here is the formula:

perimeter = (length of a) + (length of b) + (length of c), or $p = a + b + c$

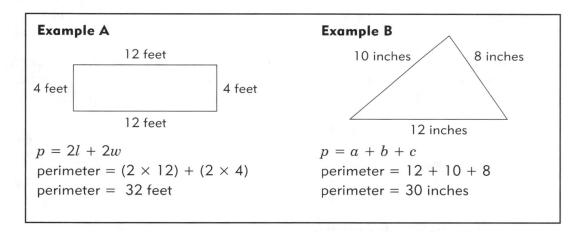

Example A

12 feet

4 feet   4 feet

12 feet

$p = 2l + 2w$
perimeter = $(2 \times 12) + (2 \times 4)$
perimeter = 32 feet

Example B

10 inches   8 inches

12 inches

$p = a + b + c$
perimeter = $12 + 10 + 8$
perimeter = 30 inches

CLASS PRACTICE

Find the perimeter of each rectangle described below, using the formula
$p = 2l + 2w$.

a. 6 in. long
   3 in. wide
      18 in.

b. 9 ft. long
   5 ft. wide
      28 ft.

c. 15 yd. long
   7 yd. wide
      44 yd.

d. 11 m long
   9 m wide
      40 m

Find the perimeter of each triangle described below, using the formula
   p = a + b + c.

e. a = 23 cm   **f.** a = 9 ft.   **g.** a = 30 m   **h.** a = 42 km
   b = 18 cm b = 9 ft. b = 27 m b = 35 km
   c = 14 cm c = 4 ft. c = 23 m c = 34 km
       55 cm   22 ft.   80 m   111 km

WRITTEN EXERCISES

A. *Find the perimeter of each rectangle described below, using the formula*
   p = 2l + 2w.

1. 5 in. long   **2.** 8 ft. long   **3.** 14 yd. long   **4.** 4 mi. long
   4 in. wide   6 ft. wide   9 yd. wide   3 mi. wide
       18 in.   28 ft.   46 yd.   14 mi.
5. l = 8 in.   **6.** l = 15 ft.   **7.** l = 18 yd.   **8.** l = 28 mi.
   w = 7 in. w = 11 ft. w = 12 yd. w = 16 mi.
       30 in.   52 ft.   60 yd.   88 mi.

B. *Find the perimeter of each triangle described below, using the formula*
   p = a + b + c.

9. a = 15 cm   **10.** a = 18 m   **11.** a = 18 km   **12.** a = 32 km
   b = 12 cm b = 12 m b = 15 km b = 27 km
   c = 8 cm c = 14 m c = 9 km c = 18 km
       35 cm   44 m   42 km   77 km

C. *Measure the length and width of each rectangle to the nearest $\frac{1}{2}$ inch.*
   Then use your measurements to find the perimeter.

13.

6 inches

14.

7 inches

D. *Solve these reading problems.*

15. The Oakdale Mennonite Meetinghouse is a rectangular building 84 feet long and
45 feet wide. What is the perimeter of the building?   258 feet

16. One day after a heavy thunderstorm, Dale's father asked him to walk around the meadow
to see if any branches had fallen on the electric fence. The meadow was a rectangle
800 feet long and 650 feet wide. How many feet long was the fence?   2,900 feet

17. An acre is equal to a square plot of land with sides of nearly 209 feet. What is the
perimeter of a plot of land 209 feet square?   836 feet

Introduction

Review finding the perimeters of squares and other polygons.

Squares

    a. 4 in. (16 in.)

    b. 9 ft. (36 ft.)

    c. 7 mi. (28 mi.)

Polygons

    d. 12 in., 15 in., 18 in. (45 in.)

    e. 23 ft., 18 ft., 16 ft. (57 in.)

    f. 18 m, 19 m, 31 m, 16 m, 18 m
      (102 m)

Now find the perimeter of a rectangle by using the same method as that used for any polygon.

    length = 7 in., width = 3 in.

    perimeter = 7 + 3 + 7 + 3 = 20 in.

Can the students think of an easier way to find the perimeter?

Teaching Guide

1. **To find the perimeter of a rectangle, use the formula $p = 2l + 2w$.** That is, multiply the length by 2, multiply the width by 2, and add the two products.

    a. $l = 9$ in., $w = 8$ in., $p = $ (34 in.)

    b. $l = 7$ ft., $w = 5$ ft., $p = $ (24 ft.)

    c. $l = 22$ m, $w = 8$ m, $p = $ (60 m)

2. **To find the perimeter of a triangle, use the formula $p = a + b + c$.** Add the lengths of all the sides as for finding the perimeter of other polygons.

    a. $a = 12$ in., $b = 15$ in., $c = 13$ in.
      $p = $ (40 in.)

    b. $a = 38$ ft., $b = 45$ ft., $c = 41$ ft.
      $p = $ (124 ft.)

    c. $a = 15$ cm, $b = 35$ cm, $c = 35$ cm
      $p = $ (85 cm)

Further Study

As the lesson makes clear, the formula $p = 2l + 2w$ is simpler to use than $p = l + w + l + w$. An even simpler version of the formula is $p = 2(l + w)$. But since this version is written in a more advanced form, it is not taught until Grade 7.

18. A rectangle 220 feet long and 198 feet wide contains exactly one acre. How long a fence would be needed to enclose a plot of this size?   836 feet

19. Laurel painted a border around the top of the living room wall. How long was the border if the room measured $15\frac{1}{2}$ feet by 16 feet?   63 feet

20. Alta mowed the back lawn one afternoon. It is a rectangle measuring 90 feet by 55 feet. How far is it around the outside edge of the lawn?   290 feet

REVIEW EXERCISES

E. *Draw the following figures, and label them with letters if they are given.* *(Lesson 137)*

21. line segment RS
23. right angle XYZ

22. parallelogram
24. intersecting lines NO and PQ (Intersecting lines do not need to be perpendicular.)

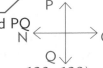

F. *Find what percent the first number is of the second. (Lessons 122, 123)*

25. 6, 30   20%   **26.** 9, 45   20%   **27.** 7, 42 $16\frac{2}{3}$% **28.** 8, 200   4%

G. *Express the fractions as decimals to the nearest hundredth. Express the decimals as fractions in lowest terms. (Lessons 73, 74)*

29. $\frac{17}{25}$ 0.68   **30.** $\frac{17}{20}$ 0.85   **31.** $\frac{9}{16}$ 0.56   **32.** $\frac{2}{9}$ 0.22

33. 0.72 $\frac{18}{25}$ **34.** 0.24 $\frac{6}{25}$ **35.** 0.59 $\frac{59}{100}$ **36.** 0.91 $\frac{91}{100}$

H. *Add or subtract mentally. (Lessons 7, 10)*

37. 45 + 38   83   **38.** 59 + 71   130 **39.** 98 − 37   61   **40.** 81 − 27   54

140. Working With Area

Area is the amount of surface that an object covers. For example, the floor area of a room is the amount of space that the floor covers. The size of a tract of land is its area. The area of land is usually measured in acres.

You learned how to find the perimeter of a rectangle in Lesson 139. This lesson will teach you how to find the area of a rectangle.

Look at the rectangle below. There are 20 squares in the rectangle, and each square represents an area 1 inch by 1 inch, or 1 **square inch.** A square inch is different from an inch. A square inch is not a *length* of 1 inch but an *area* of 1 inch by 1 inch. The area of the rectangle below is 20 square inches.

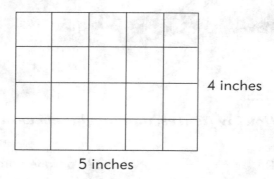

4 inches

5 inches

The area of this rectangle can be found by counting the squares. It can also be found by multiplication. Since the rectangle is 5 inches long and 4 inches wide, it contains 5 x 4 or 20 square inches. The formula is as follows:

$$\textbf{area = length} \times \textbf{width, or } a = lw$$

To find the area of a rectangle by this formula, multiply the length and the width. But remember that area cannot be expressed in units such as feet or inches. The answer must be labeled in square units such as square inches or square feet.

CLASS PRACTICE

Find the area of each rectangle described below. Include square in your labels for a–d, and the exponent 2 in your labels for e–h.

a. 8 in. long
   5 in. wide
      40 sq. in.

b. 12 ft. long
   7 ft. wide
      84 sq. ft.

c. 25 yd. long
   18 yd. wide
      450 sq. yd.

d. 54 ft. long
   28 ft. wide
      1,512 sq. ft.

e. 78 cm long
   40 cm wide
      3,120 cm^2

f. 46 m long
   32 m wide
      1,472 m^2

g. 14 km long
   7 km wide
      98 km^2

h. 67 m long
   54 m wide
      3,618 m^2

LESSON 140

Objectives

- To review the concept of area.
- To review finding the area of a rectangle.

Review

1. *Finding perimeters* (Lessons 138, 139).
   a. square with each side 13 in. (52 in.)
   b. rectangle 28 ft. by 25 ft. (106 ft.)
   c. triangle with sides 12 in., 15 in., 13 in. (40 in.)

2. *Finding interest* (Lessons 131, 132).
   a. $600 at 8% for 2 yr. ($96.00)
   b. $800 at 7% for 3 yr. ($168.00)
   c. $900 at 9% for 4 months ($27.00)
   d. $1,500 at 8% for 10 months ($100.00)

3. *Reading maps and blueprints* (Lessons 107, 108).
   1/2 inch = 10 miles
     a. 3 in. = (60 mi.)
     b. 5 1/2 in. = (110 mi.)
   1 inch = 2 feet
     c. 6 1/2 in. = (13 ft.)
     d. 9 3/4 in. = (19 1/2 ft.)

4. *Comparing decimals* (Lesson 75).
   a. 0.05 (>) 0.0451
   b. 0.52 (<) 0.5201
   c. 0.62 (<) 0.6209

Introduction

Draw a 3-foot by 2-foot rectangle on the board, and divide it into 1-foot squares. Ask a student to measure the dimensions of 1 square. The area of one square is 1 square foot. Have the students find the number of squares in the rectangle by counting and then by multiplying. The number of square feet is found by multiplying the length and the width.

Teaching Guide

To find the area of a rectangle, use the formula $a = lw$. That is, multiply the length and width of the rectangle. Label the answer as a square measure, using the square unit corresponding to the linear unit in the dimensions. If the dimensions are given in feet, the answer will be square feet. If the dimensions are given in yards, the answer will be square yards.

Solve several problems in class, and have a student give the correct label for each answer.
a. $l = 6$ in., $w = 5$ in., $a = $ (30 sq. in.)
b. $l = 12$ in., $w = 9$ in., $a = $ (108 sq. in.)
c. $l = 18$ m, $w = 14$ m, $a = $ (252 m^2)
d. $l = 9$ yd., $w = 4$ yd., $a = $ (36 sq. yd.)
e. $l = 12$ cm, $w = 15$ cm, $a = $ (180 cm^2)
f. $l = 16$ km, $w = 12$ km, $a = $ (192 km^2)

An Ounce of Prevention

1. Problems 17 and 18 are multistep reading problems.

2. In working with area, using the proper label can hardly be overemphasized. Students often use the label for linear units instead of square units. Stress that *inches* instead of *square inches* is actually a wrong label, and give only partial credit for answers with the correct numerals but the wrong labels.

WRITTEN EXERCISES

A. *Find the area of each rectangle described below. Include* square *in your labels for 1–8, and the exponent 2 in your labels for 9–12.* *(cm², m², km²)*

1. 7 in. long
   4 in. wide
   28 sq. in.

2. 18 in. long
   14 in. wide
   252 sq. in.

3. 17 in. long
   15 in. wide
   255 sq. in.

4. 9 in. long
   7 in. wide
   63 sq. in.

5. l = 7 yd.
   w = 5 yd.
   35 sq. yd.

6. l = 28 yd.
   w = 16 yd.
   448 sq. yd.

7. l = 33 mi.
   w = 28 mi.
   924 sq. mi.

8. l = 42 mi.
   w = 31 mi.
   1,302 sq. mi.

9. l = 23 cm
   w = 18 cm
   414 cm²

10. l = 7 m
    w = 6 m
    42 m²

11. l = 18 km
    w = 14 km
    252 km²

12. l = 63 km
    w = 49 km
    3,087 km²

B. *Solve these reading problems.*

13. At the Roseville Mennonite School, the sixth grade classroom measures 27 feet by 21 feet. What is the area of the floor?
    567 square feet

14. The Weavers' meadow is 800 feet long and 650 feet wide. What is the area of the meadow?
    520,000 square feet

15. Darwin is helping to shingle a roof. What is the area of one side of the roof if it measures 64 feet by 28 feet?
    1,792 square feet

16. The instructions on a kerosene heater say that there should be 80 square inches of ventilation when the heater is operated. If a window 36 inches wide is opened $2\frac{1}{4}$ inches, will that provide enough ventilation?
    yes

17. The Millers are planning to put carpet on their living room floor. The living room measures 6 yards by 5 yards, and the carpet costs $12.00 per square yard. What will be the cost of the carpet?
    $360.00

18. The Mussers are spreading fertilizer on their front lawn, which measures 90 feet by 50 feet. One bag of fertilizer covers 10,000 square feet. After they finish the front lawn, how many square feet of the back lawn can they cover with the rest of the fertilizer?
    5,500 square feet

REVIEW EXERCISES

C.   *Find the perimeter of each polygon.* *(Lessons 138, 139)*

19. square—9 in.   36 in.   **20.** square—15 in.   60 in.
21. rectangle—9 in. by 6 in.   30 in.   **22.** rectangle—18 ft. by 25 ft.   86 ft.
23. triangle—18 in., 25 in., 16 in. 59 in. **24.** triangle—28 ft., 18 ft., 22 ft.   68 ft.

D.   *Find the interest.* *(Lessons 131, 132)*

25. $400 at 6% for 2 yr. $48.00   **26.** $900 at 9% for 3 yr. $243.00
27. $800 at 8% for 8 mo. $42.67   **28.** $1,200 at 10% for 9 mo. $90.00

**E.   *Find the distance represented by each measurement when the scale is
1 inch = 4 feet.*** *(Lesson 108)*

29. $\frac{1}{2}$ in.   2 ft.   **30.** 5 in.   20 ft.   **31.** $4\frac{3}{4}$ in.   19 ft.   **32.** $3\frac{1}{8}$ in. $12\frac{1}{2}$ ft.

**F.   *Find the distance represented by each measurement when the scale is
$\frac{1}{4}$ inch = 8 miles.*** *(Lesson 107)*

33. 4 in.   128 mi. **34.** $\frac{3}{4}$ in.   24 mi. **35.** $5\frac{1}{2}$ in. 176 mi. **36.** $3\frac{1}{4}$ in. 104 mi.

**G.   *Copy these decimal fractions, compare them, and write > or < between
them.*** *(Lesson 75)*

37. 0.03 _>_ 0.0033   **38.** 0.31 _>_ 0.3045
39. 0.98 _>_ 0.909   **40.** 0.81 _<_ 0.811

LESSON 141

Objective

*   To review finding the area of a square.

Review

1. Give Lesson 141 Quiz (Finding Perimeters).

2. *Finding the areas of rectangles* (Lesson 140).
    a.   12 in. by 7 in.   (84 sq. in.)
    b.   23 ft. by 14 ft.   (322 sq. ft.)
    c.   45 cm by 35 cm   (1,575 cm²)

3. *Finding perimeters* (Lessons 138, 139).
    a.   square with sides 41 in.   (164 in.)
    b.   rectangle 8 in. by 5 in.   (26 in.)
    c.   triangle with sides 7 m, 12 m, 25 m   (44 m)

4. *Drawing geometric figures* (Lesson 137).
    a.   angle CDE
    b.   parallel lines FG and HI
    c.   triangle JKL

5. *Adding and subtracting decimals* (Lesson 76).

    a.   31.79
         + 45.98
         (77.77)

    b.   43.8635
          95.51
           1.369
          + 8.8
         (149.5425)

    c.   77.599
         − 38.6
         (38.999)

    d.   74.1
         − 28.6395
         (45.4605)

Introduction

Find the area of a rectangle that measures 8 feet by 7 feet. (8 × 7 = 56 sq. ft.) Can the students find the area of a square that measures 8 feet by 8 feet? (8 × 8 = 64 sq. ft.) Ask the students if it is necessary to know both dimensions of a square to find its area. That is actually an illogical question; for if you know the length of one side of a square, you know the length of all sides. Therefore, to find the area of a square, multiply the length of a side by itself.

Teaching Guide

To find the area of a square, use the formula $a = s \times s$. That is, multiply the length of one side by itself. Remember to label the answer in square units.
    a. s = 5 in., a = (25 sq. in.)
    b. s = 10 ft., a = (100 sq. ft.)
    c. s = 22 yd., a = (484 sq. yd.)
    d. s = 16 mi., a = (256 sq. mi.)
    e. s = 60 cm, a = (3,600 cm²)
    f. s = 25 m, a = (625 m²)
    g. s = 55 km, a = (3,025 km²)
    h. s = 75 m, a = (5,625 m²)

In higher grades, the formula for the area of a square is taught as $a = s^2$.

141. Finding the Area of a Square

A square is a special rectangle in that all four sides are equal. The formula $a = lw$ can be used to find the area of the square below.

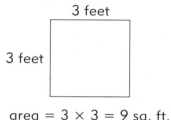

3 feet

3 feet

area = 3 × 3 = 9 sq. ft.

However, since the length and width of a square are equal, the length of any side can simply be multiplied by itself. The formula is as follows:

area = length of a side × length of a side, or $a = s \times s$

When you find the area of a square, remember to label your answer in square units, such as square feet or square inches.

CLASS PRACTICE

Find the areas of squares with these sides.

a. 9 in.   81 sq. in.   **b.** 12 ft.   144 sq. ft.   **c.** 21 yd. 441 sq. yd.   **d.** 16 mi.
256 sq. mi.

e. 32 cm 1,024 cm² **f.** 50 m   2,500 m²   **g.** 11 mm 121 mm² **h.** 18 km   324 km²

WRITTEN EXERCISES

A.   *Find the areas of these squares in square inches.*

1.

4 square inches

2.

$6\frac{1}{4}$ square inches

285

B. **Find the areas of squares with these sides.** (Answers on facing page)

3. 6 in.	**4.** 8 in.	**5.** 9 ft.	**6.** 14 yd.
7. 13 ft.	**8.** 28 yd.	**9.** 7 mi.	**10.** 17 mi.
11. 15 mm	**12.** 12 mm	**13.** 14 cm	**14.** 15 cm
15. 20 m	**16.** 65 m	**17.** 10 km	**18.** 40 km

C. **Solve these reading problems.**

19. Large areas are measured by the English unit of area called the township. A township is as large as a square with sides 6 miles long. How many square miles are in a township?

36 square miles

20. Dale's bedroom is a square with sides 12 feet long. What is the area of the floor?

144 square feet

21. One classroom at the Pleasant View Mennonite School measures 28 feet by 22 feet. Each ceiling tile covers an area of 1 square foot. How many ceiling tiles were needed to cover the ceiling?

616 tiles

22. Revelation 21 describes the glories and the size of New Jerusalem. Its length, breadth, and height are all 12,000 furlongs, or about 1,500 miles. What is the area of a square with 1,500-mile sides?

2,250,000 square miles

23. Myron and his father are planning to paint the concrete floor in the garage. The floor is 30 feet square (30 feet by 30 feet). How many gallons of paint will they need to buy if 1 gallon covers 200 square feet? (If the answer includes part of a gallon, another whole gallon is needed.)

5 gallons

24. The Nolts are buying vinyl flooring for their laundry, which measures 4 yards square. How much will the flooring cost at $18.00 per square yard?

$288.00

REVIEW EXERCISES

D. **Find the areas of rectangles with these dimensions.** *(Lesson 140)*

25. 7 in. by 4 in.   28 sq. in.   **26.** 90 ft. by 60 ft.   5,400 sq. ft.

27. 35 cm by 25 cm   875 cm²   **28.** 65 km by 45 km   2,925 km²

E. **Find the perimeters of these figures.** *(Lessons 138, 139)*

29. square—5 ft.   20 ft.   **30.** square—28 in.   112 in.

31. rectangle—8 ft by 7 ft.   30 ft.   **32.** rectangle—24 in. by 16 in.   80 in.

F. **Draw the following geometric figures. Label them with letters when they are given.** *(Lesson 137)*   (Answers on facing page)

33. line QR   **34.** ray ST

35. rectangle   **36.** perpendicular lines UV and WX

G. **Solve these addition and subtraction problems.** *(Lesson 76)*

37.	38.	39.	40.
14.56	52.9825	68.9	65.2
+ 28.93	12.87	− 29.979	− 14.7761
43.49	3.912	38.921	50.4239
	+ 5.76		
	75.5245		

An Ounce of Prevention

1. Problems 23 and 24 are multistep problems. For problem 23, explain the reason for rounding to the next higher gallon. If 1 1/2 gallons are needed, it is necessary to buy 2 whole gallons.

2. Problems 23 and 24 also refer to the measurements 30 feet square and 4 yards square. Be sure the students understand the difference between 30 square feet and 30 feet square (30 feet × 30 feet), and between 4 square yards and 4 yards square (4 yards × 4 yards).

3. 36 sq. in.	**4.** 64 sq. in.	**5.** 81 sq. ft.	**6.** 196 sq. yd.
7. 169 sq. ft.	**8.** 784 sq. yd.	**9.** 49 sq. mi.	**10.** 289 sq. mi.
11. 225 mm²	**12.** 144 mm²	**13.** 196 cm²	**14.** 225 cm²
15. 400 m²	**16.** 4,225 m²	**17.** 100 km²	**18.** 1,600 km²

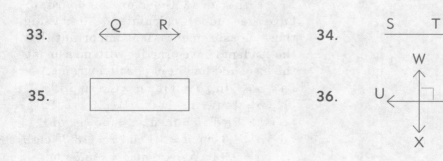

33.

34.

35.

36.

LESSON 142

Objective

- To teach *finding the area of a parallelogram.

Review

1. *Finding the areas of squares* (Lesson 141).
   a. $s = 18$ in.   (324 sq. in.)
   b. $s = 24$ ft.   (576 sq. ft.)
   c. $s = 26$ cm   (676 cm²)
   d. $s = 81$ m   (6,561 m²)

2. *Finding the areas of rectangles* (Lesson 140).
   a. 18 in. by 15 in.   (270 sq.in.)
   b. 35 ft. by 18 ft.   (630 sq. ft.)
   c. 75 cm by 45 cm   (3,375 cm²)
   d. 250 m by 110 m   (27,500 m²)

3. *Finding perimeters* (Lessons 138, 139).
   a. square with sides 23 in.   (92 in.)
   b. rectangle 250 ft. by 110 ft.   (720 ft.)
   c. triangle with sides 28 m, 32 m, 31 m   (91 m)

Introduction

Draw a rectangle 15 inches by 10 inches on the board. Have the students find the area. (150 sq. in.)

Now draw a parallelogram with a base of 15 inches and a height of 10 inches.

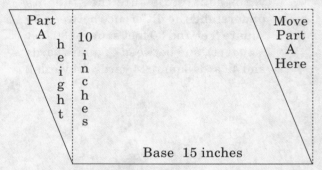

What figure would you have if you moved Part A as indicated? You would have a rectangle measuring 15 inches by 10 inches, with an area of 150 square inches. This shows that finding the area of a parallelogram is much like finding the area of a rectangle.

Teaching Guide

To find the area of a parallelogram, use the formula $a = bh$. That is, multiply the length of the base (usually the lower horizontal side) times the height (the perpendicular distance between the two bases). Usually the height of a parallelogram is shown by a dotted line.

Either draw these on the board, or have the students calculate the area using these measurements. It is important that the students have practice with measuring the base and height of parallelograms.
   a. $b = 6$ in., $h = 3$ in., $a = $ (18 sq. in.)
   b. $b = 14$ ft., $h = 11$ ft., $a = $ (154 sq. ft.)
   c. $b = 9$ yd., $h = 5$ yd., $a = $ (45 sq. yd.)
   d. $b = 4.3$ cm, $h = 3.1$ cm, $a = $ (13.33 cm²)
   e. $b = 9.9$ m, $h = 4.6$ m, $a = $ (45.54 m²)
   f. $b = 5\frac{1}{4}$ ft., $h = 3\frac{1}{2}$ ft., $a = $ ($18\frac{3}{8}$ sq. ft.)

142. Finding the Area of a Parallelogram

A **parallelogram** is like a rectangle in that it has four sides and the opposite sides are parallel. But the corners of a parallelogram are usually not right angles. This is why the figure is called a parallelogram and not a rectangle.

The area of a parallelogram is found by multiplying the length of the **base** and the **height.** The base is usually the lower horizontal side. The height is the perpendicular distance between the two bases, as shown by a dotted line below. The height is *not* found by measuring the slanted sides.

The formula for the area of a parallelogram is written as follows:

area = length of base × height, or $a = bh$

$a = bh$ area = 5 × 2 = 10 square inches

CLASS PRACTICE

Find the areas of parallelograms having these dimensions.

a. b = 8 in.
h = 5 in.
40 sq. in.

b. b = 9 ft.
h = 6 ft.
54 sq. ft.

c. b = $6\frac{3}{4}$ ft.
h = $3\frac{1}{2}$ ft.
$23\frac{5}{8}$ sq. ft.

d. b = $8\frac{1}{2}$ in.
h = $5\frac{1}{2}$ in.
$46\frac{3}{4}$ sq. in.

e. b = 15 cm
h = 6 cm
90 cm²

f. b = 24 m
h = 13 m
312 m²

g. b = 32.4 cm
h = 25.1 cm
813.24 cm²

h. b = 21 km
h = 16.8 km
352.8 km²

WRITTEN EXERCISES

A.   *Find the areas of parallelograms having these dimensions.*

1. b = 9 in
h = 4 in.
36 sq. in.

2. b = 6 in.
h = 2 in.
12 sq. in.

3. b = 7 ft.
h = 4 ft.
28 sq. ft.

4. b = 5 ft.
h = 6 ft.
30 sq.ft.

5. b = 18 in.
h = 12 in.
216 sq. in.

6. b = 12 ft.
h = 16 ft.
192 sq. ft.

7. b = $1\frac{1}{2}$ in.
h = $1\frac{3}{4}$ in.
$2\frac{5}{8}$ sq. in.

8. b = $2\frac{3}{4}$ ft.
h = $1\frac{1}{4}$ ft.
$3\frac{7}{16}$ sq.ft.

9. b = 18 cm
h = 14 cm
252 cm²

10. b = 42 cm
h = 28 cm
1,176 cm²

11. b = 12 m
h = 7 m
84 m²

12. b = 23 m
h = 14 m
322 m²

13. b = 41 m
h = 16.5 m
676.5 m²

14. b = 36 m
h = 28.5 m
1,026 m²   289

15. b = 7 yd.
h = 6 yd.
42 sq. yd.

16. b = 15 yd.
h = 11 yd.
165 sq. yd.

B.   Measure each parallelogram, and find its area in square inches.

17.

$2\frac{1}{4}$ square inches

18.

$2\frac{5}{8}$ square inches

C.   Solve these reading problems.

19. During math class, Brother Zimmerman drew a parallelogram on the board. The base was 20 inches long, the slanted sides were 17 inches long, and the height was 16 inches. What was the area of the parallelogram?   320 square inches

20. Sister Ruth drew a parallelogram on the board. The base was 16 inches long, the slanted sides were $12\frac{5}{8}$ inches long, and the height was 6 inches. What was the area of the parallelogram?   96 square inches

21. The auditorium of the Lakeside Church is a rectangle 60 feet long and 38 feet wide. What is the floor area of the auditorium?   2,280 square feet

22. The sizes of houses are often compared by figuring the square feet of living area in the house. How many square feet of living area does a single-story house contain if it measures 46 feet by 30 feet?   1,380 square feet

23. In a Cape Cod house, the second floor is smaller than the first floor. How many square feet are in a Cape Cod house if the first floor measures 44 feet by 32 feet and the second floor measures 44 feet by 17 feet?   2,156 square feet

24. Paul is preparing to paint the living room ceiling. It measures 18 feet by 14 feet. How many quarts of paint will Paul need if one quart covers 100 square feet? (Remember to round your answer up to the next quart.)   3 quarts

REVIEW EXERCISES

D.   Find the areas of squares with these dimensions. *(Lesson 141)*

4,225 sq. ft.

25. 15 in. 225 sq. in.   **26.** 28 in. 784 sq. in.   **27.** 16 ft. 256 sq. ft.   **28.** 65 ft.

E.   Find the areas of rectangles with these dimensions. *(Lesson 140)*

29. 30 in. by 18 in.   540 sq. in.   30. 90 ft. by 65 ft.   5,850 sq.ft.
31. 125 ft. by 115 ft.   14,375 sq. ft.   32. 300 ft. by 120 ft.   36,000 sq. ft.

F.   Find the perimeters of these polygons. *(Lessons 138, 139)*

33. square—15 in.   60 in.   34. square—28 in.   112 in.
35. rectangle—30 in. by 18 in.   96 in.   36. rectangle—300 ft. by 120 ft.   840 ft.
37. triangle—28 in., 15 in., 22 in. 65 in.   38. triangle—18 ft., 26 ft., 15 ft.   59 ft.

An Ounce of Prevention

1. Problems 19 and 20 also give the lengths of the slanted sides. Make it clear that the *base* and the *perpendicular height* are to be used for finding the area of a parallelogram.

2. Problems 23 and 24 are multistep problems.

LESSON 143

Objective

- To teach *finding the area of a triangle.

Review

1. Give Lesson 143 Speed Test (Finding Perimeters).

2. *Finding the areas of parallelograms* (Lesson 142).
   a. $b = 55$ in., $h = 16$ in.   (880 sq. in.)
   b. $b = 50$ in., $h = 22$ in.   (1,100 sq. in.)
   c. $b = 65$ cm, $h = 32$ cm   (2,080 cm²)
   d. $b = 90$ cm, $h = 38$ cm   (3,420 cm²)

3. *Finding the areas of rectangles* (Lesson 140).
   a. 22 in. by 18 in.   (396 sq. in.)
   b. 65 ft. by 45 ft.   (2,925 sq. ft.)
   c. 125 m by 100 m   (12,500 m²)

4. *Multiplying by 10, 100, and 1,000* (Lesson 78).
   a. 100×2.9 (290)
   b. 10×0.48 (4.8)
   c. $1,000 \times 4.65$ (4,650)
   d. $1,000 \times 0.362$ (362)

Introduction

Cut a paper to a measurement of 8 inches by 10 inches for easy calculations. After measuring the paper, ask the students to find the area of the rectangle. (80 sq. in.) Then cut the paper diagonally to make two right triangles. Do the students know what the area of each triangle is? If they have no idea, point out that the area of the rectangle was 80 square inches and that you cut the paper in half. So the area of each triangle is 40 square inches.

Now arrange the pieces in the form of a parallelogram, with the two 8-inch edges together and a 10-inch side as the base. Tell the students that any triangle is half of a parallelogram with the same base and height. (A rectangle is also a parallelogram.) This can be further demonstrated by the diagrams in the text and by other triangles of various shapes.

Teaching Guide

To find the area of a triangle, use the formula $a = \frac{1}{2}bh$. That is, multiply $\frac{1}{2}$ times the length of the base times the height.

The factors in this formula can be grouped in any way: $(\frac{1}{2} \times b) \times h$, $(\frac{1}{2} \times h) \times b$, or $(b \times h) \times \frac{1}{2}$. Encourage students to look for combinations that let them find the areas mentally.

   a. $b = 9$ in., $h = 4$ in., $a = $ (18 sq. in.)
   b. $b = 10$ ft., $h = 10$ ft., $a = $ (50 sq. ft.)
   c. $b = 9$ yd., $h = 6$ yd., $a = $ (27 sq. yd.)
   d. $b = 11$ in., $h = 11$ in., $a = $ (60.5 sq. in.)
   e. $b = 15$ ft., $h = 14$ ft., $a = $ (105 sq. ft.)
   f. $b = 5\frac{1}{2}$ in., $h = 3\frac{1}{2}$ in., $a = $ ($9\frac{5}{8}$ sq. in.)
   g. $b = 22$ cm, $h = 20$ cm, $a = $ (220 cm²)
   h. $b = 35$ cm, $h = 30$ cm, $a = $ (525 cm²)
   i. $b = 29$ m, $h = 24$ m, $a = $ (348 cm²)

143. Finding the Area of a Triangle

Finding the area of a triangle is much like finding the area of a parallelogram with the same base and height. Notice the two equal triangles in each parallelogram below. (One is a rectangle.) Each triangle is half as large as a parallelogram with the same base and height.

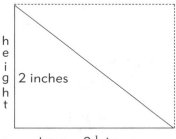

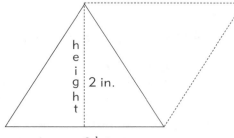

To find the area of a triangle, multiply $\frac{1}{2}$ times the length of the base (b) times the height (h). The formula is given below, and it is used to show that the area of both triangles above is $2\frac{1}{2}$ square inches.

area = $\frac{1}{2}$ × length of base × height, or $a = \frac{1}{2} bh$

$$\text{area} = \frac{1}{2} \times 2\frac{1}{2} \times 2 = 2\frac{1}{2} \text{ sq. in.}$$

CLASS PRACTICE

Find the area of triangles with the dimensions given.

a. $b = 14$ in.
$h = 6$ in.
   42 sq. in.

b. $b = 10$ ft.
$h = 9$ ft.
   45 sq. ft.

c. $b = 16$ ft.
$h = 7$ ft.
   56 sq. ft.

d. $b = 13$ in.
$h = 6$ in.
   39 sq. in.

e. $b = 22$ cm
$h = 20$ cm
   220 cm²

f. $b = 12$ m
$h = 11$ m
   66 m²

g. $b = 15$ cm
$h = 14$ cm
   105 cm²

h. $b = 19$ m
$h = 14$ m
   133 m²

WRITTEN EXERCISES

A. *Find the area of triangles with the dimensions given.*

1. $b = 8$ in.
$h = 3$ in.
   12 sq. in.

2. $b = 2$ in.
$h = 2$ in.
   2 sq. in.

3. $b = 6$ ft.
$h = 3$ ft.
   9 sq. ft.

4. $b = 5$ ft.
$h = 4$ ft.
   10 sq. ft.

5. $b = 8$ in.
$h = 4$ in.
   16 sq. in.

6. $b = 5$ ft.
$h = 2$ ft.
   5 sq. ft.

7. $b = 4$ in.
$h = 7$ in.
   14 sq. in.

8. $b = 3$ ft.
$h = 4$ ft.
   6 sq. ft.

9. $b = 17$ cm
$h = 6$ cm
   51 cm²

10. $b = 12$ cm
$h = 8$ cm
   48 cm²

11. $b = 11$ m
$h = 6$ m
   33 m²

12. $b = 40$ m
$h = 20$ m
   400 m²

13. $b = 16$ m
$h = 15$ m
   120 m²

14. $b = 25$ m
$h = 26$ m
   325 m²

15. $b = 8$ yd.
$h = 7$ yd.
   28 sq. yd.

16. $b = 16$ yd.
$h = 12$ yd.
   96 sq. yd.

293

B.   *Measure in inches, and find the areas of these triangles.*

17.

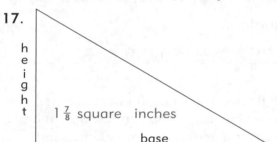

18.

C.   *Solve these reading problems.*

19. The Myers have a small triangular field in a corner where two roads meet. What is the area of the field? (Use the diagram on the right.) 160,000 square feet

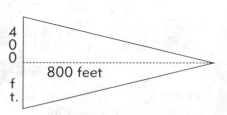

20. Find the area of a triangular garden if the base of the triangle measures 60 feet and its height measures 80 feet.   2,400 square feet

21. Mary cut a piece of $8\frac{1}{2}$-by-11-inch construction paper into two equal triangles. What is the area of each triangle? $46\frac{3}{4}$ square inches

22. Erma is helping to make a quilt for a mission in Paraguay. One piece of the quilt pattern is a triangle with a base of $6\frac{1}{2}$ inches and a height of $4\frac{1}{4}$ inches. What is the area of the pattern? $13\frac{13}{16}$ square inches

23. The Meadville Christian Day School is built on a rectangular plot of land 400 feet long and 300 feet wide. What is the area of the land?   120,000 square feet

24. The softball diamond at the Meadville School is a 60-foot square. What is the area of the diamond?   3,600 square feet

REVIEW EXERCISES

D.   *Find the areas of parallelograms with these dimensions.* (Lesson 142)

25. $b = 8$ in.	26. $b = 15$ in.	27. $b = 40$ cm	28. $b = 70$ cm
$h = 4$ in.	$h = 6$ in.	$h = 26$ cm	$h = 45$ cm
32 sq. in.	90 sq. in.	1,040 cm²	3,150 cm²

E.   *Find the areas of rectangles with these dimensions.* (Lesson 140)

29. 16 inches by 25 inches   400 sq. in.   30. 40 feet by 30 feet   1,200 sq. ft.
31. 50 feet by 45 feet   2,250 sq. ft.   32. 200 feet by 175 feet   35,000 sq. ft.

F.   *Find each answer mentally by moving the decimal point.* (Lesson 78)

33. 4.5×100 34. 0.67×10 35. $8.64 \times 1,000$ 36. $0.823 \times 1,000$
                450   6.7   8,640   823

LESSON 144

Objectives

- To review reading line graphs.
- To teach *drawing line graphs.

Review

1. *Finding areas* (Lessons 140–143).
   a. Triangles
      $b = 7$ in., $h = 4$ in.   (14 sq. in.)
      $b = 12$ ft., $h = 8$ ft.   (48 sq. ft.)
   b. Parallelograms
      $b = 7$ cm, $h = 4$ cm   (28 cm²)
      $b = 15$ m, $h = 8$ m   (120 m²)
   c. Squares
      $s = 7$ in.   (49 sq. in.)
      $s = 15$ ft.   (225 sq. ft.)
   d. Rectangles
      $l = 8$ cm, $w = 7$ cm   (56 cm²)
      $l = 12$ m, $w = 9$ m   (108 m²)

2. *Multiplying decimals* (Lesson 79).

   a.   5.3   b.   11.5
      × 2.8   × 4.3
      (14.84)   (49.45)

   c.   22.5   d.   2.12
      × 0.011   × 0.03
      (0.2475)   (0.0636)

Introduction

Have the students compare the first graph in this lesson with Bar Graph 2 in Lesson 109. How is the subject matter different?

The bar graph in Lesson 109 shows the population of six different countries at the same time. The line graph in this lesson shows the population of the same state at different times. Although a bar graph could also have been used in this lesson, a line graph would not have been suitable in Lesson 109. A line graph usually shows how a given value changes over a period of time.

Teaching Guide

1. Use the first line graph in the lesson to give practice with reading line graphs. Explain how to read the graph by finding the population of Pennsylvania in 1800. Then have the students find the population figures given for the remainder of the graph.

2. Draw a line graph based on the following facts, using the steps listed below.

Population of Ontario, Canada, 1851–1991 (rounded)

1851 1,000,000
1871 1,500,000
1891 2,000,000
1911 2,500,000
1931 3,500,000
1951 4,500,000
1971 7,500,000
1991 9,500,000

(1) Number the vertical scale as directed, putting the numbers on the correct lines. The numbers must increase at the same rate, such as by tens or by hundreds. Number to one line higher

144. Working With Graphs: The Line Graph

READING LINE GRAPHS

Line graphs are used to show how values change with time. A rising line shows an increase in value, and a falling line shows a decrease in value.

Line graphs are read much like bar graphs. The scale along the left edge of the graph shows the value of the line at any point on the graph. Like bar graphs, line graphs usually show approximate values.

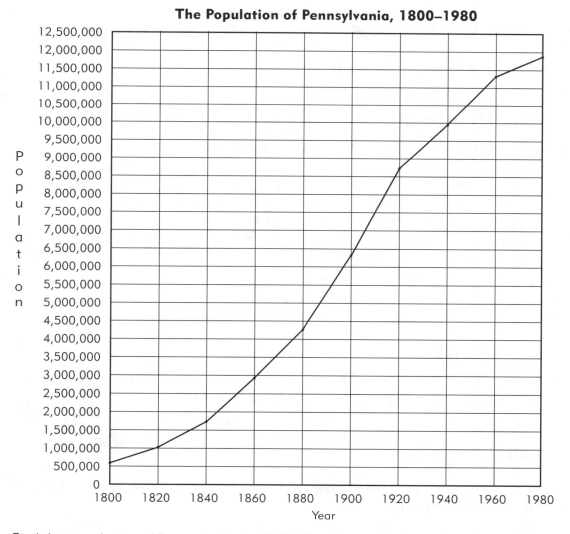

The Population of Pennsylvania, 1800–1980

Find the population of Pennsylvania in 1980. The line graph shows that the population of Pennsylvania in 1980 was about 11,900,000.

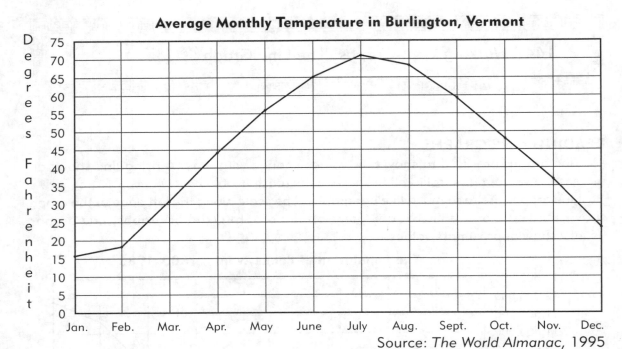

Average Monthly Temperature in Burlington, Vermont

Source: *The World Almanac*, 1995

DRAWING LINE GRAPHS

To draw a line graph, use the following steps.

1. Number the vertical scale as directed, putting the numbers beside the correct lines. The numbers must increase at the same rate. For example, they must not increase by tens and then suddenly increase by hundreds. Number to one line higher than what is needed for the greatest value to be shown.

2. Space the labels for each point across the bottom of the graph, allowing an equal distance between the labels.

3. Use a dot or a small x to mark the location of each value that is to be shown. Then use a straightedge to connect all the points marked on the graph.

5. Label the vertical scale, and write a good title for the graph.

CLASS PRACTICE

Estimate the population of Pennsylvania in the following years. Refer to the graph "The Population of Pennsylvania."

a. 1820	b. 1860	c. 1900	d. 1940	e. 1960	f. 1980
1,000,000	2,900,000	6,300,000	9,900,000	11,300,000	11,900,000

WRITTEN EXERCISES

A. *Give the average monthly temperature in Burlington, Vermont, for each month of the year.*

1. January	16°	2. February	18°	3. March	31°	4. April	44°
5. May	56°	6. June	65°	7. July	71°	8. August	68°
9. September	59°	10. October	48°	11. November	37°	12. December	23°

than what is needed for the highest point of the line.

The population of Ontario begins at 1,000,000 and increases to nearly 10,000,000, and the data is rounded to the nearest 500,000. So the vertical scale should be numbered by 500,000's to 10,000,000.

Note: The vertical scale for a bar graph must begin at zero so that the bars give a true impression of the relative values that they represent. This is not so important for a line graph, which merely shows changes over a period of time.

(2) Space the labels for each point across the bottom of the graph, allowing an equal distance between the labels. (To calculate the distance between each label, divide the width of the graph by the number of labels needed.)

(3) Use a dot or a small x to mark the location of each value that is to be shown. Then use a straightedge to connect all the points marked on the graph.

(4) Label the vertical scale, and write a good title for the graph. Note that the title of the graph below is similar to that of the first graph in the text.

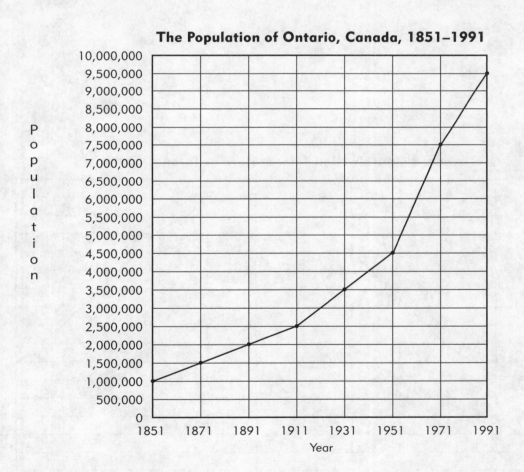

The Population of Ontario, Canada, 1851–1991

299

25.

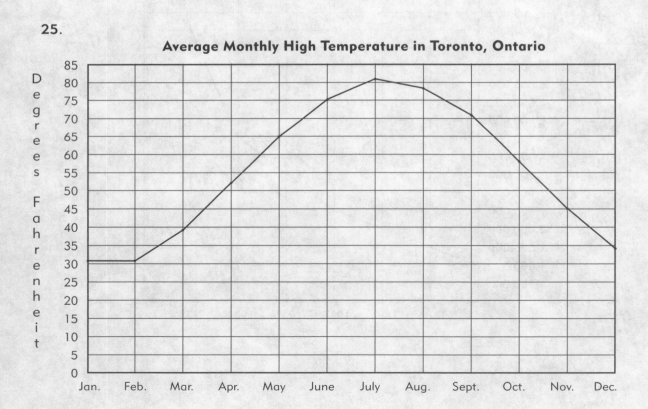

Average Monthly High Temperature in Toronto, Ontario

Average Monthly Precipitation in St. Louis, Missouri

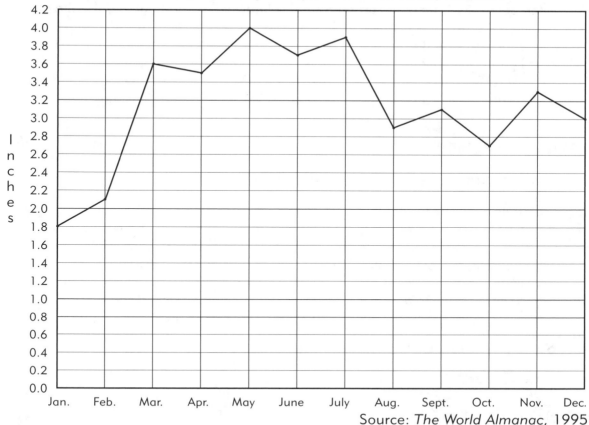

Source: *The World Almanac*, 1995

B. **What is the average precipitation in St. Louis in these months?**

13. January 1.8 in. **14.** February 2.1 in. **15.** March   3.6 in. **16.** April   3.5 in.
17. May   4.0 in. **18.** June   3.7 in. **19.** July   3.9 in. **20.** August 2.9 in.
21. September   **22.** October   **23.** November   **24.** December
      3.1 in.   2.7 in.   3.3 in.   3.0 in.

C. **Prepare line graphs according to the instructions.**

25. The average monthly high temperatures in the city of Toronto, Ontario are listed
below. Prepare a line graph from this information. For a guide, use the graph "Average
Monthly Temperature in Burlington, Vermont."   (Sample graph on facing page)

January	31	May	65	September	71
February	31	June	75	October	58
March	39	July	81	November	45
April	52	August	78	December	34

26. The average monthly precipitation in the cities of Dallas and Fort Worth, Texas, are listed below. Prepare a line graph from this information. For a guide, use the graph "Average Monthly Precipitation in St. Louis, Missouri." (Sample graph on facing page)

January	1.8 in.	May	4.9 in.	September	3.4 in.
February	2.2 in.	June	3.0 in.	October	3.5 in.
March	2.8 in.	July	2.3 in.	November	2.3 in.
April	3.5 in.	August	2.2 in.	December	1.8 in.

REVIEW EXERCISES

D.   Find the area of each polygon. (Lessons 140–143)

27. rectangle
4 ft. by 3 ft.
  12 sq. ft.

28. rectangle
60 ft. by 40 ft.
  2,400 sq. ft.

29. square
28 in.
  784 sq. in.

30. square
48 ft.
  2,304 sq. ft.

31. parallelogram
$b = 16$ in.
$h = 12$ in.
  192 sq. in.

32. parallelogram
$b = 4$ ft.
$h = 3$ ft.
  12 sq. ft.

33. triangle
$b = 18$ in.
$h = 14$ in.
  126 sq. in.

34. triangle
$b = 86$ ft.
$h = 40$ ft.
  1,720 sq. ft.

E.   Solve these multiplication problems. (Lesson 79)

35.   4.6
  × 2.5
  11.50

36. 18.1
  × 7.2
  130.32

37. 16.2
  × 0.015
  0.2430

38. 1.18
  × 0.03
  0.0354

39. 0.45
  × 0.08
  0.0360

40. 0.89
  × 0.06
  0.0534

26.

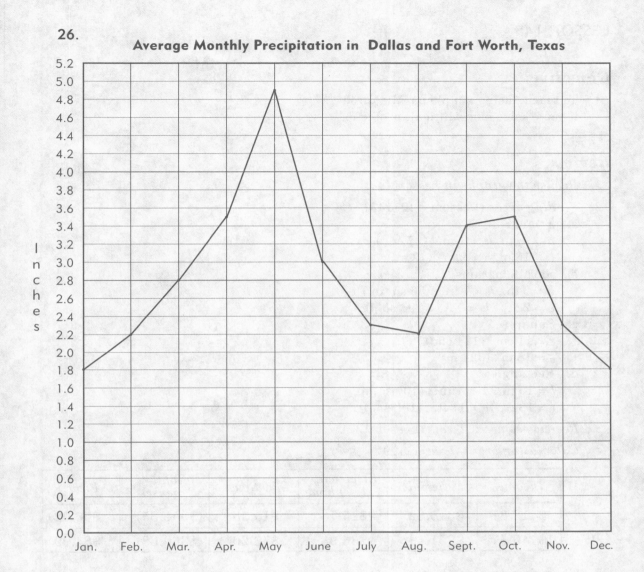

Average Monthly Precipitation in Dallas and Fort Worth, Texas

LESSON 145

Objective

- To teach *using simple parallel problems to solve more difficult problems.

Review

1. *Review the graphs in Lesson 144.*

2. *Finding areas* (Lessons 140–143).
   a. Triangles
      $b = 9$ cm, $h = 6$ cm   (27 cm²)
      $b = 16$ m, $h = 9$ m   (72 m²)
   b. Parallelograms
      $b = 8$ in., $h = 7$ in.   (56 sq. in.)
      $b = 22$ ft., $h = 9$ ft.   (198 sq. ft.)
   c. Squares
      $s = 11$ cm   (121 cm²)
      $s = 18$ m   (324 m²)
   d. Rectangles
      $l = 15$ in., $w = 7$ in.   (105 sq. in.)
      $l = 18$ ft., $w = 11$ ft.   (198 sq. ft.)

3. *Review geometric terms* (Lesson 137).

4. *Calculating profit* (Lesson 129).

	Income	Materials	Electricity & Telephone	Postage	Total Expenses	Profit
a.	$412.87	$315.52	$25.78	$15.55	($356.85)	($56.02)
b.	$445.67	$251.49	$36.93	$72.26	($360.68)	($84.99)

5. *Changing percents to decimals and fractions* (Lesson 115).
   a. 35% = (0.35 = 7/20)
   b. 58% = (0.58 = 29/50)

6. *Multiplying decimals* (Lesson 79).

   a.   1.3
      × 0.13
     (0.169)

   b.   1.12
      × 0.05
     (0.0560)

   c.   1.48
     × 0.011
     (0.01628)

   d.   0.25
      × 0.12
     (0.0300)

145. Reading Problems: Using Parallel Problems

Sometimes a reading problem seems difficult because it contains fractions, decimals, or large numbers. One help for understanding such a problem is to replace the difficult numbers with simple whole numbers. Decide how the problem with the simple numbers should be solved, and then put the original numbers back into the problem. Solve the original problem by using the same method that you used for the problem with simpler numbers.

> David and Walter took a walk through the woods to school. They walked $2\frac{1}{3}$ miles in $\frac{2}{3}$ hour. What was their average rate of speed?
>
> **Parallel Problem**
>
> David and Walter took a walk through the woods one Saturday afternoon. They walked 4 miles in 2 hours. What was their average rate of speed?

In the example above, the parallel problem is very easy to solve. Divide the distance (4 miles) by the time (2 hours) to obtain an average rate of 2 miles per hour. The parallel problem is the same kind as the original except that the values are whole numbers instead of fractions.

To find the average rate of speed in the original problem, divide the distance ($2\frac{1}{3}$ miles) by the time ($\frac{2}{3}$ hour) as shown below. The answer is $3\frac{1}{2}$ miles per hour.

$$2\frac{1}{3} \div \frac{2}{3} = \frac{7}{3} \div \frac{2}{3} = \frac{7}{\overset{1}{\cancel{3}}} \times \frac{\overset{1}{\cancel{3}}}{2} = \frac{7}{2} = 3\frac{1}{2} \text{ miles per hour}$$

CLASS PRACTICE

These problems are in pairs. Solve problem a, and then use the same method to solve problem b. Do the same with problems c and d.

a. On a family trip, the Zimmermans crossed a 2-mile-long bridge. If the toll was $4.00, what was the cost per mile of the bridge? $2.00

b. Later the Zimmermans traveled 176 miles on a turnpike. If their toll was $7.04, what was the cost per mile? $0.04

c. The Allen family drove 180 miles to visit a church in a neighboring state. If their average speed was 45 m.p.h., how long did it take?   4 hours

d. Gregorio lived $1\frac{3}{4}$ miles from the market. If he walked to the market at a rate of $2\frac{5}{8}$ miles per hour, how long did it take? $\frac{2}{3}$ hour

WRITTEN EXERCISES

A.   *These exercises are pairs of parallel problems. Problems 1 and 2 are the same kind, but problem 2 has more difficult numbers. Solve the first problem in each pair, and then use the same method to solve the second problem.*

1. Father helped to distribute the *Star of Hope* one Sunday afternoon. He walked for 2 hours at an average rate of 2 miles per hour. How many miles did he walk?   4 miles

2. Brother Sweigart traveled by jet to visit a distant church. The jet flew at an average rate of 425 miles per hour, and the flight lasted $5\frac{1}{2}$ hours. How far did Brother Sweigart fly?   2,337.5 miles

3. The Stauffers traveled 150 miles to visit their cousins. They traveled at an average rate of 50 miles per hour. How long did it take to drive the 150 miles?   3 hours

4. Marvin and Harvey rode their bicycles to school one morning. They covered the $4\frac{1}{5}$ miles at an average speed of $12\frac{3}{5}$ miles per hour. How long did it take them to ride to school? $\frac{1}{3}$ hour *or* 20 minutes

5. Marvin and Harvey rode their bicycles at an average speed of $12\frac{1}{2}$ miles per hour. The Kauffmans drove their van to school at an average speed that was 3 times as fast. What was the average speed that the Kauffmans drove? $37\frac{1}{2}$ miles per hour

6. Marvin and Harvey rode their bicycles at an average speed of $12\frac{1}{2}$ miles per hour. A few years ago they could ride only $\frac{2}{3}$ as fast as they can now. What was their average speed several years ago? $8\frac{1}{3}$ miles per hour

7. The Plainview Church pays $2.00 per copy to buy New Testaments for distribution. How many Testaments can they buy for $100?   50 Testaments

8. If the price of the *Star of Hope* is $0.18 per copy, how many copies can the Plainview church buy for $126.00?   700 copies

9. Five years ago, 48 pupils attended the Stony Run Mennonite School. This year, 68 pupils attend the school. How many more pupils attend the school now than did five years ago?   20 pupils

Introduction

Read the first problem below to the students. Do they know how to solve it? Perhaps a few will, but most of them will find the problem quite difficult.

a. The Long Valley Christian School is in session 6 1/2 hours each school day. The sixth grade is having class for 2 3/5 hours each day. Write a fraction showing what part of the school day the sixth grade is in class.

Now read exactly the same problem with different numbers.

b. The Long Valley Christian School is in session 6 hours each school day. The sixth grade is having class for 3 hours each day. Write a fraction showing what part of the school day the sixth grade is in class.

Are the students able to solve the second problem? Tell the class that the only difference is that the first problem has mixed numbers and the second problem has whole numbers. Show them the solution as follows:

$$\frac{\text{number of hours in class}}{\text{number of hours in school}} \quad \frac{3}{6} = \frac{1}{2}$$

Can they solve the first problem now? A seemingly difficult problem is often easy to understand if fractions or decimals are replaced by simple whole numbers.

$$\frac{2\frac{3}{5}}{6\frac{1}{2}} = 2\frac{3}{5} \div 6\frac{1}{2} = \frac{2}{5}$$

Teaching Guide

Many difficult reading problems can be simplified by replacing large numbers, fractions, or decimals with simple whole numbers. Discuss the sample problem in the text and the parallel problem, and then discuss the reading problems below. Work through the first and easier one and then the second and more difficult one. The problems in each pair are kept as nearly parallel as possible to help the students see the relationship between them.

a. This year Mother canned twice as many peaches as last year. If she canned 66 quarts last year, how many quarts did she can this year?
$2 \times 66 = 132$ quarts

b. This year Mother canned 2/3 as many peaches as last year. If she canned 66 quarts last year, how many quarts did she can this year?
$2/3 \times 66 = 44$ quarts

c. Linda and Mabel picked 9 rows of green beans in 3 hours. How many rows of beans did they pick each hour?
$9 \div 3 = 3$ rows

d. Linda and Mabel picked 8 3/4 rows of green beans in 3 1/2 hours. How many rows of beans did they pick each hour?
$8 3/4 \div 3 1/2 = 2 1/2$ rows

In the written exercises, the reading problems are arranged in pairs of one problem that is simpler (odd numbers) and one that is more difficult (even numbers). Solving the first problem in each pair should be a help in solving the second problem. Because of this arrangement, the problems do not follow the usual pattern in which pairs of odd- and even-numbered problems are similar. Instead, both problems in each pair must be assigned.

Further Study

Using parallel problems is not just a help for children learning to solve reading problems; it is a handy tool for adults and upper-grade students as well. For example, a difficult algebraic formula becomes much easier to comprehend when the literal numbers are replaced by single-digit numbers. Using parallel problems as the students do in this lesson is a first step in preparing them to solve those complex problems.

13.

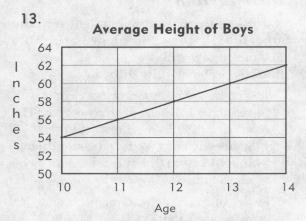

Average Height of Boys

Source: *Physicians Handbook*, 1983

14.

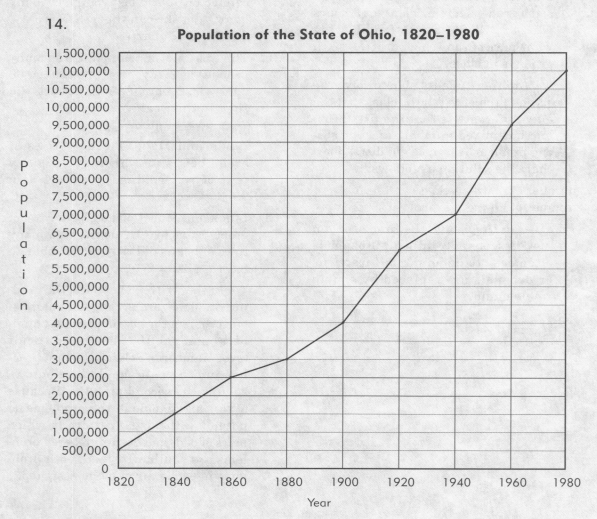

Population of the State of Ohio, 1820–1980

Source: *U.S. Census*

10. In 1850, the population of the world was 1,175,000,000. In 1990, its population was 5,333,000,000. How much did the population of the world increase during that time?   4,158,000,000 people

11. The Millers traveled on a toll road when they visited their uncle in another state. The odometer reading was 25,000.0 miles when they entered the toll road and 25,150.0 miles when they left the toll road. The toll was $0.02 per mile. How much did it cost to travel on the toll road? $3.00

12. The odometer of the Martins' car showed 54,876.7 miles when they entered a toll road and 54,925.1 miles when they left it. If the toll is $0.027 per mile, how much did they need to pay? $1.31

REVIEW EXERCISES

(Sample graphs on facing page)

B. *Do the following exercises on line graphs. (Lesson 144)*

13. Following are the average heights of boys from the ages of ten to fourteen. Draw a line graph to show this information.

Age	Average Height
10	54 inches
11	56 inches
12	58 inches
13	60 inches
14	62 inches

Source: *Physicians Handbook*, 1983

14. Make a line graph based on this table.

Population of the State of Ohio (rounded)

1820	500,000
1840	1,500,000
1860	2,500,000
1880	3,000,000
1900	4,000,000
1920	6,000,000
1940	7,000,000
1960	9,500,000
1980	11,000,000

Source: *U.S. Census*

C. *Find the area of each polygon. (Lessons 140–143)*

15. rectangle
    8 ft. by 5 ft.
        40 sq. ft.

16. rectangle
    80 ft. by 55 ft.
        4,400 sq. ft.

17. square
    45 inches
        2,025 sq. in.

18. square
    95 feet
        9,025 sq. ft.

19. parallelogram
    $b = 24$ in.
    $h = 16$ in.
        384 sq. in.

20. parallelogram
    $b = 38$ ft.
    $h = 25$ ft.
        950 sq. ft.

21. triangle
    $b = 22$ in.
    $h = 16$ in.
        176 sq. in.

22. triangle
    $b = 65$ ft.
    $h = 50$ ft.
        1,625 sq. ft.

D. Draw the following items. Label them with letters when they are given.
(Lesson 137)

23. line segment AB   A _____ B

24. right angle CDE

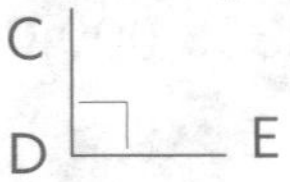

25. square

26. parallel lines FG and HI

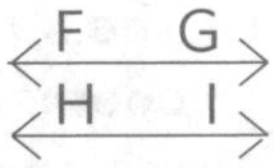

E. Find the total expenses and the profit in each line below. *(Lesson 129)*

	Income	Materials	Electricity & Telephone	Postage	Total Expenses	Profit
27.	$375.63	$225.31	$35.28	$68.93	$329.52	$46.11
28.	$415.67	$251.49	$36.93	$72.26	$360.68	$54.99

F. Copy and complete the following charts. Write the fractions in lowest terms. *(Lesson 115)*

	Percent	Decimal	Fraction
29.	44%	0.44	$\frac{11}{25}$
30.	39%	0.39	$\frac{39}{100}$

G. Solve these multiplication problems. *(Lesson 79)*

31.
```
   1.6
 × 0.1
  0.16
```

32.
```
   1.01
 × 0.02
 0.0202
```

33.
```
   0.221
 × 0.05
 0.01105
```

34.
```
   0.018
 × 0.05
 0.00090
```

LESSON 146

Objective

- To review the material taught in Chapter 11.

Teaching Guide

This review covers Lessons 137–145. Be sure to assign all the reading problems (numbers 39–44) because of the relationship between the odd- and even-numbered problems.

146. Chapter 11 Review

A.   Name each figure below. *(Lesson 137)*

1.

   square

2.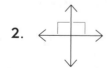

   intersecting perpendicular lines

3. [rectangle figure]

   rectangle

4. A •

   point A

5. [parallelogram figure]

   parallelogram

6. B____C

   line segment BC

7. [hexagon figure]

   hexagon

8. D____E→

   ray DE

9.

   right angle LMN

10. O←——→P
    Q←——→R

    parallel lines OP and QR

11. [triangle figure]

    triangle

12. ←G____H→

    line GH

B.   Find the perimeters of polygons with the dimensions given. *(Lessons 138, 139)*

13. square
    s = 12 in.
              48 in.

14. square
    s = 75 ft.
              300 ft.

15. rectangle
    l = 14 in.
    w = 8 in.
              44 in.

16. rectangle
    l = 225 ft.
    w = 145 ft.
              740 ft.

17. triangle
    a = 8 in.
    b = 10 in.
    c = 12 in.
              30 in.

18. triangle
    a = 20 in.
    b = 14 in.
    c = 18 in.
              52 in.

19. pentagon
    each side
    = 18 in.
              90 in.

20. octagon
    each side
    = 20 in.
              160 in.

C.   Find the areas of these polygons. *(Lessons 140–143)*

21. square
    s = 8 in.
              64 sq. in.

22. square
    s = 15 in.
              225 sq. in.

23. square
    s = 25 ft.
              625 sq. ft.

24. square
    s = 150 ft.
              22,500 sq. ft.

25. rectangle
    l = 9 in.
    w = 6 in.
              54 sq. in.

26. rectangle
    l = 22 in.
    w = 15 in.
              330 sq. in.

27. rectangle
    l = 35 ft.
    w = 25 ft.
              875 sq. ft.

28. rectangle
    l = 450 ft.
    w = 225 ft.
              101,250 sq. ft.

29. parallelogram
    b = 12 in.
    h = 8 in.
              96 sq. in.

30. parallelogram
    b = 45 in.
    h = 24 in.
              1,080 sq. in.

31. parallelogram
    b = 60 ft.
    h = 45 ft.
              2,700 sq. ft.

32. parallelogram
    b = 325 ft.
    h = 250 ft.
              81,250 sq. ft.

33. triangle
    b = 9 in.
    h = 8 in.
              36 sq. in.

34. triangle
    b = 35 in.
    h = 20 in.
              350 sq. in.

35. triangle
    b = 80 ft.
    h = 60 ft.
              2,400 sq. ft.

36. triangle
    b = 200 ft.
    h = 150 ft.
              15,000 sq. ft.

(Sample graphs on facing page)

D.   *Draw line graphs to show the following information.* *(Lesson 144)*

37. This table shows the average monthly temperature in degrees Fahrenheit in Dallas, Texas.

January	43°	May	73°	September	77°
February	48°	June	81°	October	67°
March	57°	July	85°	November	56°
April	66°	August	85°	December	47°

38. The population figures for Illinois from 1850 to 1990 are listed below. (All figures are rounded to the nearest 500,000.)

1850	1,000,000	1930	7,500,000
1870	2,500,000	1950	8,500,000
1890	4,000,000	1970	11,000,000
1910	5,500,000	1990	11,500,000

E.   *The following exercises are pairs of parallel problems. Problems 39 and 40 are the same kind, but problem 40 has more difficult numbers. Solve the first problem in each pair, and then use the same method to solve the second problem.* *(Lesson 145)*

39. The area of a rectangle is 6 square inches. The length of the rectangle is 3 inches. What is the width?
                                                                                  2 inches

40. The area of a rectangle is $15\frac{3}{4}$ square inches. The length of the rectangle is $4\frac{1}{2}$ inches. What is the width?
                                                                                  $3\frac{1}{2}$ inches

3 inches	
6 square inches	(?) inches

$4\frac{1}{2}$ inches	
$15\frac{3}{4}$ square inches	(?) inches

41. Mother bought several loaves of bread for $1.00 each and a carton of ice cream for $2.00. She gave the cashier $10 and received $5.00 in change. How many loaves of bread did Mother buy?
                                                                                  3 loaves

42. Mother bought several loaves of bread for $0.89 each and a box of cereal for $3.35. She gave the cashier a 10-dollar bill and received $3.09 in change. How many loaves of bread did Mother buy?
                                                                                  4 loaves

43. How many bags of feed can Father buy for $50 if the price of the feed is $10 per bag?
                                                                                  5 bags

44. How many rolls of transparent tape can Father buy for $24.84 if the cost is $0.69 per roll?
                                                                                  36 rolls

147. Chapter 11 Test

LESSON 147

Objective

- To test the students' mastery of the concepts in Chapter 11.

Teaching Guide

1. Correct Lesson 146.
2. Review any areas of special difficulty.
3. Administer the test.

37.

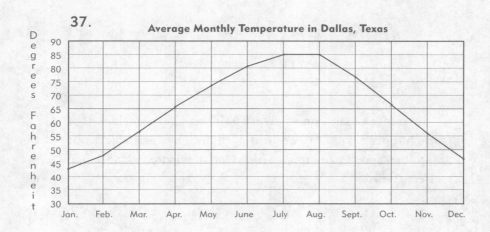

38.

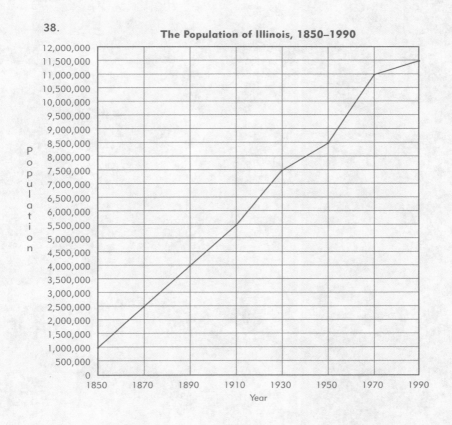

Intricate design and perfect balance characterize all of God's handiwork. Man's accurate prediction of eclipses is but an application of principles which God in wisdom established at Creation.

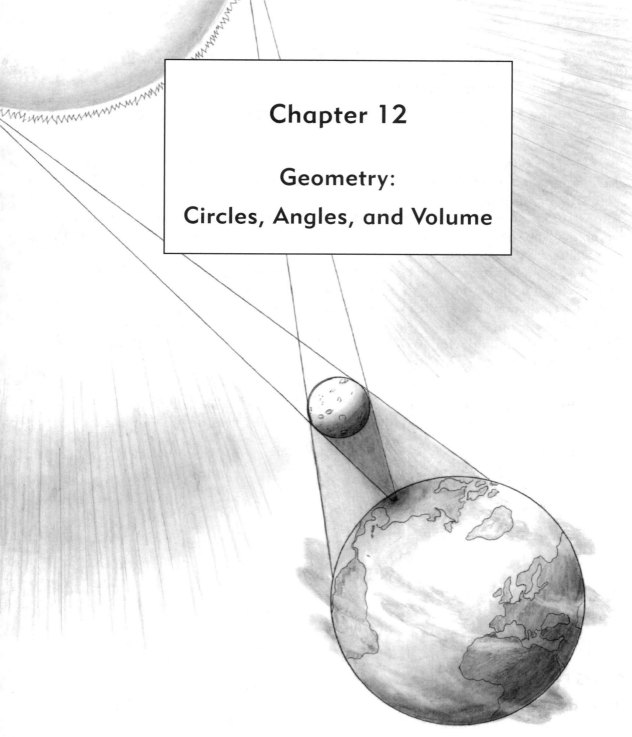

Chapter 12

Geometry:
Circles, Angles, and Volume

Wisdom crieth . . .

"I was set up from everlasting, from the beginning, or ever the earth was. . . . When he prepared the heavens, I was there: when he set a compass upon the face of the depth."

(Proverbs 8:23, 27)

148. Working With Circles

A **circle** is different from a polygon in that it does not have any straight sides. It is also different in that every point of a circle is the same distance from the center. A circle is drawn with a compass.

Any straight line drawn from the center of a circle to its edge is called a **radius.** In Example A, line segment BD is a radius. All radii (rā′ dē · ī) in a circle are equal in length. A circle has an unlimited number of radii.

Any straight line drawn from one edge of the circle through its center to the opposite edge is called a **diameter.** In Example A, line segment AC is a diameter. (B marks the center.) A circle has an unlimited number of diameters.

The diameter of a circle is twice as long as the radius. To find the diameter if the radius is known, multiply the radius by 2. To find the radius if the diameter is known, divide the diameter by 2. The formula is as follows:

diameter = 2 × radius, or $d = 2r$

Example B is a **semicircle,** or half of a circle. The broken line (FG) is its diameter.

An **arc** is any part of the curve of a circle. Example B shows an arc that is labeled E.

Example A   **Example B**

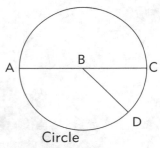   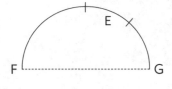

Circle   Semicircle
Radius = 6 in.   Diameter = 12 in.
Diameter = 2 × 6 in. = 12 in.   Radius = 12 in. ÷ 2 = 6 in.

CLASS PRACTICE

Write the missing numbers.

	Radius	Diameter			Radius	Diameter
a.	5 in.	10 in.		b.	9 ft.	18 ft.
c.	13 cm	26 cm		d.	25 ft.	50 ft.
e.	16 m	32 m		f.	$15\frac{1}{2}$ cm	31 cm
g.	23 in.	46 in.		h.	$13\frac{1}{4}$ ft.	$26\frac{1}{2}$ ft.

LESSON 148

Objectives

- To review the terms *radius* and *diameter*.
- To introduce the *terms *semicircle* and *arc*.
- To teach *finding the diameter when the radius is known.
- To teach *finding the radius when the diameter is known.

Review

1. Give Lesson 148 Speed Test (Finding Areas).

2. *Finding interest for months* (Lesson 132). Also review finding the new balance if the interest is added to the principal.
   a. $400 at 6% interest for 6 months
      $i = (\$12.00)$ $p = (\$412.00)$
   b. $700 at 9% interest for 4 months
      $i = (\$21.00)$ $p = (\$721.00)$
   c. $650 at 5% interest for 8 months
      $i = (\$21.67)$ $p = (\$671.67)$
   d. $1,000 at 7% interest for 7 months
      $i = (\$40.83)$ $p = (\$1,040.83)$

3. *Finding the areas of triangles* (Lesson 143).
   a. $b = 8$ in.
      $h = 4$ in.
      $a = (16$ sq. in.$)$
   b. $b = 19$ in.
      $h = 16$ in.
      $a = (152$ sq. in.$)$
   c. $b = 50$ ft.
      $h = 40$ ft.
      $a = (1,000$ sq. ft.$)$
   d. $b = 56$ ft.
      $h = 34$ ft.
      $a = (952$ sq. ft.$)$

4. *Mental multiplication.*
   By multiples of 10 (Lesson 19).
      a. $60 \times 12 = 6 \times 12 \times 10 = (720)$
      b. $40 \times 11 = 4 \times 11 \times 10 = (440)$
   By combining factors to obtain multiples of 10 (Lesson 19).
      c. $4 \times 9 \times 5 = (4 \times 5) \times 9 = (180)$
      d. $5 \times 3 \times 6 = (5 \times 6) \times 3 = (90)$
   By 50 and by 25 (Lesson 20).
      e. $50 \times 12 = 100 \times 6 = (600)$
      f. $50 \times 28 = 100 \times 14 = (1,400)$
      g. $25 \times 8 = 100 \times 2 = (200)$
      h. $25 \times 36 = 100 \times 9 = (900)$

Introduction

Use a compass to draw a circle on the board. How is a circle different from a polygon?

a. A polygon has three or more straight sides, but a circle has none.

b. The entire edge of a circle is the same distance from the center. That is not true of any polygon, even a square.

Teaching Guide

1. Teach the terms relating to circles. As you discuss the terms, illustrate them on the circle that you drew on the board.
   a. *Radius.* Draw radius AB on the board.
   b. *Diameter.* Draw diameter CD on the board.
   c. *Semicircle.* Shade one-half of the circle.
   d. *Arc.* Draw several arcs separately from the circle on the board. A semicircle is half of a full circle. An arc is any part of the outside curve of a circle.

2. Teach how to find the diameter when the radius is known, and the radius when the diameter is known.

The diameter is two times the radius. To find the diameter when the radius is known, multiply the radius by 2.
   a.   radius = 4 in., diameter = (8 in.)
   b.   radius = 7 in., diameter = (14 in.)
   c.   radius = $5\frac{1}{2}$ ft., diameter = (11 ft.)
   d.   radius = 4.3 ft., diameter = (8.6 ft.)

The radius is one-half of the diameter. To find the radius when the diameter is known, divide the diameter by 2.
   e.   diameter = 18 in., radius = (9 in.)
   f.   diameter = 28 in., radius = (14 in.)
   g.   diameter = 42 ft., radius = (21 ft.)
   h.   diameter = 17 ft., radius = (8.5 ft.)

1–5.

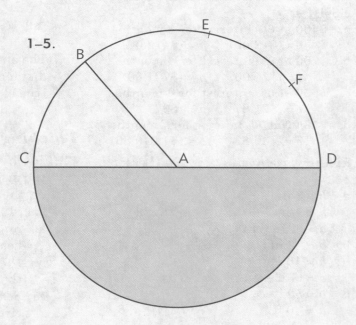

WRITTEN EXERCISES

A. *Use a compass to draw a circle. Then label it as directed.*

1. Label the center point A.   (Sample diagram on facing page)

2. Draw a radius in the circle, and use B to label the point where it touches the circle. You will draw radius AB.

3. Draw a diameter in the circle, and label its two endpoints C and D. You will draw diameter CD.

4. Use your pencil to shade the part of the circle on one side of the diameter. You will shade a semicircle.

5. Mark off an arc, and label its endpoints E and F.

B. *Write the missing numbers for the following tables.*

	Radius	Diameter
6.	8 in.	16 in.
8.	1 ft.	2 ft.
10.	15 ft.	30 ft.
12.	$16\frac{1}{2}$ in.	33 in.
14.	50 cm	100 cm
16.	$2\frac{1}{4}$ in.	$4\frac{1}{2}$ in.

	Radius	Diameter
7.	14 in.	28 in.
9.	6 ft.	12 ft.
11.	48 ft.	96 ft.
13.	$18\frac{1}{2}$ in.	37 in.
15.	44 m	88 m
17.	$3\frac{1}{4}$ in.	$6\frac{1}{2}$ in.

C. *Solve these reading problems.*

18. The radius of a silo is 10 feet. What is the diameter?   20 feet

19. The diameter of a grain bin is 30 feet. What is the radius?   15 feet

20. David wants to draw a circle with a 5-inch radius. Will it fit on a sheet of paper that is $8\frac{1}{2}$ inches wide?   no

21. The Beilers' family car needs a radius of 15 feet to be turned around without backing. Can their car be turned around on a parking lot 32 feet wide?   yes

REVIEW EXERCISES

D. *Solve these parallel reading problems on finding interest for months.* (*Lessons 145, 132*)

22. At the beginning of the year, Father had $500 in a savings account with an interest rate of 5%. The balance stayed the same for 6 months, and then interest was added to the account. What was the new balance? $512.50

23. Father borrowed $775 at 8% interest. Nine months later he paid back both the loan and the interest. How much did Father need to pay? $821.50

E. *Find the areas of triangles having these measurements.* (*Lesson 143*)

24. $b = 6$ in.   **25.** $b = 12$ in.   **26.** $b = 14$ ft.   **27.** $b = 30$ ft.
      $h = 5$ in. $h = 10$ in. $h = 11$ ft. $h = 20$ ft.
      15 sq. in.   60 sq. in.   77 sq. ft.   300 sq. ft.

F. *Subtract these percents from 100%.* (*Lesson 116*)

28. 42%   **29.** 36%   **30.** 8%   **31.** 7%   **32.** 91%   **33.** 99%
      58%   64%   92%   93%   9%   1%

G. *Solve these multiplication problems mentally.* (*Lessons 19, 20*)

34. 30×12 360   **35.** 20×32 640   **36.** $5 \times 3 \times 8$ 120   **37.** $6 \times 9 \times 5$ 270
38. 14×50 700   **39.** 26×50 1,300 **40.** 24×25 600   **41.** 36×25 900

LESSON 149

Objectives

- To teach that the *value of π is about 3.14 or 3 1/7.
- To introduce the *term *circumference*.
- To teach *finding the circumference when the diameter is known.

Review

1. *Terms relating to circles* (Lesson 148). Read the following definitions, and have the students give the terms.
   a. Half of a circle (semicircle)
   b. The distance from one edge of a circle through the center to its opposite edge (diameter)
   c. Any part of the curve of a circle (arc)
   d. The distance from the center of a circle to its edge (radius)
   e. The plural form of *radius* (radii)

2. *Finding areas of rectangles and squares* (Lessons 140, 141).
   a. rectangle: $l = 14$ ft., $w = 8$ ft. (112 sq. ft.)
   b. rectangle: $l = 50$ m, $w = 30$ m (1,500 m²)
   c. square: $s = 17$ in.   (289 sq. in.)
   d. square: $s = 28$ cm   (784 cm²)

3. *Finding percentages* (Lessons 117, 118).
   a. 42% of 70 = (29.4)
   b. 36% of 82 = (29.52)
   c. 8% of 92 = (7.36)
   d. 3% of 79 = (2.37)

Introduction

Draw a circle with a 6-inch diameter on the board. Explain that the circumference of the circle is the distance around it (the length of the curved line). Have several of the students measure the circumference. How do their answers compare? Is it easy to measure the circumference of a circle?

Now explain and use the formula in the text to compute the circumference of the circle.

Teaching Guide

To find the circumference of a circle, multiply the diameter of the circle by π. Use 3.14 or 3 1/7 for π, as the directions indicate.

circumference = π × diameter
$$c = \pi d$$

Practice using 3.14 for π.
   a. $d = 6$ in. [circle on board]
      $c = $ (18.84 in.)
   b. $d = 11$ in., $c = $ (34.54 in.)
   c. $d = 9$ ft., $c = $ (28.26 ft.)
   d. $d = 40$ ft., $c = $ (125.6 ft.)

Practice using 3 1/7 for π. To multiply, change π to the improper fraction 22/7.
   e. $d = 28$ in., $c = $ (88 in.)
   f. $d = 56$ ft., $c = $ (176 ft.)
   g. $d = 16$ ft., $c = $ (50 2/7 ft.)

149. Finding the Circumference of a Circle

The distance around a circle is called its **circumference.** Unlike the perimeter of a polygon, the circumference of a circle cannot be found by adding the lengths of all the sides. It is difficult to measure the circumference of a circle by using a ruler. Instead, the circumference is usually calculated from the diameter of the circle.

When King Solomon built the temple, it was known that there was a relationship between the diameter of a circle and its circumference. According to 1 Kings 7:23, the circumference of a circle was considered to be about 3 times its diameter.

Since that time, a more exact relationship between the diameter and the circumference of a circle has been calculated. Today we use the Greek letter π, called **pi** and pronounced like *pie*, to represent that relationship. The value of π has been established as about $3\frac{1}{7}$ ($\frac{22}{7}$) in fraction form or about 3.14 in decimal form. That is, the circumference of a circle is about $3\frac{1}{7}$ or 3.14 times as long as its diameter. But these numbers are approximate; the exact value of π cannot be stated with numerals.

The formula for finding the circumference of a circle is as follows:

$$\textbf{circumference} = \pi \times \textbf{diameter, or } c = \pi d$$

Example A	**Example B**
The rim of a bucket has a diameter of 10 inches. Find its circumference, using 3.14 for π.	The diameter of a silo is 14 feet. Find its circumference, using $3\frac{1}{7}$ ($\frac{22}{7}$) for π.
$c = \pi \times d$	$c = \pi \times d$
$c = 3.14 \times 10$	$c = \frac{22}{7} \times 14$
$c = 31.4$ inches	$c = 44$ feet

CLASS PRACTICE

Find the circumferences of circles with these diameters. Use $\pi = 3.14$.

a. 13 cm   **b.** 9 in.   **c.** 22 ft.   **d.** 15 m
     40.82 cm   28.26 in.   69.08 ft.   47.1 m

Find the circumferences of circles with these diameters. Use $\pi = \frac{22}{7}$.

e. 14 m   **f.** 56 ft.   **g.** 28 in.   **h.** 5 cm
     44 m   176 ft.   88 in. $15\frac{5}{7}$ cm

WRITTEN EXERCISES

A. *Find the circumferences of circles with these diameters. Use $\pi = 3.14$.*

1. 4 in. 12.56 in.   **2.** 5 in. 15.7 in.   **3.** 15 in. 47.1 in.   **4.** 18 ft. 56.52 ft.

5. 12 m 37.68 m   **6.** 16 m 50.24 m   **7.** 30 cm 94.2 cm   **8.** 25 cm 78.5 cm

B.   Find the circumferences of circles with these diameters. Use π = $\frac{22}{7}$.

9. 7 in.   22 in.   **10**. 21 in.   66 in.   **11**. 35 in.   110 in.   **12**. 49 ft.   154 ft.

13. 6 m $18\frac{6}{7}$ m   **14**. 8 m $25\frac{1}{7}$ m   **15**. 42 cm   132 cm   **16**. 63 cm   198 cm

C.   Solve these reading problems. In problems 21 and 22, you must change the radius to the diameter before you can find the circumference.

17. The silo on the Miller farm has a diameter of 20 feet. What is the distance around the silo? (π = 3.14)   62.8 feet

18. Mother baked a cake in a 9-inch round cake pan. What is the circumference of the cake pan? (π = 3.14)   28.26 inches

19. Dwight's bicycle has 26-inch tires. How far does the bicycle travel each time the wheels make one complete revolution? (π = $\frac{22}{7}$) $81\frac{5}{7}$ inches

20. The tires on the family car have a diameter of 22 inches. How far does the car travel each time the wheels make one revolution? (π = $\frac{22}{7}$) $69\frac{1}{7}$ inches

21. The tires on the Millers' pickup truck have a *radius* of 12 inches. How far does the pickup travel each time the wheels make one revolution? (π = 3.14) 75.36 inches

22. A large grain bin has a *radius* of 15 feet. What is its circumference? (π = 3.14)
                                                                                       94.2 feet

REVIEW EXERCISES

D.   Write the correct term for each definition. *(Lessons 148, 149)*

arc	radius	diameter
pi	semicircle	circumference

23. Distance from the center of a circle to its edge   radius

24. Half of a circle   semicircle

25. Distance around a circle   circumference

26. Any part of the curved line of a circle   arc

27. Distance from one edge of a circle through the center to the opposite edge diameter

28. Value represented by π and equal to about $\frac{22}{7}$ or 3.14   pi

E.   Find the areas of polygons with these dimensions. *(Lessons 140, 141)*

29. rectangle
l = 12 in.
w = 11 in.
132 sq. in.

30. rectangle
l = 65 ft.
w = 48 ft.
3,120 sq. ft.

31. rectangle
l = 142 m
w = 98 m
13,916 m²

32. rectangle
l = 82 cm
w = 78 cm
6,396 cm²

33. square
s = 15 in.
225 sq. in.

34. square
s = 38 in.
1,444 sq. in.

35. square
s = 45 cm
2,025 cm²

36. square
s = 82 cm
6,724 cm²

F.   Find these percentages. *(Lesson 117)*

37. 45% of 92 41.4   **38**. 38% of 55 20.9   **39**. 8% of 95 7.6   **40**. 5% of 60 3

An Ounce of Prevention

Make certain the students understand that they are to use π = 3.14 in problems 1–8, and π = 22/7 in problems 9–16. Because of rounding, failure to follow directions will result in wrong answers.

The students need to use the radius to find the diameter in problems 21 and 22.

Further Study

The ratio of the circumference to the diameter of a circle is represented by the Greek letter π (p). This letter stands for the Greek word *periphereia*, which is the source of the English word *periphery* (a synonym of *circumference*).

Saying that π = 3.14 or π = 3 1/7 is not exactly true; both figures are approximate. The exact value of π has long intrigued mathematicians. Modern computers have calculated π to more than 100 million decimal places, but no exact value has ever been found. The reason is that π is an irrational number; that is, it cannot be stated in terms of any exact figures *a* to *b*.

In 1 Kings 7:23, the value of π was taken to be 3. The Greek mathematician Archimedes correctly stated that the value is between 3 10/70 and 3 10/71. Later in this math series, students will be told that 3.14159 is more nearly accurate than either 3.14 or 3 1/7. For most practical purposes, however, the values taught in this lesson will serve the students well throughout life.

LESSON 150

Objectives

- To teach *finding the area of a circle when the radius is known.

- To teach that *squaring a number means multiplying the number by itself.

Review

1. *Finding circumference, diameter, and radius* (Lessons 148, 149). Review the meaning of each term.

radius	diameter [2 × radius]	circumference [diameter × 3.14]
a. 8 in.	(16 in.)	(50.24 in.)
b. 12 in.	(24 in.)	(75.36 in.)
c. (15 in.)	30 in.	(94.2 in.)
d. (21 in.)	42 in.	(131.88 in.)

2. *Finding the areas of parallelograms* (Lesson 142).

   a. b = 8 in.
      h = 7 in.
      a = (56 sq. in.)
   b. b = 26 in.
      h = 13 in.
      a = (338 sq. in.)
   c. b = 17 ft.
      h = 16 ft.
      a = (272 sq. ft.)

3. *Dividing and casting out nines* (Lesson 21).

   a. $48\overline{)38,598}$ (804 R 6)   Check number: 6

   b. $175\overline{)49,981}$ (285 R 106)   Check number: 4

Introduction

Call attention to the circle in the students' text. Find the area as instructed—by counting all the squares that are more than halfway inside the circle, and not counting any square that is less than halfway inside the circle. You should count 12 squares (12 square inches).

Teaching Guide

To find the area of a circle, square the radius and multiply the result by π.

$$\text{area} = \pi \times \text{radius} \times \text{radius}$$
$$a = \pi r^2$$

1. Square the radius by multiplying it by itself. The exponent 2 means that r is used as a factor two times.

2. Multiply the result by π. Use π = 3.14.

3. Label the answer in square units.
   a. r = 2 in.
      a = 3.14 × 2 × 2 = (12.56 sq. in.)
   b. r = 5 in.
      a = 3.14 × 5 × 5 = (78.5 sq. in.)
   c. r = 22 in.
      a = 3.14 × 22 × 22 = (1,519.76 sq. in.)
   d. r = 31 in.
      a = 3.14 × 31 × 31 = (3,017.54 sq. in.)

150. Finding the Area of a Circle

The circle below has a radius of 2 inches and a diameter of 4 inches. Each square measures 1 square inch. Count the number of squares to estimate the area of the circle. For part squares, count each one that is more than half as a full square, and do not count the ones that are less than half squares. You should find that the area of the circle is about 12 square inches.

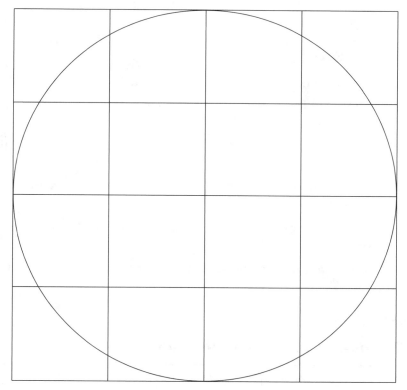

The area of a circle can be found by a method that is much more precise than counting squares. The formula for finding the area of a circle is as follows:

area = π × radius × radius, or $a = \pi r^2$

The small raised 2 after r is an **exponent.** It means that the radius needs to be used two times as a factor. That is, the radius is to be multiplied by itself: $r \times r$. The following examples show how to use the formula to find the areas of circles.

Example A

Find the area of a circle with a radius of 2 inches.

$a = \pi \times r \times r$
$a = 3.14 \times 2 \times 2$
$a = 12.56$ square inches

Example B

Find the area of a circle with a radius of 15 inches.

$a = \pi \times r \times r$
$a = 3.14 \times 15 \times 15$
$a = 706.5$ square inches

CLASS PRACTICE

Find the areas of circles with these radii.

a. 5 in.   78.5 sq. in.   b. 11 ft.   379.94 sq. ft.   c. 14 m   615.44 m²

d. 20 in.   1,256 sq. in.   e. 15 cm   706.5 cm²   f. 22 cm   1,519.76 cm²

WRITTEN EXERCISES

A.   *Find the areas of circles with these radii.*

1. 4 in.   2. 6 in.   3. 7 in.   4. 8 in.   5. 9 in.
50.24 sq. in.   113.04 sq. in.   153.86 sq. in.   200.96 sq. in.   254.34 sq. in.

6. 10 in.   7. 12 ft.   8. 16 ft.   9. 25 ft.   10. 30 ft.
314 sq. in.   452.16 sq. ft.   803.84 sq. ft.   1,962.5 sq. ft.   2,826 sq. ft.

B.   *Solve these reading problems.*

11. What is the area of a circle that has a radius of 40 inches?   5,024 sq. in.

12. The blade of a rotary lawn mower cuts a circle with a radius of 11 inches. What is
the area of this circle?   379.94 sq. in.

13. A garden sprinkler irrigates a circle with an 18-foot radius. What is the area of this
circle?   1,017.36 sq. ft.

14. A field sprinkler irrigates a circle with a radius of 200 feet. What is the area of the
circle irrigated by this sprinkler?   125,600 sq. ft.

15. The circular face of a clock has a diameter of 8 inches. What is its area? Hint: First
find the radius.   50.24 sq. in.

16. A round table has a diameter of 48 inches. What is its area? (Remember to start
with the radius.)   1,808.64 sq. in.

REVIEW EXERCISES

C.   *Write the missing numbers for this table. Use $\pi = 3.14$. (Lessons 148–150).*

Radius	Diameter $(d = 2r)$	Circumference $(c = \pi d)$	Area $(a = \pi r^2)$
14 in.	17. 28 in.	18. 87.92 in.	19. 615.44 sq. in.
20. 13 in.	26 in.	21. 81.64 in.	22. 530.66 sq. in.
17 in.	23. 34 in.	24. 106.76 in.	25. 907.46 sq. in.

D.   *Find the areas of parallelograms with these dimensions. (Lesson 142)*

26. $b = 9$ in.   27. $b = 15$ ft.   28. $b = 25$ cm   29. $b = 20$ m
$h = 8$ in. $h = 11$ ft. $h = 18$ cm $h = 18$ m
72 sq. in.   165 sq. ft.   450 cm²   360 m²

E.   *Solve these problems, and check by casting out nines. (Lesson 21)*

$$\begin{array}{llll} \quad\ 528 \text{ R } 3 & \quad\ 1{,}764 \text{ R } 37 & \quad\ 543 \text{ R } 37 & \quad\ 377 \text{ R } 116 \end{array}$$

30. $32\overline{)16{,}899}$ 31. $56\overline{)98{,}821}$ 32. $125\overline{)67{,}912}$ 33. $215\overline{)81{,}171}$

An Ounce of Prevention

Make certain that the students understand the meaning of the exponent 2 in math. Be sure they multiply the number by itself and not just by 2.

LESSON 151

Objectives

- To teach that volume is space occupied by a figure that has length, width, and height.

- To introduce English units of cubic measure such as the cubic inch, cubic foot, and cubic yard.

- To teach finding the volume of a rectangular solid.

Review

1. *Circumferences and areas of circles* (Lessons 149, 150).
   a. $d = 10$ in., $c = $ (31.4 in.)
   b. $d = 14$ cm, $c = $ (43.96 cm)
   c. $r = 5$ in., $a = $ (78.5 sq. in.)
   d. $r = 13$ m, $a = $ (530.66 m²)

2. *Areas of triangles* (Lesson 143).
   a. $b = 8$ in., $h = 3$ in., $a = $ (12 sq. in.)
   b. $b = 7$ cm, $h = 5$ cm, $a = $ (17.5 cm²)

3. *Subtracting percents from 100* (Lesson 116). No class review is necessary.

4. *Division with decimals* (Lessons 85–87).
   a. $3.5\overline{)7.7}$ (2.2)

   b. $0.48\overline{)5.4}$ (11.25)

   c. $0.55\overline{)6.6}$ (12)

5. *Short division* (Lesson 22).
   a. $3\overline{)5,923}$ (1,974 R 1)

   b. $6\overline{)8,381}$ (1,396 R 5)

   c. $7\overline{)6,732}$ (961 R 5)

Introduction

Bring a cardboard box to class. Have the class calculate the area of its base. Ask: "Does the area tell you how much space is in the entire box?" (No; it tells only the area of the bottom.) The capacity is the volume of the box. Capacity includes not only length and width but also height.

Teaching Guide

1. **Volume is measured in cubic units.** A cubic inch is the volume of a cube measuring 1 inch long, 1 inch wide, and 1 inch high. Can the students guess the dimensions of the following units?
   a. 1 cubic foot—The volume of a cube measuring 1 foot by 1 foot by 1 foot. The amount of air in a room is often measured in cubic feet. Natural gas is sold by the cubic foot. The density of materials is often expressed in pounds per cubic foot.
   b. 1 cubic yard—The volume of a cube measuring 1 yard by 1 yard by 1 yard. Concrete is usually sold by the cubic yard.
   c. 1 cubic mile—The volume of a cube measuring 1 mile by 1 mile by 1 mile. This unit is used for extremely large measurements, such as the amount of air in the atmosphere or water in the ocean.

2. **A rectangular solid is a box-shaped object whose sides are all rectangular and whose opposite sides are parallel.** Mention a few common rectangular solids, such as a box, a brick, and a rectangular room.

151. Introduction to Volume

You have had much practice with linear units such as inches, feet, and yards. These units measure length, which has one dimension. You have also worked with square units such as square inches, square feet, and square yards. These units measure area, which has two dimensions (length and width).

In this lesson you will work with units that measure three dimensions: length, width, and height. For example, if the base of a box is 12 inches long and 9 inches wide, it covers an area of 108 square inches. But square inches cannot measure the amount of space occupied by the entire box. The space occupied by an object is the **volume** of the object.

As area is measured in square units, so volume is measured in cubic units. Some English units of cubic measure are the cubic inch, cubic foot, and cubic yard. A cubic inch is the volume equal to a cube 1 inch long, 1 inch wide, and 1 inch high.

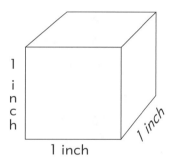

1 inch · 1 inch · 1 inch

One of the simplest three-dimensional objects is the **rectangular solid.** This is any box-shaped object whose sides are all rectangles, whose corners all form right angles, and whose opposite sides are parallel. To find the volume of a rectangular solid, multiply the length times the width times the height. The formula is as follows:

volume = length × width × height, or $v = lwh$

Example A

Find the volume of a rectangular solid that measures 5 inches by 4 inches by 2 inches.

$v = l \times w \times h$
$v = 5 \times 4 \times 2$
$v = 40$ cu. in.

Example B

Find the volume of a rectangular solid that measures 6 inches by 5 inches by 3 inches.

$v = l \times w \times h$
$v = 6 \times 5 \times 3$
$v = 90$ cu. in.

CLASS PRACTICE

Find the volumes of rectangular solids with these dimensions. Remember to label your answers as cubic units.

	Length	Width	Height			Length	Width	Height	
a.	5 in.	4 in.	4 in.	80 cu. in.	b.	9 in.	7 in.	9 in.	567 cu. in.
c.	8 ft.	6 ft.	5 ft.	240 cu. ft.	d.	14 ft.	10 ft.	5 ft.	700 cu. ft.
e.	6 yd.	4 yd.	3 yd.	72 cu. yd.	f.	24 ft.	18 ft.	7 ft.	3,024 cu. ft.

WRITTEN EXERCISES

A. Name a cubic unit for each linear unit.

1. inch cubic inch   2. foot cubic foot   3. yard cubic yard   4. mile cubic mile

B. Find the volumes of rectangular solids with these dimensions. Remember to label your answers as cubic units.

	Length	Width	Height			Length	Width	Height	
5.	3 in.	2 in.	3 in.	18 cu. in.	6.	4 in.	3 in.	4 in.	48 cu. in.
7.	7 in.	6 in.	4 in.	168 cu. in.	8.	8 in.	5 in.	3 in.	120 cu. in.
9.	6 ft.	4 ft.	5 ft.	120 cu. ft.	10.	9 ft.	3 ft.	4 ft.	108 cu. ft.
11.	7 ft.	4 ft.	7 ft.	196 cu ft.	12.	10 ft.	8 ft.	3 ft.	240 cu ft.
13.	2 yd.	2 yd.	1 yd.	4 cu. yd.	14.	6 yd.	5 yd.	3 yd.	90 cu. yd.
15.	20 ft.	18 ft.	8 ft.	2,880 cu. ft.	16.	45 ft.	35 ft.	12 ft.	18,900 cu. ft.

C. Solve these reading problems.

17. A cardboard box is 16 inches long, 15 inches wide, and 12 inches high. What is the volume of the box?   2,880 cubic inches

18. A coat closet is 4 feet long, 3 feet wide, and 8 feet high. What is the volume of the coat closet?   96 cubic feet

19. Concrete is usually sold by the cubic yard. Father is planning to pour a concrete garage floor with a length of 10 yards, a width of 10 yards, and a thickness of 6 inches ($\frac{1}{6}$ yard). How many cubic yards of concrete will he need? Round your answer to the next higher cubic yard.   17 cubic yards

20. The basement of the Maysville Mennonite School is 20 yards long and 15 yards wide. How many cubic yards of concrete will be needed to pour a concrete floor with a thickness of 4 inches ($\frac{1}{9}$ yard)? Round your answer to the next higher cubic yard.   34 cubic yards

21. The sixth and seventh grade classroom at the Maysville School is 30 feet long, 25 feet wide, and 8 feet high. If air weighs 0.08 pound per cubic foot, what is the weight of the air in the empty room? (First find the volume of the room.) 6,000 cubic feet
                                   480 pounds

3. **To find the volume of a rectangular solid, multiply the length by the width by the height.** Label the answer in cubic units.

   Find the volume of the box that you brought to class. Most students also enjoy calculating the weight of the air in their classroom. First find the volume of the room; then multiply that by the density of air (0.08 pound per cubic foot).

   a. What is the weight of air in a classroom that measures 30 feet by 30 feet by 8 feet?

      volume = 30 × 30 × 8 = 7,200 cu. ft.

      weight of air = 7,200 × 0.08 lb. per
         cu. ft. = 576 lb.

      (Students will probably find this hard to believe. The weight does vary a bit according to the relative humidity of the air and the elevation of the school, but such variation is generally insignificant.)

   Find the volume of these rectangular solids.

   b. 4 in. by 6 in. by 3 in.
      (72 cu. in.)

   c. 9 ft. by 8 ft. by 6 ft.
      (432 cu. ft.)

   d. 6 yd. by 4 yd. by 5 yd.
      (120 cu. yd.)

   e. 40 ft. by 35 ft. by 12 ft.
      (16,800 cu. ft.)

   f. 60 ft. by 40 ft. by 12 ft.
      (28,800 cu. ft.)

   g. 27 ft. by 22 ft. by 13 ft.
      (7,722 cu. ft.)

An Ounce of Prevention

Problems 19, 20, and 22 involve both inches and yards. Remind the students that they must use all yard measurements to arrive at the correct answers.

22. The Brubaker family is pouring concrete for the basement floor of their house. The basement is 15 yards long and 10 yards wide, and the floor will be 4 inches ($\frac{1}{9}$ yard) thick. At $58 per cubic yard, how much will the concrete cost? (Round the volume of concrete to the next higher cubic yard before finding the cost.) $986

REVIEW EXERCISES

D. Find the areas of circles with these radii. *(Lesson 150)*

23. 4 in.
50.24 sq. in.

24. 9 ft.
254.34 sq. ft.

25. 17 cm
907.46 cm²

26. 26 m
2,122.64 m²

E. Find the circumferences of circles with these diameters. *(Lesson 149)*

27. 8 ft.
25.12 ft.

28. 18 in.
56.52 in.

29. 34 m
106.76 m

30. 52 cm
163.28 cm

F. Find the areas of these triangles. *(Lesson 143)*

31. b = 7 in.
h = 5 in.
$17\frac{1}{2}$ sq. in.

32. b = 9 in.
h = 6 in.
27 sq. in.

33. b = 15 ft.
h = 12 ft.
90 sq. ft.

34. b = 20 ft.
h = 15 ft.
150 sq. ft.

G. Subtract these percents from 100%. *(Lesson 116)*

35. 16%   84%

36. 23%   77%

37. 8%   92%

38. 4%   96%

H. Solve these division problems. *(Lessons 85–87)*

39. $4.5\overline{)90.9}$ → 20.2

40. $0.32\overline{)6.4}$ → 20

41. $0.82\overline{)0.1804}$ → 0.22

42. $1.1\overline{)0.0396}$ → 0.036

I. Solve these problems by short division. *(Lesson 22)*

43. $4\overline{)4,184}$ → 1,046

44. $5\overline{)9,189}$ → 1,837 R 4

45. $8\overline{)6,821}$ → 852 R 5

46. $9\overline{)2,843}$ → 315 R 8

152. Finding the Volume of a Cube

A **cube** is a special kind of rectangular solid because its length, width, and height are the same. Since all three dimensions are equal, they are not called the length, width, and height. Instead, the dimensions are simply called the edges of the cube. The length of any edge is the length, width, or height of the cube.

The formula for finding the volume of a cube is as follows:

volume = edge × edge × edge, or $v = e \times e \times e$

Example A	Example B
Find the volume of a cube with edges that measure 3 feet.	Find the volume of a cube with edges that measure 12 inches.
$v = e \times e \times e$	$v = e \times e \times e$
$v = 3 \times 3 \times 3$	$v = 12 \times 12 \times 12$
$v = 27$ cubic feet (cu. ft.)	$v = 1{,}728$ cubic inches (cu.in.)
The edges of this cube are 3 feet or 1 yard long. So the volume of this cube is 27 cubic feet or 1 cubic yard.	The edges of this cube are 12 inches or 1 foot long. So the volume of this cube is 1,728 cubic inches or 1 cubic foot.
27 cu. ft. = 1 cu. yd.	1,728 cu. in. = 1 cu. ft.

CLASS PRACTICE

Find the volumes of cubes with these edges. Label your answers in cubic units.

a. 5 ft.   125 cu. ft.   **b.** 3 in.   27 cu. in.   **c.** 16 in.   4,096 cu. in.

d. 12 ft.   1,728 cu. ft.   **e.** 26 in.   17,576 cu. in.   **f.** 15 in.   3,375 cu. in.

WRITTEN EXERCISES

A.   *Find the volumes of cubes with these edges. Label your answers in cubic units.*

1. 4 in.
  64 cu. in.

2. 2 in.
  8 cu. in.

3. 6 ft.
  216 cu. ft.

4. 9 yd.
  729 cu. yd.

5. 10 in.
  1,000 cu. in.

6. 8 ft.
  512 cu. ft.

7. 20 ft.
  8,000 cu. ft.

8. 7 ft.
  343 cu. ft.

9. 11 yd.
  1,331 cu. yd.

10. 22 in.
  10,648 cu. in.

11. 30 ft.
  27,000 cu. ft.

12. 18 ft.
  5,832 cu. ft.

13. 20 in.
  8,000 cu. in.

14. 13 yd.
  2,197 cu. yd.

15. 40 ft.
  64,000 cu. ft.

16. 50 ft.
  125,000 cu. ft.

B.   *Solve these reading problems.*

17. The most holy place in the tabernacle was in the form of a cube. Each edge of the cube is thought to have measured 15 feet in English units. What is the volume of a 15-foot cube?

3,375 cubic feet

LESSON 152

Objective

- To teach finding the volume of a cube.

Review

1. Give Lesson 152 Quiz (Working With Circles).

2. *Volumes of rectangular solids* (Lesson 151).
   a. $l = 6$ in., $w = 5$ in., $h = 4$ in.
      (120 cu. in.)
   b. $l = 8$ in., $w = 3$ in., $h = 2$ in.
      (48 cu. in.)
   c. $l = 9$ ft., $w = 8$ ft., $h = 7$ ft.
      (504 cu. ft.)

3. *Areas of circles* (Lesson 150).
   Use $\pi = 3.14$.
   a. $r = 3$ in., $a = $ (28.26 sq. in.)
   b. $r = 6$ in., $a = $ (113.04 sq. in.)
   c. $r = 4$ ft., $a = $ (50.24 sq. ft.)
   d. $r = 5$ ft., $a = $ (78.5 sq. ft.)

4. *Discount prices and sale prices* (Lesson 120).

	Regular Price	Percent of Discount	Discount	Sale Price
a.	$30.00	8%	($2.40)	($27.60)
b.	$15.00	12%	($1.80)	($13.20)
c.	$65.00	10%	($6.50)	($58.50)

5. *Rounding decimals* (Lesson 88). Round each to the nearest tenth and the nearest hundredth.
   a. 0.378 (0.4, 0.38)
   b. 0.245 (0.2, 0.25)
   c. 0.831 (0.8, 0.83)

Introduction

Find the volume of a rectangular solid measuring 3 feet by 4 feet by 2 feet (24 cubic feet). Now find the volume of a rectangular solid measuring 2 feet by 2 feet by 2 feet (8 cubic feet). What is special about the second rectangular solid? It has the same length, width, and height. A rectangular solid that has equal length, width, and height is a cube.

Teaching Guide

1. **A cube is a rectangular solid whose length, width, and height are equal.** Because the dimensions are all the same, they are called the edges of the cube.

2. **To find the volume of a cube, multiply edge × edge × edge.** The formula is $v = e \times e \times e$. To apply the formula, use the following steps.
   (1) Multiply one edge by itself, and multiply the result by one edge again.
   (2) Label the answer in cubic units.
      a. $e = 5$ in.
         $v = 5 \times 5 \times 5 = $ (125 cu. in.)
      b. $e = 8$ ft.
         $v = 8 \times 8 \times 8 = $ (512 cu. ft.)
      c. $e = 17$ in.
         $v = 17 \times 17 \times 17 = $ (4,913 cu. in.)
      d. $e = 2.5$ ft.
         $v = 2.5 \times 2.5 \times 2.5 = $
                          (15.625 cu. ft.)
      e. $e = 60$ ft.
         $v = 60 \times 60 \times 60 = $
                          (216,000 cu. ft.)
      f. $e = 19$ in.
         $v = 19 \times 19 \times 19 = $
                          (6,859 cu. in.)

18. The most holy place in Solomon's temple was larger than the one in the tabernacle. This cube is thought to have measured 30 feet along each edge. What is the volume of a 30-foot cube?   27,000 cubic feet

19. The average annual rainfall in the United States is enough water to fill a cube whose edges are nearly 11.5 miles long. What is the volume of a cube with edges of 11.5 miles?
                                                                         1,520.875 cubic miles

20. If all the gold that was mined in the world from 1492 to 1946 were at one place, it would be enough to fill a cube whose edges are more than 44 feet long. What is the volume of a cube with 44-foot edges?   85,184 cubic feet

21. The Troyers' cistern measures 8 feet by 6 feet by 4 feet. One cubic foot is equal to about $7\frac{1}{2}$ gallons. How many gallons of water can the cistern hold? 1,440 gallons

22. The Zimmermans' milk tank measures 8 feet by 6 feet by 3 feet. If milk weighs 64 pounds per cubic foot, how many pounds of milk can the milk tank hold?   9,216 pounds

REVIEW EXERCISES

C. **Find the volumes of rectangular solids with these dimensions.** *(Lesson 151)*

	Length	Width	Height			Length	Width	Height	
23.	8 in.	4 in.	2 in.	64 cu. in.	**24.**	5 in.	3 in.	2 in.	30 cu. in.
25.	8 ft.	4 ft.	3 ft.	96 cu. ft.	**26.**	9 ft.	7 ft.	2 ft.	126 cu. ft.

D. **Find the areas of circles with these radii. Use $\pi = 3.14$.** *(Lesson 150)*

27. 2 ft.	**28.** 8 ft.	**29.** 6.5 in.	**30.** 11 in.
12.56 sq. ft.	200.96 sq. ft.	132.665 sq. in.	379.94 sq. in.

E. **Write the correct word for each blank.** *(Lesson 148)*

31. A line segment extending from edge to edge through the center of a circle is the <u>diameter</u>.

32. Half of a circle is a <u>semicircle</u>.

33. A line segment extending from the center of a circle to its edge is the <u>radius</u>.

34. The value of π is about equal to the mixed number <u>$3\frac{1}{7}$</u>, the improper fraction <u>$\frac{22}{7}$</u>, or the decimal fraction <u>3.14</u>.

F. **Find the discount and the sale price of each item.** *(Lesson 120)*

	Regular Price	Percent of Discount				Regular Price	Percent of Discount		
35.	$20.00	6%	$1.20	$18.80	**36.**	$15.00	8%	$1.20	$13.80
37.	$80.00	15%	$12.00	$68.00	**38.**	$90.00	12%	$10.80	$79.20

G. **Round each decimal to the nearest hundredth.** *(Lesson 88)*

39. 0.458   0.46   **40.** 0.533   0.53   **41.** 0.681   0.68   **42.** 0.588   0.59

153. Metric Units of Volume

In the past two lessons you worked with English units of volume, such as the cubic inch and the cubic foot. One cubic foot is the volume of a cube with 1-foot edges. This lesson introduces metric units of volume such as the cubic meter and the cubic centimeter. One cubic meter is the volume of a cube with edges of 1 meter.

You know that abbreviations for metric units of area are different from abbreviations for English units. *Square meter*, for example, is not abbreviated as "sq. m" but as "m². " Abbreviations for metric units of volume are also different. **Cubic meter** is abbreviated as "m³" rather than "cu. m." The exponent 3 is used because volume has three dimensions: length, width, and height.

Example A

Find the volume of a rectangular solid that is 4 meters long, 3 meters wide, and 2 meters high.

$v = l \times w \times h$
$v = 4 \times 3 \times 2 = 24 \text{ m}^3$

Example B

Find the volume of a cube with edges of 8 centimeters.

$v = e \times e \times e$
$v = 8 \times 8 \times 8 = 512 \text{ cm}^3$

CLASS PRACTICE

Find the volumes of rectangular solids with these dimensions. Be sure to use the exponent 3 for all metric units of volume.

a. $l = 7$ cm	**b.** $l = 10$ m	**c.** $l = 12$ mm	**d.** $l = 14$ cm
$w = 5$ cm	$w = 8$ m	$w = 10$ mm	$w = 12$ cm
$h = 4$ cm	$h = 4$ m	$h = 10$ mm	$h = 7$ cm
140 cm³	320 m³	1,200 mm³	1,176 cm³

Find the volumes of cubes having these edges. Be sure to use the exponent 3 for all metric units of volume.

e. $e = 8$ m	**f.** $e = 7$ cm	**g.** $e = 11$ mm	**h.** $e = 15$ cm
512 m³	343 cm³	1,331 mm³	3,375 cm³

Find the areas of circles with these radii, using π = 3.14. Be sure to use the exponent 2 for all metric units of area.

i. $r = 3$ cm	**j.** $r = 6$ m	**k.** $r = 8$ mm	**l.** $r = 7$ cm
28.26 cm²	113.04 m²	200.96 mm²	153.86 cm²

LESSON 153

Objectives

- To give more practice with finding the volume of rectangular solids.
- To introduce *metric units of cubic measure.

Review

1. *Geometric figures* (Lesson 137). Draw and label the geometric figures named here.

   a. line AB

   b. ray CD

   c. line segment EF

   d. angle GHI

   e. right angle JKL

   f. parallel lines MN and OP

2. *Sales commissions* (Lesson 121).

   a. sales = \$400, rate = 9%
      commission = (\$36.00)

   b. sales = \$800, rate = 7%
      commission = (\$56.00)

3. *Expressing common fractions as decimals* (Lesson 89). Divide to the hundredths' place, and express any remainder as a fraction.

   a. $\frac{1}{7}$ $(0.14\frac{2}{7})$

   b. $\frac{2}{11}$ $(0.18\frac{2}{11})$

   c. $\frac{1}{6}$ $(0.16\frac{2}{3})$

4. *Long division and casting out nines* (Lessons 23, 24).

   a. $61\overline{)34,921}$ $(572 \text{ R } 29)$ Check number: 1

   b. $361\overline{)35,998}$ $(99 \text{ R } 259)$ Check number: 7

Introduction

Using metric units, practice finding the area of rectangles. The abbreviations for metric units of area use the exponent 2 because area involves two dimensions (length and width). Can the pupils guess what the abbreviations are for metric units of volume? Because three dimensions are involved (length, width, and height), the exponent 3 is used.

Teaching Guide

1. **In abbreviations for metric units of volume, the exponent 3 is used to designate cubic measure.** This exponent is used because volume has three dimensions: length, width, and height.

   Find the volume of these rectangular solids.

   a. $l = 8$ m, $w = 6$ m, $h = 6$ m
      $v = (288 \text{ m}^3)$

   b. $l = 9$ cm, $w = 7$ cm, $h = 9$ cm
      $v = (567 \text{ cm}^3)$

   c. $l = 20$ mm, $w = 16$ mm, $h = 15$ mm
      $v = (4,800 \text{ mm}^3)$

   Find the volume of these cubes.

   d. $e = 9$ m, $v = (729 \text{ m}^3)$

   e. $e = 6$ cm, $v = (216 \text{ cm}^3)$

   f. $e = 23$ mm, $v = (12,167 \text{ mm}^3)$

2. **The rest of the lesson text before the Review Exercises is a review of the**

concepts learned about circles in this
chapter.
Finding circumferences.
    a. $d = 6$ m
        $c = (18.84$ m$)$
    b. $d = 45$ cm
        $c = (141.3$ cm$)$
    c. $d = 100$ mm
        $c = (314$ mm$)$
Finding areas.
    d. $r = 3$ m
        $a = (28.26$ m$^2)$
    e. $r = 10$ cm
        $a = (314$ cm$^2)$
    f. $r = 25$ mm
        $a = (1{,}962.5$ mm$^2)$

WRITTEN EXERCISES

A. *Find the volumes of rectangular solids with these dimensions. Be sure to use the exponent 3 for all metric units of volume.*

1. $l = 5$ m
   $w = 3$ m
   $h = 3$ m
   45 m³

2. $l = 8$ m
   $w = 4$ m
   $h = 5$ m
   160 m³

3. $l = 15$ cm
   $w = 13$ cm
   $h = 6$ cm
   1,170 cm³

4. $l = 12$ cm
   $w = 11$ cm
   $h = 10$ cm
   1,320 cm³

B. *Find the volumes of cubes having these edges. Be sure to use the exponent 3 for all metric units of volume.*

5. $e = 5$ m
   125 m³

6. $e = 7$ m
   343 m³

7. $e = 10$ m
   1,000 m³

8. $e = 14$ cm
   2,744 cm³

C. *Find the circumferences of circles with these diameters. Use π = 3.14. (Lesson 149)*

9. $d = 4$ m
   12.56 m

10. $d = 9$ m
    28.26 m

11. $d = 15$ mm
    47.1 mm

12. $d = 7$ mm
    21.98 mm

D. *Find the areas of circles with these radii, using π = 3.14. Be sure to use the exponent 2 for all metric units of area. (Lesson 150)*

13. $r = 2$ m
    12.56 m²

14. $r = 4$ m
    50.24 m²

15. $r = 5$ cm
    78.5 cm²

16. $r = 9$ in.
    254.34 sq. in.

E. *Use your metric ruler to measure this circle. Then answer the following questions.*

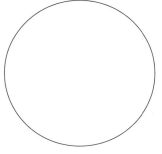

17. What is the diameter?   4 cm

18. What is the circumference?   12.56 cm

19. What is the radius?   2 cm

20. What is the area?   12.56 cm²

F. *Solve these reading problems. Use π = 3.14.*

21. Mother wants to buy a border for the edge of a round flower bed. The distance through the center of the flower bed is 6 feet. How much edging should Mother buy?
    18.84 feet   (19 feet)

22. Solomon made a molten sea for the temple. According to 1 Kings 7:23, the diameter of the sea was 10 cubits. If 10 cubits is 15 feet, what was the circumference of the sea in feet?
    47.1 feet

23. What is the area of the flower bed in problem 21? (Remember to find the radius first.)
    28.26 square feet

24. Suppose that Solomon's molten sea was filled to the brim with water. If it had a diameter of 15 feet, what was the area of the water's surface? (Remember to find the radius first.)
    176.625 square feet

REVIEW EXERCISES

G.   Draw the following geometric figures. *(Lesson 137)*

25. line MN $\longleftrightarrow$ M   N

26. angle OPQ   P, O, Q

27. point R   R

28. ray ST   S   T

H.   Find the sales commission in each problem. *(Lesson 121)*

	Sales	Rate	
29.	$800	6%	$48.00
30.	$700	5%	$35.00

I.   Express each common fraction as a decimal fraction to the hundredths' place. Write any remainder as a fraction. *(Lesson 89)*

31. $\frac{1}{3}$ $0.33\frac{1}{3}$ **32.** $\frac{5}{6}$ $0.83\frac{1}{3}$ **33.** $\frac{5}{9}$ $0.55\frac{5}{9}$ **34.** $\frac{4}{7}$ $0.57\frac{1}{7}$

J.   Solve these problems. Check by casting out nines. *(Lessons 23, 24)*

35. $52\overline{)34,921}$ 671 R 29

36. $252\overline{)35,998}$ 142 R 214

LESSON 154

Objectives

- To review the meaning of the term *vertex.*

- To review acute and obtuse angles.

- To introduce right angles and *straight angles.

- To teach *naming angles by using either one letter or three letters.

Review

1. *Volume of cubes* (Lesson 152).
   a. $e = 10$ in., $v = (1,000$ cu. in.)
   b. $e = 14$ m, $v = (2,744$ m^3)
   c. $e = 6$ in., $v = (216$ cu. in.)
   d. $e = 1.8$ m, $v = (5.832$ m^3)

2. *Area of circles* (Lesson 150).
   Use $\pi = 3.14$.
   a. $r = 6$ in., $a = (113.04$ sq. in.)
   b. $r = 5$ ft., $a = (78.5$ sq. ft.)
   c. $r = 14$ cm, $a = (615.44$ cm^2)
   d. $r = 3.2$ m, $a = (32.1536$ m^2)

3. *Perimeter of rectangles and squares* (Lessons 138, 139).
   a. square: $s = 9$ in., $p = (36$ in.)
   b. square: $s = 13.4$ cm, $p = (53.6$ cm)
   c. rectangle: $l = 25$ ft., $w = 20$ ft., $p = (90$ ft.)
   d. rectangle: $l = 18$ m, $w = 16$ m, $p = (68$ m)

4. *Multiplying mentally by changing decimals to common fractions* (Lesson 90).
   a. 0.2 of 35 = (7)
   b. 0.5 of 46 = (23)
   c. 0.8 of 40 = (32)
   d. 0.75 of 44 = (33)

Introduction

Draw a ray on the board, and have the students identify it. Draw an angle by using two rays. Can the students identify the two rays joined at the vertex as an angle?

Draw a right angle, an acute angle, and an obtuse angle. How are the three different from each other? The students may not have the correct terminology, but they will probably identify the acute angle as having sides that are closer together, and the obtuse angle as having sides that are farther apart.

Teaching Guide

1. **An angle is defined as two rays with the same endpoint.** This common endpoint is the vertex of the angle. However, angles usually consist of line segments rather than rays. The two line segments are the sides of an angle.

2. **Angles are measured in degrees, which are based on the circle.** A full circle has 360 degrees, a half circle (semicircle) has 180 degrees, and a quarter circle has 90 degrees. The symbol for *degrees* is a small raised circle (°).

3. **The size of an angle depends on the number of degrees between the two sides.** It has nothing to do with the lengths of the sides.

4. **Angles are called by different names according to their sizes.** Draw an acute angle, a straight angle, a right angle, and an obtuse angle on the board. Label each angle with three capital letters, but do not label the types of angles. Have the students identify each one as you discuss it.

154. Working With Angles

An **angle** is defined as two rays with the same endpoint. This common endpoint is the **vertex** of the angle. However, angles usually consist of line segments rather than rays. The two line segments are the **sides** of an angle.

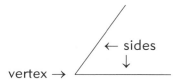

Angles are measured in **degrees,** which are based on the circle. A full circle has 360 degrees, a half circle (semicircle) has 180 degrees, and a quarter circle has 90 degrees. The symbol for *degrees* is a small raised circle, as in 90°.

The size of an angle depends on the number of degrees between the two sides. It has nothing to do with the lengths of the sides. For example, the hands of a clock form a larger angle at 4 o'clock than at 2 o'clock because the opening between the sides is larger at 4 o'clock.

Angles are called by different names according to their sizes. A **right angle** is an angle whose sides are perpendicular. It has 90 degrees—as many degrees as there are in a quarter circle. A right angle is shown by the symbol ⌐ in the vertex. On a clock, the hands form a right angle at 3 o'clock and 9 o'clock.

An **acute angle** has less than 90 degrees. (The word *acute* means "sharp.") The hands of a clock form acute angles at times such as 1 o'clock and 10 o'clock.

An **obtuse angle** is of a size between 90 degrees and 180 degrees. (The word *obtuse* means "blunt.") The hands of a clock form obtuse angles at times such as 4 o'clock and 7 o'clock.

A **straight angle** has 180 degrees—as many degrees as there are in a semicircle. The two sides extend in opposite directions from the vertex. The hands of a clock form a straight angle at 6 o'clock.

Angles are commonly named by using three capital letters—one for the vertex and one for each of the other endpoints. The letter for the vertex must be in the middle. For example, the right angle below may be called ∠ABC or ∠CBA. (The symbol ∠ means "angle.")

An angle can also be named by using a letter inside the angle (usually a small letter). The acute angle below may be called ∠*a*.

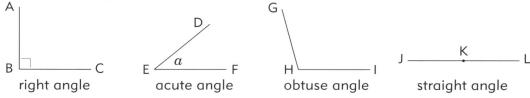

CLASS PRACTICE

Identify each angle as right, acute, obtuse, or straight.

a.
acute

b.
straight

c.
obtuse

d.
right

e.
obtuse

f.
acute

g.
right

h.
straight

WRITTEN EXERCISES

A.   *Identify each angle as right, acute, obtuse, or straight.*

1.
straight

2.
acute

3.
right

4.
obtuse

5. A B C
right

6. D E F
acute

7. G H I
acute

8. J K L
obtuse

9. M a N O
straight

10. P Q d R
obtuse

11. U S c T
acute

12. V W b X
obtuse

B.   *Name the angles in numbers 5–8 above by using the angle symbol and three letters. Give two names for each angle.*

13. (number 5)   **14.** (number 6)   **15.** (number 7)   **16.** (number 8)

$\angle ABC, \angle CBA$ $\angle DFE, \angle EFD$ $\angle GHI, \angle IHG$ $\angle JKL, \angle LKJ$

C.   *Name each angle in numbers 9–12 above by using the angle symbol and one letter.*

17. (number 9)   **18.** (number 10)   **19.** (number 11)   **20.** (number 12)

$\angle a$ $\angle d$ $\angle c$ $\angle b$

a. A *right angle* is an angle whose sides are perpendicular. It has 90 degrees (the number of degrees in a quarter circle). It is shown by the symbol ⌐ in the vertex.

Have the students identify the right angle on the board. Place the symbol in the vertex to indicate that it is a right angle. At what times do the hands of a clock form a right angle? (3 o'clock and 9 o'clock)

b. An *acute angle* has less than 90 degrees. *Acute* means "sharp"; can the students guess why this term is used? (The point of an acute angle is sharp.)

Do clock hands form acute angles at the following times?

2 o'clock   (yes)
5 o'clock   (no)
10 o'clock   (yes)
1 o'clock   (yes)

c. An *obtuse angle* has more than 90 degrees but less than 180 degrees. *Obtuse* means "blunt"; can the students see why this term is used? (The point of an obtuse angle is blunt.)

Do clock hands form obtuse angles at the following times?

3 o'clock?   (no)
5 o'clock?   (yes)
4 o'clock?   (yes)
6 o'clock?   (no)

d. A *straight angle* has 180 degrees. It is a straight line segment, with its vertex on that line.

When do the hands of a clock form a straight angle?   (at 6 o'clock)

5. **Angles are commonly named by using three capital letters.** One letter is for the vertex, and two are for the other endpoints of the two sides. The letter for the vertex must be in the middle.

Name the angles on the board by using the letters with which you labeled them. Arrange them in two ways, such as ∠ABC and ∠CBA. (Call attention to the symbol for angle.)

Mention that an angle can also be named by using a letter inside the angle, usually a small letter. Illustrate by writing small letters inside two of the angles on the board.

D. *Solve these reading problems.*

21. What kind of angle is a 35-degree angle?   acute

22. What kind of angle is a 90-degree angle?   right

23. What kind of angle is a 180-degree angle?   straight

24. What kind of angle is a 115-degree angle?   obtuse

25. Father is buying wire fencing to enclose a rectangular sheep meadow that measures 165 feet by 145 feet. How many feet of fencing will he need?   620 feet

26. A field sprinkler irrigates a circle with a 125-foot radius. What is the area of this circle? (Use π = 3.14.)   49,062.5 square feet

REVIEW EXERCISES

E. *Find the volumes of cubes with these dimensions. (Lesson 152)*

27. $e = 11$ in.   **28.** $e = 4.5$ in.   **29.** $e = 20$ m   **30.** $e = 3.5$ m
  1,331 cu. in.   91.125 cu. in.   8,000 m^3 42.875 m^3

F. *Find the areas of circles with these radii, using π = 3.14. (Lesson 150).*

31. $r = 5$ in.   **32.** $r = 8$ in.   **33.** $r = 1.5$ m   **34.** $r = 9$ cm
  78.5 sq. in.   200.96 sq. in.   7.065 m^2 254.34 cm^2

G. *Find the perimeters of these rectangles and squares. (Lesson 138, 139)*

35. square   **36.** square   **37.** rectangle   **38.** rectangle
  $s = 8$ ft. $s = 15.5$ cm $l = 16$ in. $l = 14.5$ m
        $w = 12$ in. $w = 11.5$ m
  32 ft.   62 cm   56 in.   52 m

H. *Find each answer mentally by changing the decimal to a common fraction before multiplying. (Lesson 90)*

39. 0.25 of 24   6   **40.** 0.33$\frac{1}{3}$ of 33   11

41. 0.75 of 32   24   **42.** 0.6 of 45   27

155. Using Protractors to Measure Angles

The sizes of angles are measured by using an instrument called a **protractor** (prō-trăk'tər). Most protractors are semicircular, with an arrow or line indicating the center of the straight edge. The curved edge has two scales that are marked off in degrees. One scale begins with 0 on the left side of the protractor and increases to 180 degrees on the right side. The other scale begins with 0 on the right side and increases to 180 degrees on the left side.

To measure an angle, use the following steps.

1. If necessary, extend the sides of the angle with the straight edge of the protractor until they are long enough to measure.

2. Lay the protractor on the angle so that the center mark is at the vertex and the straight edge is exactly on one side.

3. Read the number of degrees on the correct scale of the protractor. Be sure it is the scale that begins with 0 on the side toward which the angle opens.

4. Check to make sure your answer is logical. An acute angle has less than 90 degrees, and an obtuse angle has more than 90 degrees.

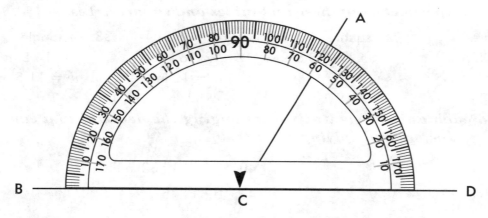

In the illustration above, ∠ ACD measures 60°, and ∠ ACB measures 120°. This is logical because ∠ ACD is an acute angle, and ∠ ACB is an obtuse angle.

To draw an angle with a given number of degrees, use the following steps.

1. Draw one side of the angle with a straightedge, and mark one end as the vertex.

2. Place the straight edge of the protractor on the side you drew, with the center mark at the vertex.

3. Find the desired number of degrees on the correct scale of the protractor, and put a dot on the paper at that point. Be sure it is the scale that begins with 0 on the side toward which the angle opens.

4. Using a straightedge, draw a line from the vertex through the dot you made in step 3.

LESSON 155

Objectives

- To teach *measuring angles with a protractor.
- To teach *using a protractor to draw an angle of a given size.

Review

1. Give Lesson 155 Quiz (Computing Volume).

2. *Volume of rectangular solids* (Lesson 151).
   a. 7 in. × 4 in. × 5 in. (140 cu. in.)
   b. 8 in. × 6 in. × 4 in. (192 cu. in.)
   c. 13 ft. × 7 ft. × 8 ft. (728 cu. ft.)
   d. 18 ft. × 8 ft. × 6 ft. (864 cu. ft.)

3. *Finding what percent one number is of another* (Lessons 122, 123).
   a. 3 is (20%) of 15
   b. 9 is (25%) of 36
   c. 5 is ($41\frac{2}{3}$%) of 12
   d. 16 is ($48\frac{16}{33}$%) of 33

4. *Long division* (Lesson 24). Cast out nines to check the solutions.

   a. $58\overline{)61,328}$ (1,057 R 22)   Check number: 2

   b. $171\overline{)87,912}$ (514 R 18)   Check number: 0

Introduction

Draw an acute, an obtuse, a right, and a straight angle on the board, and have the students identify them. Draw another acute angle, which is obviously not congruent to the first acute angle. Ask the students if both angles are acute. (yes) Are they exactly the same? (no) These angles can be compared by using a protractor.

Each pupil will need a protractor to complete this lesson.

Teaching Guide

1. **Angles are measured in degrees by using a protractor.** To measure an angle, use the following steps.
   (1) If necessary, extend the sides of the angle with the straight edge of the protractor until they are long enough to measure.
   (2) Lay the protractor on the angle so that the center mark is at the vertex and the straight edge is exactly on one side.
   (3) Read the number of degrees on the correct scale of the protractor. Be sure it is the scale that begins with 0 on the side toward which the angle opens.
   (4) Check to make sure your answer is logical. An acute angle has less than 90 degrees, and an obtuse angle has more than 90 degrees.

   Have the pupils practice measuring the angles in the textbook. Make sure that each one is measuring the angles properly, and especially that he is reading the correct scale.

   Also have students measure and compare the angles you drew on the board. Some variation is understandable because of the thickness of the chalk lines.

2. **Angles can be drawn by using a protractor.** To draw an angle with a given number of degrees, use the following steps.

    (1) Draw one side of the angle with a straightedge, and mark one end as the vertex.

    (2) Place the straight edge of the protractor on the side you drew, with the center mark at the vertex.

    (3) Find the desired number of degrees on the correct scale of the protractor, and put a dot on the paper at that point. Be sure it is the scale that begins with 0 on the side toward which the angle opens.

    (4) Using a straightedge, draw a line from the vertex through the dot you made in the preceding step.

    Draw a 55-degree angle on the board, having the students follow the same steps on their papers. Then have them draw a 135-degree angle by themselves. Examine their work for accuracy, especially in using the correct scale.

An Ounce of Prevention

The most common error in measuring angles is to read the wrong scale. Be sure the students understand how to read the protractor. The side on which the protractor is placed points to zero on the correct scale.

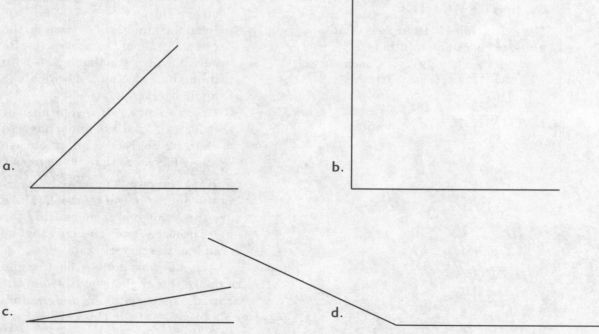

a.

b.

c.

d.

CLASS PRACTICE

Use a protractor to draw angles of the following sizes.   (See facing page.)

   a. 45°   **b.** 90°   **c.** 10°   **d.** 155°

WRITTEN EXERCISES

A.   *Identify each angle as* acute, obtuse, **or** right. **Then measure the size of each angle. All the answers are multiples of 5 degrees.**

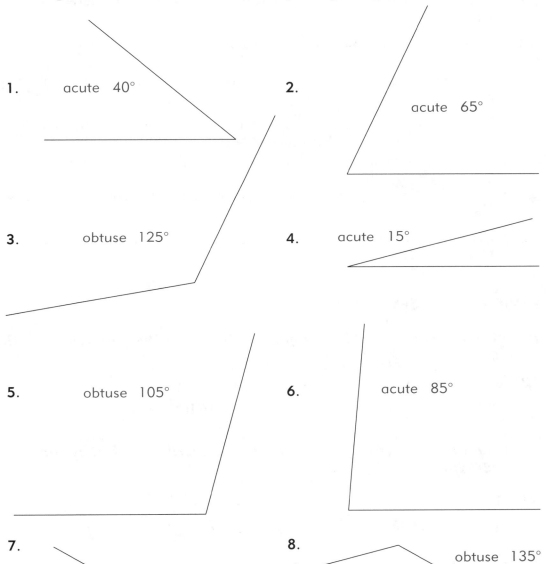

1.   acute 40°

2.   acute 65°

3.   obtuse 125°

4.   acute 15°

5.   obtuse 105°

6.   acute 85°

7.

obtuse 150°

8.   obtuse 135°

B.   Use a protractor to draw angles of the following sizes.

(See facing page.)

9. 55°   **10.** 80°   **11.** 105°   **12.** 160°

13. 15°   **14.** 30°   **15.** 130°   **16.** 100°

C.   Solve these reading problems.

17. David measured an angle of a triangle and found it to be 90 degrees. What kind of angle was it?   right angle

18. Another angle in the same triangle measured 40 degrees. What kind of angle was this?

acute angle

19. The Beilers' living room is 16 feet long, 14 feet wide, and 8 feet high. How many cubic feet does it contain?   1,792 cubic feet

20. The Beilers are planning to spray their milking parlor with fly spray. According to the directions, they should spray 5 seconds for each 1,000 cubic feet of space. If the room is 25 feet long, 20 feet wide, and 8 feet high, how long should they spray?

20 seconds

21. In a Bible assignment, Jennifer had 23 out of 26 answers correct. Find her score to the nearest whole percent.   88%

22. Louise had 19 out of 20 spelling words correct. What was her score as a percent?

95%

REVIEW EXERCISES

D.   Find the volumes of rectangular solids with these dimensions. *(Lesson 151)*

23. 8 in. x 5 in. x 3 in.   120 cu. in.   **24.** 6 in. x 4 in. x 3 in.   72 cu. in.

25. 12 ft. x 9 ft. x 7 ft.   756 cu. ft.   **26.** 15 ft. x 8 ft. x 9 ft.   1,080 cu. ft.

E.   Find these percents. Some of the answers will include fractions. *(Lessons 122, 123)*

27. 4 is $16\frac{2}{3}$ % of 24   **28.** 7 is 20 % of 35

29. 8 is $16\frac{2}{3}$ % of 48   **30.** 7 is $38\frac{8}{9}$ % of 18

F.   Solve these problems. Check by casting out nines. *(Lessons 23, 24)*

31. $88\overline{)44{,}721}$ 508 R 17   **32.** $171\overline{)827{,}912}$ 4,841 R 101

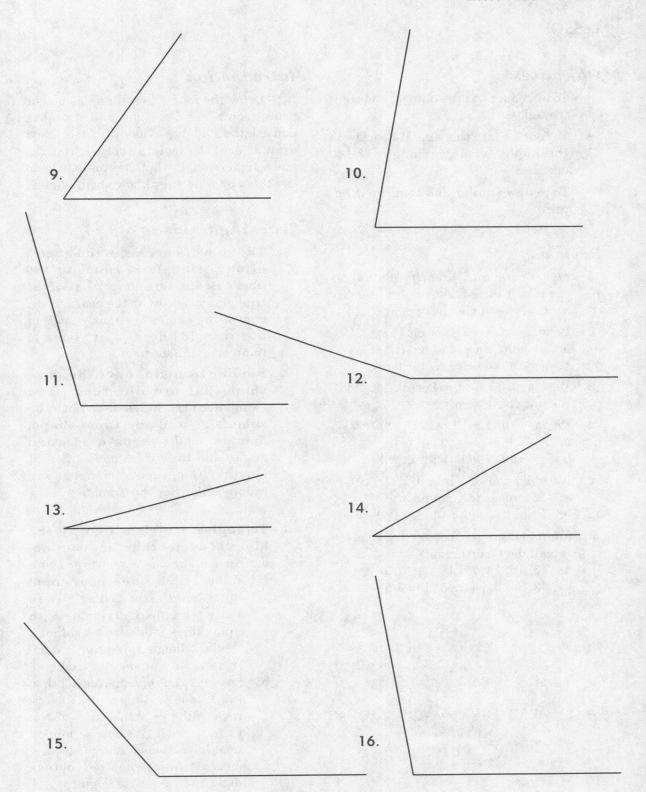

LESSON 156

Objectives

- To introduce *acute, obtuse, and right triangles.

- To teach that *the sum of degrees in the angles of any triangle is 180 degrees.

- To review similar and congruent figures.

Review

1. *Measuring and identifying angles* (Lesson 155). Measure and identify some of the angles in Lesson 155.

2. *Volumes of cubes* (Lesson 152).
   a. $e = 8$ ft., $v =$ (512 cu. ft.)
   b. $e = 14$ ft., $v =$ (2,744 cu. ft.)

3. *Working with circles* (Lesson 148, 149). Review circle terms.

4. *Areas of squares* (Lesson 141).
   a. $s = 7$ ft., $a =$ (49 sq. ft.)
   b. $s = 15$ ft., $a =$ (225 sq. ft.)

5. *Writing ratios* (Lesson 92).
   a.   16 ounces to 1 pound $(\frac{16}{1})$
   b.   1 ton to 2,000 pounds $(\frac{1}{2,000})$

6. *Finding averages* (Lesson 27). Express remainders as fractions.
   a.   15, 16, 14, 17, 19   (16 1/5)
   b.   32, 34, 31, 41, 45   (36 3/5)

Introduction

Draw the four types of angles on the board (acute, obtuse, right, and straight), and ask the students to identify them. Next draw an acute triangle, an obtuse triangle, and a right triangle. Can the students identify them by what they know about angles?

Teaching Guide

1. **The sum of degrees in the angles of any triangle is equal to 180 degrees.** Measure one or more of the triangles you drew on the board. If the sum of the angles is slightly more or less than 180 degrees, it is due to imprecise measurement.

2. **Similar triangles have the same shape but are different sizes. Congruent triangles have both the same size and the same shape.** Similar triangles have identical angles, but their sides have different lengths. Congruent triangles are exactly alike. See the examples in the text.

3. **Triangles are classified by the kinds of angles that they contain.**
   a. An *acute triangle* has three acute angles. If all three sides are of equal length, the triangle is an acute triangle. (A triangle with equal sides may also be called a regular triangle, an equilateral triangle, or an equiangular triangle.)
   b. An *obtuse triangle* has one obtuse angle. Is it possible to draw a triangle with two obtuse angles? No; a figure with two obtuse angles must have at least four sides. Any obtuse triangle has one obtuse angle and two acute angles.

156. Working With Triangles

All triangles are the same in that they have three straight sides and three angles. They are also the same in that the sum of the degrees of the three angles is always 180. For example, the angles may be 90 degrees, 40 degrees, and 50 degrees. Or all three angles may be 60 degrees. In either case, the sum of the angles is 180 degrees.

Triangles are compared by their shapes and sizes. If two triangles have the same shape but one is larger than the other, the two are **similar triangles.** If two triangles are exactly the same shape and size, they are **congruent triangles.** Study the pairs of triangles below.

similar triangles   congruent triangles

Triangles are classified by the kinds of angles that they contain. In an **acute triangle,** all three angles are acute (less than 90 degrees). In an **obtuse triangle,** one of the angles is obtuse (greater than 90 degrees). In a **right triangle,** one angle is a right angle (exactly 90 degrees). These three kinds of triangles are illustrated below. Notice that if all three sides are of equal length, the triangle is an acute triangle.

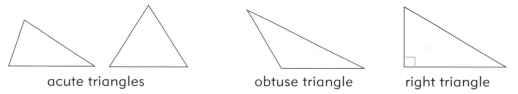

acute triangles   obtuse triangle   right triangle

CLASS PRACTICE

Find the size of the third angle in each triangle.

Angle 1	Angle 2	Angle 3
a. 55°	45°	80°
b. 30°	65°	85°
c. 56°	73°	51°
d. 24°	42°	114°

Write whether each pair of triangles is *similar* or *congruent.*

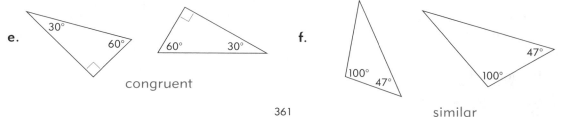

e.   f.

congruent   similar

Write whether each triangle is *acute, obtuse,* **or** *right.*

g. acute

h. 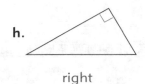 right

i. 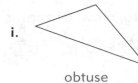 obtuse

j. 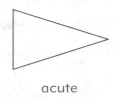 acute

WRITTEN EXERCISES

A. Write the missing number of degrees for each triangle.

1. 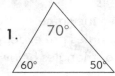 70° 60° 50°

2. 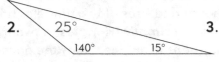 25° 140° 15°

3. 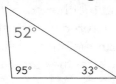 52° 95° 33°

4. 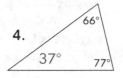 66° 37° 77°

B. Write whether each pair of triangles is *similar* **or** *congruent.*

5. 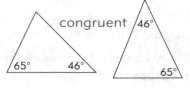 congruent 46° 65° 46° 65°

6. 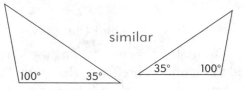 similar 100° 35° 35° 100°

7. 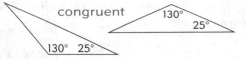 congruent 130° 25° 130° 25°

8. 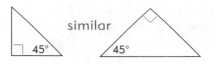 similar 45° 45°

C. Write whether each triangle is *acute, obtuse,* **or** *right.*

9. right

10. acute

11. right

12. 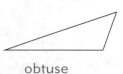 obtuse

13. acute

14. acute

D. Solve these reading problems.

15. A triangle has angles of 75 degrees, 45 degrees, and 60 degrees. What kind of triangle is it?   acute

16. A triangle has angles of 48 degrees, 42 degrees, and 90 degrees. What kind of triangle is it?   right

17. A triangle has angles of 32 degrees, 45 degrees, and 103 degrees. What kind of triangle is it?   obtuse

c. A *right triangle* has one right angle. It can have only one right angle. As in the obtuse triangle, the other two angles must be acute.

18. A triangle has angles of 10 degrees, 15 degrees, and 155 degrees. What kind of triangle is it?   obtuse

19. A triangle has a 55-degree angle and a 65-degree angle. What is the size of the third angle?   60 degrees

20. A triangle has a 105-degree angle and a 50-degree angle. What is the size of the third angle?   25 degrees

REVIEW EXERCISES

E. *Measure each angle with a protractor. All the answers are multiples of 5 degrees.* (Lesson 155)

21.

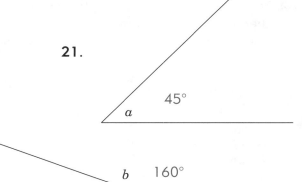

22.

F. *Identify each angle above as* acute, obtuse, right, **or** straight. *(Lesson 154)*

23. ∠ *a*   acute   **24.** ∠ *b*   obtuse

G. *Find the volumes of cubes having these dimensions. (Lesson 152)*

25. *e* = 7 in.   **26.** *e* = 5 in.   **27.** *e* = 13 in.   **28.** *e* = 22 in.
  343 cu. in.   125 cu. in.   2,197 cu. in.   10,648 cu. in.

H. *Write the correct word for each blank. (Lesson 148, 149)*

29. The distance around a circle is the circumference .

30. The distance from edge to edge through the center of a circle is the diameter .

I. *Find the areas of squares having these dimensions. (Lesson 141)*

31. *s* = 12 in.   **32.** *s* = 18 in.   **33.** *s* = 21 in.   **34.** *s* = 30 in.
  144 sq. in.   324 sq. in.   441 sq. in.   900 sq. in.

J. *Write ratios to compare the following numbers. (Lesson 92)*

35. 25 verses to 11 students   **36.** 5 songs to 20 minutes
                $\frac{25}{11}$ or 25:11 $\frac{1}{4}$ or 1:4

K. *Find the average of each set of numbers. Express any remainder as a fraction. (Lesson 27)*

37. 22, 16, 19, 20, 21 $19\frac{3}{5}$ **38.** 44, 25, 39, 48, 46 $40\frac{2}{5}$

157. Working With Graphs: The Circle Graph

A **circle graph** shows how a whole amount is divided into different parts. Bar graphs and picture graphs show how different things compare with each other, but a circle graph shows how each part compares with the whole. Each **sector** (section) of a circle graph has a label and a percent showing what part of the whole that part is. In the circle graph below, the number of students in each class is shown as a part of the whole school.

Students at Lakeville Christian School	
Grades 1–3	20
Grades 4–6	13
Grades 7–10	+ 17
Total	50

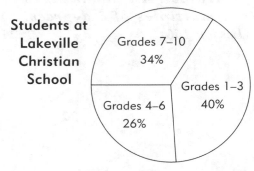

Students at Lakeville Christian School

Remember that there are 360 degrees in a full circle. (Your protractor is a semicircle showing 180 degrees.) To find the number of degrees for each sector of a circle graph, use the following steps.

1. Write a fraction showing what part of the entire circle each sector will be. The numerator should be the number for that sector, and the denominator should be the total amount that the graph represents.

2. Change the fraction you found in step 1 to a percent, rounded to the nearest whole number.

3. A circle has 360 degrees. To find the number of degrees for each part of the circle graph, multiply 360 by the percent for each part.

Check your answers to make sure they are logical. The total of the percents in all the parts should equal 100%, and the total of the degrees in all the parts should equal 360 degrees. Because of rounding, however, there may be a difference of 1 or 2 from the total of 100% and 360 degrees.

The following table shows how these steps were applied to construct the circle graph in the lesson.

	Students	Percents	Degrees
Grades 1–3	20	$\frac{20}{50} = \frac{2}{5} = 40\%$	40% of 360° = 144°
Grades 4–6	13	$\frac{13}{50} = \frac{26}{100} = 26\%$	26% of 360° = 94°
Grades 7–10	17	$\frac{17}{50} = \frac{34}{100} = 34\%$	34% of 360° = 122°
Totals	50	100%	360°

LESSON 157

Objectives

- To teach *reading circle graphs.
- To teach *calculating the degrees needed to make the sectors of a circle graph.

Review

1. Give Lesson 157 Speed Test (Multiplying Decimals).

2. *Circles and rectangles.*
   Area of circles (Lesson 150).
      a. $r = 4$ in., $a = (50.24$ sq. in.)
      b. $r = 4.6$ in., $a = (66.4424$ sq. in.)
   Circumference of circles (Lesson 149).
      c. $d = 6.5$ in., $c = (20.41$ in.)
      d. $d = 9.5$ in., $c = (29.83$ in.)
   Area of rectangles (Lesson 140).
      e. $l = 25$ ft., $w = 14$ ft.
        $a = (350$ sq. ft.)
      f. $l = 125$ ft., $w = 85$ ft.
        $a = (10{,}625$ sq. ft.)

3. *Proportion problems* (Lesson 93).
      a. $\frac{5}{6} = \frac{n}{24}$, $n = (20)$
      b. $\frac{8}{9} = \frac{n}{16}$, $n = (14\frac{2}{9})$
      c. $\frac{7}{12} = \frac{16}{n}$, $n = (27\frac{3}{7})$

Introduction

Review the use of picture, bar, and line graphs. Picture graphs and bar graphs are often used to compare different things, such as the population of various states or countries. A line graph is used to compare the same thing at different times. For example, a line graph could be used to compare the population of a state in different years.

A circle graph shows how the different parts of a given quantity are related to the total quantity. The graph in the lesson shows how the number of students in each classroom is related to the number of students in the entire school.

Teaching Guide

1. **A circle graph shows how a whole amount is divided into different parts.** Discuss the graph in the lesson text. What percent of the total student body is in grades 1–3? (40%) grades 4–6? (26%) grades 7–10? (34%) Make it clear that the size of each sector of the circle graph is the same percentage of the entire circle as what the number of students in that room is of the entire school. For example, grades 1–3 make up 40% of the students in the school, and the grades 1–3 sector on the graph is 40% of the graph.

2. **To make a circle graph, first calculate the number of degrees for each sector.** Use the following steps. (Show how they apply to the table in the lesson.)
   (1) Write a fraction showing what part of the entire circle each sector will be. The numerator should be the number for that sector, and the denominator should be the total amount that the graph represents.

(2) Change the fraction you found in the first step to a percent, rounded to the nearest whole number.

(3) A circle has 360 degrees. To find the number of degrees for each part of the circle graph, multiply 360 by the percent for each part.

(4) Check your answers to make sure they are logical. The total of the percents in all the parts should equal 100%, and the total of the degrees in all the parts should equal 360 degrees. Because of rounding, however, there may be a difference of 1 or 2 from the total of 100% and 360 degrees.

Note: Be sure to assign the entire charts for calculating the degrees in each sector of a circle graph. The completed charts will be used to prepare circle graphs in Lesson 158.

	Students	Percents	Degrees
Grade 7	3	$\frac{3}{15} = \frac{1}{5} = \frac{20}{100} = 20\%$	20% of 360° = 72°
Grade 8	7	$\frac{7}{15} = 7 \div 15 = 47\%$	47% of 360° = 169°
Grade 9	3	$\frac{3}{15} = \frac{1}{5} = \frac{20}{100} = 20\%$	20% of 360° = 72°
Grade 10	2	$\frac{2}{15} = 2 \div 15 = 13\%$	13% of 360° = 47°
Totals	15	100%	360°

(Percents and degrees are rounded to the nearest whole number.)

CLASS PRACTICE

Copy and complete the following table to find how many degrees of a circle each part of the circle graph will contain. Then total the columns to make sure your calculations are correct.

Students in Wellsville Mennonite School

	Students	*Percents*		*Degrees*	
Grades 1–3	7	**a.**	32%	**b.**	115°
Grades 4–6	10	**c.**	45%	**d.**	162°
Grades 7–10	5	**e.**	23%	**f.**	83°
Totals	22	**g.**	100%	**h.**	360°

WRITTEN EXERCISES

A.   *Study the following circle graph to answer these questions.*

1. What percent of the land area on the earth is in Asia?   30%

2. What percent of the land area on the earth is in North America?   16%

3. Which two continents together contain one-half of the land area on the earth?
Asia and Africa

4. What percent of the land area on the earth is in Europe?   7%

Land Area of the Continents

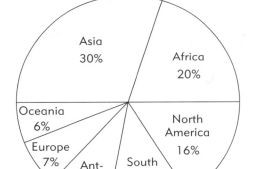

B.   *Copy and complete the following tables to find how many degrees of a circle each part of the circle graph will contain. Then total the columns to make sure your calculations are correct. (The total degrees in the second chart will be 1 off because of rounding.) Save your work; you will use these charts in Lesson 158 to construct circle graphs.*

Students in Grades 1–3

	Students	*Percents*		*Degrees*	
Grade 1	7	**5.**	35%	**6.**	126°
Grade 2	5	**7.**	25%	**8.**	90°
Grade 3	8	**9.**	40%	**10.**	144°
Totals	20	**11.**	100%	**12.**	360°

Students in Grades 4–6

	Students	Percents		Degrees	
Grade 4	4	**13.** 31%		**14.** 112°	
Grade 5	6	**15.** 46%		**16.** 166°	
Grade 6	3	**17.** 23%		**18.** 83°	
Totals	13	**19.** 100%		**20.** 361°	

REVIEW EXERCISES

C.   *Solve these reading problems. Use π = 3.14 when needed.* (Lessons 140, 149, 150)

21. A circle has a diameter of 4.5 inches. What is the circumference?   14.13 inches

22. A circle has a diameter of 9.25 inches. What is the circumference?   29.045 inches

23. What is the area of a circle that has a radius of 2.5 inches?   19.625 square inches

24. What is the area of a circle that has a radius of 3.5 inches?   38.465 square inches

25. The Witmers' garden is 85 feet long and 75 feet wide. What is its area?

6,375 square feet

26. The Witmers' one-story rectangular house is 46 feet long and 30 feet wide. What is its floor area?

1,380 square feet

D.   *Identify each triangle as* acute, obtuse, *or* right. *(Lesson 156)*

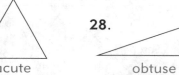

27.   acute   **28.**   obtuse   **29.**   acute   **30.**   right

E.   *Measure each angle with a protractor. All the answers are multiples of 5 degrees.* (Lesson 155)

31.

115°

32.

90°

F.   *Find the missing numbers in these proportions. Express any remainders as fractions.* (Lesson 93)

33. $\frac{3}{5} = \frac{n}{7}$ **34.** $\frac{6}{7} = \frac{n}{15}$ **35.** $\frac{9}{14} = \frac{6}{n}$ **36.** $\frac{8}{15} = \frac{10}{n}$

$n = 4\frac{1}{5}$ $n = 12\frac{6}{7}$ $n = 9\frac{1}{3}$ $n = 18\frac{3}{4}$

An Ounce of Prevention

Stress accuracy in finding each percent figure. An error in the percentage calculation will also cause an error when the degrees are calculated.

LESSON 158

Objective

- To teach *constructing circle graphs by using a protractor and a compass.

Review

1. *Types of angles* (Lesson 154). Identify these angles as *acute, obtuse, right,* or *straight* angles.
   a. 180 degrees (straight)
   b. 90 degrees (right)
   c. 91 degrees (obtuse)
   d. 89 degrees (acute)

2. *Types of triangles* (Lesson 156). Identify these triangles.
   a. 50 degrees, 40 degrees, 90 degrees (right triangle)
   b. 54 degrees, 63 degrees, 63 degrees (acute triangle)
   c. 95 degrees, 35 degrees, 50 degrees (obtuse triangle)
   d. 60 degrees, 60 degrees, 60 degrees (acute triangle)

3. *Finding areas.*
   Circles (Lesson 150).
   a. $r = 5$ in., $a =$ (78.5 sq. in.)
   b. $r = 4$ ft., $a =$ (50.24 sq. ft.)
   c. $r = 4.4$ m, $a =$ (60.7904 m²)
   Parallelograms. (Lesson 142)
   d. $b = 8$ in., $h = 5$ in.
      $a =$ (40 sq. in.)
   e. $b = 14$ in., $h = 7$ in.
      $a =$ (98 sq. in.)
   f. $b = 52$ cm, $h = 20$ cm
      $a =$ (1,040 cm²)

4. *Writing proportions to solve reading problems* (Lesson 94).
   a. One day Melanie completed 3 math problems in 5 minutes. At that rate, how long will it take to complete her assignment if there are 33 problems in all?
      3 problems in 5 min.
      33 problems in n min.
      $\frac{3}{5} = \frac{33}{n}$ $5 \times 33 \div 3 = 55$ min.
   b. The next day, Melanie completed 4 math problems in 5 minutes. At that rate, how many problems can she do in 45 minutes?
      4 problems in 5 min.
      n problems in 45 min.
      $\frac{4}{5} = \frac{n}{45}$ $4 \times 45 \div 5 = 36$ problems

Introduction

Point out the information shown for making a circle graph in the lesson text. Look at the first row (Grade 4). How was each number calculated? Why does the sum of all the percents equal 100%? (These three grades include all the students in the room.) Why does the sum of all the degrees equal 360 degrees? (There are 360 degrees in a full circle.)

A circle has 360 degrees. Can anyone guess how to use the degrees that were calculated to make a circle graph? (The degrees calculated will be used in drawing the sectors of the circle graph.)

CLASS PRACTICE

Distribution of Hours
on Weekdays

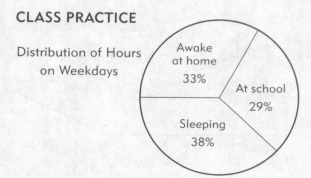

Awake at home 33%

At school 29%

Sleeping 38%

158. Working With Graphs: Constructing Circle Graphs

In Lesson 157 you learned about circle graphs and how to find the number of degrees for each sector. In this lesson you will use the degrees you calculated to construct a circle graph. You can do this by following the steps below.

1. Using a compass, draw a circle with a 2-inch radius.
2. Draw a radius in the circle to use as a starting point.
3. Using the calculated degrees, draw an angle for the first sector. Use the second side of this angle as the base for the next angle. Continue around the circle until all the sectors are drawn.

   The last sector will be what is left when all the other sectors are drawn. Its size should be close to the number of degrees calculated for the last sector.
4. Write the appropriate label and percent in each sector.
5. Write a title for the graph.

The following illustration shows the information needed to prepare a circle graph, and the graph that is prepared from the information.

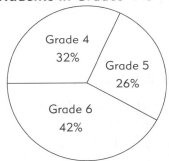

Students in Grades 4–6

	Students	Percents	Degrees
Grade 4	6	32%	115°
Grade 5	5	26%	94°
Grade 6	8	42%	151°
Totals	19	100%	360°

Students in Grades 4–6

CLASS PRACTICE

Use the following table to construct a circle graph.

Distribution of Hours on Weekdays

	Hours	Percents		Degrees	
Awake at home	8	a.	33%	b.	119°
At school	7	c.	29%	d.	104°
Sleeping	9	e.	38%	f.	137°
Totals	24	g.	100%	h.	360°

(Sample graph on facing page)

WRITTEN EXERCISES

A. Draw these circle graphs, using your answers from Lesson 157.

1–5. Prepare a circle graph based on the information in problems 5–12 of Lesson 157.

6–10. Prepare a circle graph based on the information in problems 13–20 of Lesson 157.

(Sample graphs on page T–386)

B.   *Solve these reading problems.*

11. In a triangle, one angle has 42 degrees and another has 57 degrees. How many degrees are in the third angle?   81°

12. A triangle has a right angle and a 48-degree angle. How many degrees are in the third angle?   42°

13. The angles of a triangle are 38 degrees, 62 degrees, and 80 degrees. What kind of triangle is it?   acute

14. The angles of a triangle are 28 degrees, 45 degrees, and 107 degrees. What kind of triangle is it?   obtuse

15. A circular table top has a radius of 21 inches. What is its area?

1,384.74 square inches

16. The top of a tree stump has a radius of 9 inches. What is its area?

254.34 square inches

REVIEW EXERCISES

C.   *Identify triangles with these angles as* acute, obtuse, *or* right. *(Lesson 156)*

17. 35°, 48°, 97°   obtuse   18. 60°, 60°, 60°   acute

19. 28°, 90°, 62°   right   20. 87°, 50°, 43°   acute

D.   *Find the areas of circles with these radii. (Lesson 150)*

21. 9 in.   22. 4 ft.   23. 4.4 m   24. 3.8 m
     254.34 sq. in.   50.24 sq. ft.   60.7904 m²   45.3416 m²

E.   *Find the areas of these parallelograms. (Lesson 142)*

25. b = 9 in.   26. b = 12 in.   27. b = 23 cm   28. b = 28 mm
     h = 7 in. h = 6 in. h = 16 cm h = 21 mm
     63 sq. in.   72 sq. in.   368 cm²   588 mm²

F.   *Use proportions to solve these reading problems. (Lesson 94)*

29. Dale had 7 out of every 8 of his math problems correct. There were 40 math problems in the assignment. How many of them did he do correctly? $\frac{7}{8} = \frac{n}{40}$ n = 35 problems

30. The Stauffer family has 48 dairy cows. They are presently milking 5 out of every 6 of them. How many cows are they milking? $\frac{5}{6} = \frac{n}{48}$ n = 40 cows

Teaching Guide

To construct a circle graph, use the degrees calculated for each sector of the graph. The steps are as follows:

1. Using a compass, draw a circle of a suitable size (a 2-inch radius is suggested).
2. Draw a radius in the circle to use as a starting point.
3. Using the calculated degrees, draw an angle for the first sector. Use the second side of this angle as the base for the next angle. Continue around the circle until all the sectors are drawn.

    The last sector will be what is left when all the other sectors are drawn. Its size should be close to the number of degrees calculated for the last sector. (*Note:* You may have the students place a small x in the vertex of the last sector to show that it may not be quite as accurate as the other sectors.)
4. Write the appropriate label and percent in each sector.
5. Write a title for the graph.

Have the students use their protractors to see how the circle graph in the lesson was constructed from the degrees that were calculated. Then draw a circle on the board, and prepare a circle graph based on the information below. Have the students prepare the same graph on paper as you make it on the board.

To do the written work, the students will need their answers for problems 5–20 in Lesson 157. Either have them use their homework papers, or give them the degrees for each graph.

In checking the lesson, allow a tolerance of 2 degrees for each sector. Do not count the sector marked with an x wrong if it has too many or too few degrees. This can happen either because of allowable tolerance in the other sectors or because of a mistake in one of the other sectors.

	Students	Percents	Degrees
Grade 7	3	$\frac{3}{15} = \frac{1}{5} = \frac{20}{100} = 20\%$	20% of 360° = 72°
Grade 8	7	$\frac{7}{15} = 7 \div 15 = 47\%$	47% of 360° = 169°
Grade 9	3	$\frac{3}{15} = \frac{1}{5} = \frac{20}{100} = 20\%$	20% of 360° = 72°
Grade 10	2	$\frac{2}{15} = 2 \div 15 = 13\%$	13% of 360° = 47°
Totals	15	100%	360°

(Percents and degrees are rounded to the nearest whole number.)

WRITTEN EXERCISES

1–5. Students in Grades 1–3

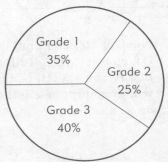

6–10. Students in Grades 4–6

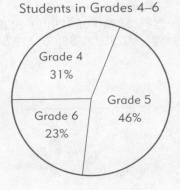

LESSON 159

Objective

*   To practice using sketches to solve reading problems.

Review

1. Give Lesson 159 Speed Test (Addition). Time limit: 2 minutes. Speed tests on the basic operations will be repeated during the remainder of the course. If the students finish easily in 2 minutes, reduce the time to 1 3/4 or 1 1/2 minutes.

2. *Angles and circle graphs* (Lesson 155, 159). Exercises in the lesson are sufficient review.

3. *Volumes of rectangular solids* (Lesson 151).
    a. $l = 5$ in., $w = 2$ in., $h = 7$ in.
        $v = $ (70 cu. in.)
    b. $l = 8$ in., $w = 4$ in., $h = 8$ in.
        $v = $ (256 cu. in.)
    c. $l = 14$ ft., $w = 10$ ft., $h = 7$ ft.
        $v = $ (980 cu. ft.)

4. *Areas of triangles* (Lesson 143).
    a. $b = 5$ in., $h = 2$ in., $a = $ (5 sq. in.)
    b. $b = 8$ in., $h = 4$ in., $a = $ (16 sq. in.)
    c. $b = 14$ ft., $h = 10$ ft., $a = $ (70 sq. ft.)

5. *Counting out change* (Lesson 127).
    a. Amount of sale: $3.67
        Amount given: $5.00
        ($3.67 out of $5.00, $3.70, $3.75, $4.00, $5.00)
    b. Amount of sale: $5.89
        Amount given: $20.00
        ($5.89 out of $20.00, $5.90, $6.00, $7.00, $8.00, $9.00, $10.00, $20.00)

Introduction

Ask the students, "If you have 4 fence posts and place them 10 feet apart, how long a fence can you build?" If someone offers 40 feet as the answer, draw a sketch, and then repeat the question. It is beneficial to draw sketches for some reading problems.

Teaching Guide

1. Call attention to Examples A and B in the text. Point out the following things about the sketches.
    a. The sketches are drawn neatly and accurately.
    b. The sketches are drawn simply. In artwork, extra details often add to the attractiveness of a picture. But on a math sketch, extra details are unnecessary and distracting. They clutter the sketch in the same way that a blueprint would be cluttered if it showed all the home furnishings.

2. Read the problems below, and have the students suggest the sketches needed. Their sketches may vary somewhat from the ones shown below, but they should be accurate and should help to find the correct solutions.
    a. The Martins are planting strawberries in short rows. The rows are 20 feet long, and the plants are set 2 feet apart. How many plants can be put in each row if they leave 2 feet at each end for a border?

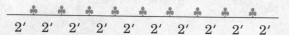

2'   2'   2'   2'   2'   2'   2'   2'   2'   2'

Nine plants can be put in each row. (If you let the students guess before the sketch is drawn, they will probably guess either 8 plants or 10 plants.)

159. Reading Problems: Using Sketches

A builder often uses a blueprint to calculate how much lumber he will need for a building before any work is done. Using a sketch of the building helps him to visualize it as he plans the project.

Solving a reading problem is somewhat similar. You must usually find the answer without seeing the actual objects that the problem is about. For many problems like this, a simple sketch or drawing—like a builder's blueprint—will help you to see the situation and plan how to find the solution.

Sketches are for the benefit of the person solving the problem. They are not artwork and are not graded as such. Sketches must be complete enough to be clear and accurate, or they will be useless. Sketches are most useful when they contain only the important information.

To draw a sketch for a problem, use the following steps.

1. Picture the problem and sketch it, using simple shapes.
2. Write the information given in the problem where it belongs on the sketch.
3. Solve the problem. Make sure your answer works on the sketch.

Example A

Father is buying posts for the school yard fence. The posts will be spaced 10 feet apart. How many posts will be needed for a 50-foot fence?

I 10' I 10' I 10' I 10' I 10' I

Six posts will be needed. If this problem were solved without a sketch, many people would answer "5 posts"—forgetting that a post is needed at the beginning.

Example B

Gary is sawing an 8-foot board into 1-foot pieces. How many cuts will he need to make?

| 1 | 2 | 3 | 4 | 5 | 6 | 7 | 8 |

Gary will need to make 7 cuts. If this problem were solved without a sketch, many people would answer "8 cuts"—forgetting that the last cut results in two 1-foot pieces.

CLASS PRACTICE

Make a simple, neat sketch for each reading problem. Use your sketches to find the solutions to the problems. (Sample sketches on page T–388)

a. Mother is setting the table, which measures 12 feet by 4 feet. If she sets the plates 2 feet apart, beginning 1 foot from each corner, how many plates will she set on the table?

16 plates

b. The Smiths are laying one row of concrete blocks to make a sandbox with outside dimensions of 8 feet by 4 feet. How many blocks will they use if the blocks are 16 inches long and 8 inches wide?

16 blocks

WRITTEN EXERCISES

A. ***Make a simple, neat sketch for each reading problem. Use your sketches to find the solutions to the problems.***   (Sample sketches on facing page)

1. Father plans to dig postholes to make a clothesline. He wants the clothesline to be 40 feet long with posts every 20 feet. How many postholes will Father need to dig?
3 postholes

2. Esther hung 8 towels on the clothesline, using 1 clothespin between each 2 towels and 1 at each end of the row. How many clothespins did she use in all?   9 clothes pins

3. Father is buying posts to build a fence around a pasture. The pasture measures 100 feet by 60 feet, and the fence posts will be placed every 20 feet. How many posts will he need?
16 posts

4. Two cows were tied in a pasture to stakes 140 feet apart. One cow had 50 feet of rope, and the other had 75 feet. How close to each other could the cows graze?
15 feet

5. Mother is helping to make dresses at the sewing circle. How many dresses can be made from 10 yards of fabric if each dress requires $1\frac{1}{2}$ yards? (Drop any remainder because only whole dresses can be made.)
6 dresses

6. Father asked Marlin to cut an 8-foot board into 2-foot pieces. How many times will he need to cut the board?
3 times

7. How far is 3 inches on a map if the scale is $\frac{1}{2}$ inch = 15 miles?   90 miles

8. How many days is it from April 16 to April 29, counting both the sixteenth and the twenty-ninth?
14 days

9. Wayne rode his bicycle 3 miles in 15 minutes. At that rate, how far can he ride in 1 hour?
12 miles

10. A rectangle is 5 inches long and 4 inches wide. What is its area?   20 square inches

11. Two cars left town at exactly the same time, one traveling east and one traveling west. The eastbound car traveled at an average speed of 52 miles per hour, and the westbound car traveled at 54 miles per hour. After 2.5 hours, how far were the cars from each other?
265 miles

12. A car and a train both left Ashville at the same time and traveled in the same direction. The car averaged 50 miles per hour and the train averaged 65 miles per hour. How far will the train be ahead of the car in 3 hours?   45 miles

World Population

REVIEW EXERCISES

B. ***Answer these questions by using the circle graph at the right.*** *(Lesson 159)*

13. What percent of the world's population lives in North America?   5%

14. What percent of the world's population lives in Latin America?   8%

15. What percent lives in Asia?   56%

16. What percent lives in Europe?   9%

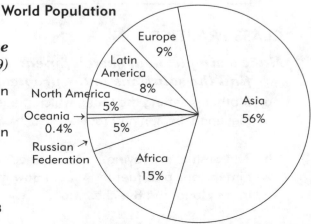

b. Mother planted flowers along the edge of a 4-foot square. The flowers are 1 foot apart. How many flowers did Mother plant?

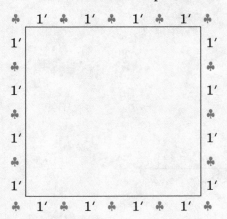

Mother planted 16 flowers.

CLASS PRACTICE

a.
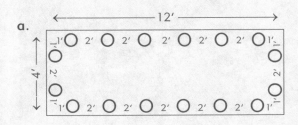

b.
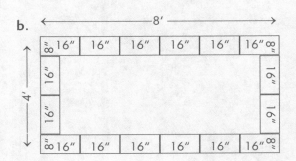

WRITTEN EXERCISES

1.
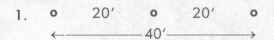

2.

3.
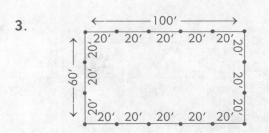

4.
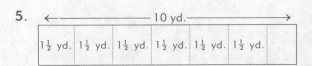

5.

| 1½ yd. | 1½ yd. | 1½ yd. | 1½ yd. | 1½ yd. | 1½ yd. | |

← 10 yd. →

6.

| 2' | 2' | 2' | 2' |

← 8' →

7.

| 15 mi. | 15 mi. | 15 mi. | 15 mi. | 15 mi. | 15 mi. |
| ½" | ½" | ½" | ½" | ½" | ½" |

← 3" →

8.

| 16 | 17 | 18 | 19 | 20 | 21 | 22 |
| 23 | 24 | 25 | 26 | 27 | 28 | 29 |

9.

| 3 mi. | 3 mi. | 3 mi. | 3 mi. |
| 15 min. | 15 min. | 15 min. | 15 min. |

← 1 hr. →

(Continued on next page)

10.

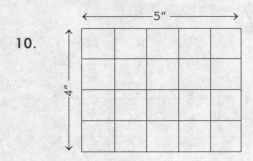

11.

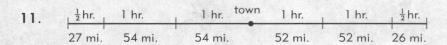

12.

C. Measure each angle with a protractor. All the answers are multiples of 5 degrees. *(Lesson 155)*

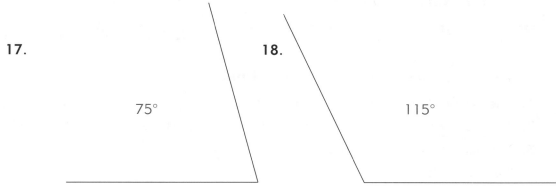

17.   75°   **18.**   115°

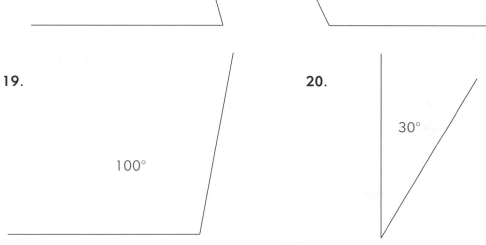

19.   100°   **20.**   30°

D. Find the volumes of rectangular solids with these dimensions. *(Lesson 151)*

21. l = 4 in.	**22.** l = 9 in.	**23.** l = 12 ft.	**24.** l = 15 ft.
w = 3 in.	w = 7 in.	w = 11 ft.	w = 12 ft.
h = 4 in.	h = 5 in.	h = 9 ft.	h = 18 ft.
48 cu. in.	315 cu. in.	1,188 cu. ft.	3,240 cu. ft.

E. Find the areas of triangles with these dimensions. *(Lesson 143)*

25. b = 4 in.	**26.** b = 9 in.	**27.** b = 12 ft.	**28.** b = 15 ft.
h = 3 in.	h = 7 in.	h = 11 ft.	h = 12 ft.
6 sq. in.	$31\frac{1}{2}$ sq. in.	66 sq. ft.	90 sq. ft.

F. Copy and fill in the following chart. *(Lesson 127)*

	Amount of Sale	Amount Given	1¢	5¢	10¢	25¢	$1	$5	Total Change
29.	$0.75	$1.00				1			$0.25
30.	$0.37	$1.00	3		1	2			$0.63
31.	$0.63	$5.00	2		1	1	4		$4.37
32.	$2.25	$3.00				3			$0.75

160. Chapter 12 Review

A.   Write the correct word for each blank.

1. The symbol π is called __pi__ and has a value of __$3\frac{1}{7}$__ or __3.14__.

2. The distance from the center of a circle to its edge is the __radius__.

3. The distance around a circle is its __circumference__.

4. Half of a circle is a(n) __semicircle__.

5. A(n) __arc__ is any part of the curve of a circle.

6. The distance from one edge of a circle through the center to the other edge is the __diameter__.

7. A 90-degree angle is a(n) __right__ angle.

8. An angle with more than 90 but less than 180 degrees is a(n) __obtuse__ angle.

9. An angle with less than 90 degrees is a(n) __acute__ angle.

10. A 180-degree angle is a(n) __straight__ angle.

11. Triangles with the same shape but different sizes are __similar__.

12. Triangles with the same shape and size are __congruent__.

13. A triangle with all three angles less than 90 degrees is a(n) __acute__ triangle.

14. A triangle with one 90-degree angle is a(n) __right__ triangle.

15. A triangle with equal sides and 60-degree angles is a(n) __acute__ triangle.

16. A triangle with one angle greater than 90 degrees is a(n) __obtuse__ triangle.

B.   Write the missing numbers. *(Lesson 148)*

	Radius	Diameter
17.	6 in.	12 in.
18.	3.5 in.	7 in.
19.	4 ft.	8 ft.
20.	4.5 ft.	9 ft.

C.   Find the circumferences of circles with these diameters. *(Lesson 149)*
Use the decimal form of π.

21. 6 inches   18.84 inches   **22.** 3 inches   9.42 inches

Use the fractional form of π.

23. 12 inches $37\frac{5}{7}$ inches   **24.** 14 feet   44 feet

LESSON 160

Objective

- To review the material taught in Chapter 12.

Teaching Guide

This review covers Lessons 148–159. Since the lesson is lengthy, you may wish to review the odd-numbered exercises in class and assign the even-numbered exercises. But note that exercises 53–61 all relate to one project. One possible approach would be to do the chart in class and have the students use that information to prepare the graph in exercise 62.

If an extra amount of review is needed before the test, use lessons 148–159 for review material in class. Then assign the even numbers one day and the odd numbers the next. Since numbers 53–61 all relate to one project, you could assign exercises 53–61 the first day and exercise 62 the second day.

D. Find the areas of circles with these radii. Use the decimal form of π. *(Lesson 150)*

25. 3 in.
28.26 sq. in.

26. 6 in.
113.04 sq. in.

27. 7 in.
153.86 sq. in.

28. 8 in.
200.96 sq. in.

E. For each of these linear units, write the abbreviation for the corresponding cubic unit. *(Lessons 151, 153)*

29. ft. cu. ft.

30. yd. cu. yd.

31. m m^3

32. cm cm^3

F. Find the volumes of rectangular solids with these dimensions. *(Lesson 151)*

	Length	Width	Height			Length	Width	Height	
33.	3 in.	2 in.	3 in.	18 cu. in.	**34.**	4 in.	3 in.	4 in.	48 cu. in.
35.	7 in.	6 in.	4 in.	168 cu. in.	**36.**	8 in.	5 in.	3 in.	120 cu. in.

G. Find the volumes of cubes having these edges. *(Lessons 152, 153)*

37. $e = 3$ in.
27 cu. in.

38. $e = 5$ in.
125 cu. in.

39. $e = 7$ m
343 m^3

40. $e = 8$ cm
512 cm^3

H. Measure each angle with a protractor. All the answers are multiples of 5 degrees. *(Lesson 155)*

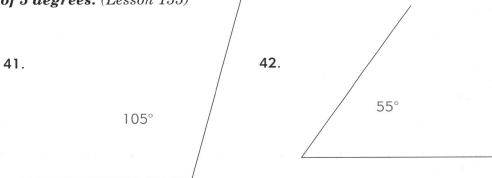

41.   105°

42.   55°

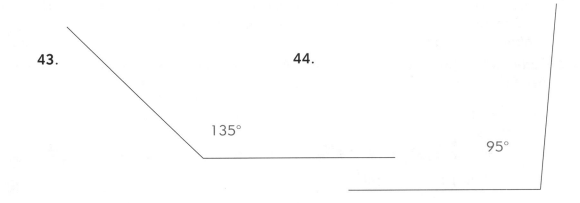

43.   135°

44.   95°

I.   **Each pair of numbers gives the sizes of two angles in a triangle. Find the size of the third angle.** *(Lesson 156)*

45. 68°, 42° 70°   **46.** 90°, 34° 56°   **47.** 122°, 25° 33°   **48.** 60°, 60° 60°

J.   **For each triangle in numbers 45–48, name the kind that it is.** *(Lesson 156)*

49. (triangle in 45)   **50.** (triangle in 46)   **51.** (triangle in 47)   **52.** (triangle in 48)

     acute   right   obtuse   acute

K.   **Write the missing numbers for the following chart, which can be used to construct a circle graph. Then do number 62.** *(Lesson 157)*

Number of Students in Grades 6 and 7

	Students	*Ratios*	*Percents*	*Degrees*
Grade 6	10	**53.** $\frac{5}{12}$	**54.** 42%	**55.** 151°
Grade 7	14	**56.** $\frac{7}{12}$	**57.** 58%	**58.** 209°
Totals	24	**59.** $\frac{12}{12}$	**60.** 100%	**61.** 360°

62. Prepare a circle graph by using your answers to numbers 53–58 above. (Lesson 158)

                                    (Sample graph on facing page)

L.   **Solve these reading problems.**

63. The diameter of a silo is 16 feet. What is its radius?   8 feet

64. An irrigation system waters a circular area with a diameter of 400 feet. What is the radius of this circle?   200 feet

65. What is the circumference of a silo with a 16-foot diameter?   50.24 feet

66. If an irrigation system waters a circle with a 400-foot diameter, what is the circumference of the circle?   1,256 feet

M.   **Draw a sketch for each reading problem to help you find the solution.**
(Lesson 159)   (Sample sketches on facing page)

67. The Rudolph family is planting a row of tall bushes to serve as a windbreak. The row is 42 feet long, and the bushes are being planted 6 feet apart. How many bushes are they planting?   8 bushes

68. Father told John to saw a 3-foot board into 9-inch pieces. How many cuts will John need to make?   3 cuts

161. Chapter 12 Test

LESSON 161

Objective

- To test the students' mastery of the concepts in Chapter 12.

Teaching Guide

1. Correct Lesson 160.
2. Review any areas of special difficulty.
3. Administer the test.

62.

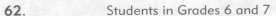

Students in Grades 6 and 7

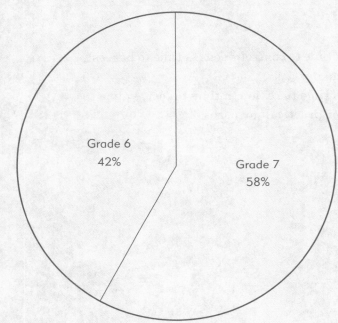

Grade 6
42%

Grade 7
58%

67.

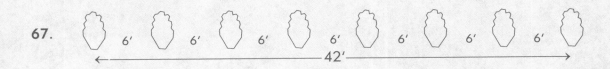

68.

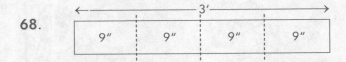

A time to plant, a time to control weeds, a time to harvest, a time to consume the harvest.

A time to learn, a time to review, a time to test, a time to use the knowledge for practical purposes.

Chapter 13

Number Sentences
and Year-End Review

To every thing there is a season, and a time to every purpose under the sun.
(Ecclesiastes 3:1)

162. Working With Number Sentences

Sometimes in math, letters or other symbols are used to represent a known or an unknown number. In formulas relating to circles, the symbol π is used to stand for the known value 3.14. In the formula for the perimeter of a triangle, $p = a + b + c$, each letter represents an unknown number. When you use the triangle formula, you replace each letter with the length of the sides of a triangle to find the perimeter.

A problem written with a letter or a symbol to stand for a number is called a **number sentence** or an **equation.** You are familiar with a number sentence such as 5 + ? = 8, and you know that the answer is 3. This problem can also be written $5 + n = 8$. The letter n stands for the unknown number, which added to 5, equals 8. In this number sentence, n is equal to 3. In the number sentence $6 - n = 5$, n is equal to 1.

When you write the answer to a number sentence in which a letter stands for a number, write the letter followed by an equal sign and then the missing number. The answer to $8 \times n = 16$ is written like this: $n = 2$.

$12 + n = 36$	$36 - n = 12$	$12 \times n = 36$	$36 \div n = 12$
$n = 24$	$n = 24$	$n = 3$	$n = 3$
Check	Check	Check	Check
$12 + 24 = 36$	$36 - 24 = 12$	$12 \times 3 = 36$	$36 \div 3 = 12$

CLASS PRACTICE

Find the value of the letter in each number sentence. Be sure to include the letter in your answer, such as n = 5.

a. $14 - n = 8$ $n = 6$ **b.** $n + 5 = 12$ $n = 7$ **c.** $n - 5 = 12$ $n = 17$ **d.** $3 + n = 12$ $n = 9$

e. $n \times 7 = 49$ $n = 7$ **f.** $15 \times n = 75$ $n = 5$ **g.** $n \div 12 = 4$ $n = 48$ **h.** $66 \div n = 6$ $n = 11$

WRITTEN EXERCISES

A.   *Write true or false for each number sentence.*

1. $7 + 6 = 13$ true   **2.** $8 + 5 = 12$ false   **3.** $12 \times 6 = 74$ false   **4.** $13 \times 12 = 156$ true

5. $63 \div 9 = 7$ true   **6.** $65 \div 5 = 15$ false   **7.** $18 - 7 = 11$ true   **8.** $91 - 27 = 54$ false

LESSON 162

Objective

- To teach *solving number sentences.

Review

1. Give Lesson 162 Speed Test (Subtraction). Time limit: 2 minutes. This is a continuation of reviewing the basic facts, which began in Lesson 159.

2. *Right, acute, obtuse, and straight angles* (Lesson 154).
   a. 99 degrees (obtuse)
   b. 75 degrees (acute)
   c. 90 degrees (right)
   d. 180 degrees (straight)

3. *Income, expense, and profit* (Lesson 129).
   a. income: $80; expenses: $35, $42; profit: ($3)
   b. income: $100; expenses: $23, $68; profit: ($9)
   c. income: $325; expenses: $148, $116; profit: ($61)
   d. income: $365; expenses: $145, $161; profit: ($59)

4. English units of linear measure (Lesson 32).
   a. 1 ft. = (12) in.
   b. 1 yd. = (36) in.
   c. 1 yd. = (3) ft.
   d. 1 mi. = (5,280) ft.
   e. 6 ft. = (72) in.
   f. 30 ft. = (10) yd.
   g. 96 in. = (8) ft.

Introduction

Write the following problems on the board.
   a. $4 + 2 = ?$
   b. $4 + ? = 6$
   c. $8 - ? = 4$
   d. $? - 4 = 4$
   e. $3 \times ? = 12$
   f. $? \div 3 = 4$

What does the question mark represent in each problem? It represents an unknown number.

Replace the question marks with the letter n. What does the letter n represent? It too represents the unknown number. Letters can be used to represent unknown quantities.

Now find the value of n in each problem.
   a. $n = 6$
   b. $n = 2$
   c. $n = 4$
   d. $n = 8$
   e. $n = 4$
   f. $n = 12$

Teaching Guide

Most of the problems in this lesson are simple enough that the students should easily be able to grasp the concept of using n for an unknown number. Using all four mathematical operations in class discussion will help to show them how to solve number sentences.
   a. $3 + n = 7$ $(n = 4)$
   b. $6 + n = 9$ $(n = 3)$
   c. $n + 4 = 11$ $(n = 7)$
   d. $n + 2 = 13$ $(n = 11)$

Ask the students, "If the sum and one of the addends are known in an addition problem, how is the other addend found?" (By subtraction: Subtract the known addend from the sum.)

e. $8 - n = 2$; $(n = 6)$
f. $9 - n = 5$; $(n = 4)$
g. $14 - n = 3$; $(n = 11)$
h. $18 - n = 4$; $(n = 14)$

Ask, "If the minuend and the difference are known in a subtraction problem, how is the subtrahend found?" (By subtraction: Subtract the difference from the minuend.)

i. $n - 3 = 2$; $(n = 5)$
j. $n - 6 = 1$; $(n = 7)$
k. $n - 5 = 8$; $(n = 13)$
l. $n - 6 = 11$; $(n = 17)$

Ask, "If the subtrahend and the difference are known in a subtraction problem, how is the minuend found?" (By addition: Add the difference and the subtrahend.)

m. $5 \times n = 20$; $(n = 4)$
n. $7 \times n = 21$; $(n = 3)$
o. $n \times 2 = 10$; $(n = 5)$
p. $n \times 8 = 32$; $(n = 4)$

Ask, "If the product and one of the factors is known, how is the unknown factor found?" (By division: Divide the product by the known factor.)

q. $6 \div n = 3$; $(n = 2)$
r. $24 \div n = 3$; $(n = 8)$
s. $15 \div n = 3$; $(n = 5)$
t. $30 \div n = 6$; $(n = 5)$

Ask, "If the quotient and the dividend are known, how is the divisor found?" (By divison: Divide the dividend by the quotient.)

u. $n \div 2 = 6$; $(n = 12)$
v. $n \div 3 = 4$; $(n = 12)$
w. $n \div 5 = 9$; $(n = 45)$
x. $n \div 3 = 6$; $(n = 18)$

Ask, " If the quotient and the divisor are known, how is the dividend found? (By multiplication: Multiply the quotient by the divisor.)

An Ounce of Prevention

Stress that when a number sentence is solved, the letter must be included in the answer. For $6 + 4 = n$, the answer is "$n = 10$," not just "10."

Further Study

A letter that represents a number is known as a literal number (a "letter number"). The students have worked with literal numbers in formulas. This lesson introduces the use of literal numbers to solve problems in general, though the term *literal number* is not used.

B.   Find the value of the letter in each number sentence. Be sure to include the letter in your answer, such as n = 5.

9. $7 - n = 1$ $n = 6$ **10.** $12 - n = 5$ $n = 7$ **11.** $23 - n = 7$ $n = 16$ **12.** $38 - n = 12$ $n = 26$

13. $n - 2 = 2$ $n = 4$ **14.** $n - 9 = 1$ $n = 10$ **15.** $n - 12 = 11$ $n = 23$ **16.** $n - 15 = 18$ $n = 33$

17. $4 + n = 11$ $n = 7$ **18.** $8 + n = 15$ $n = 7$ **19.** $9 + n = 18$ $n = 9$ **20.** $15 + n = 60$ $n = 45$

21. $4 \times n = 20$ $n = 5$ **22.** $7 \times n = 56$ $n = 8$ **23.** $8 \times n = 96$ $n = 12$ **24.** $9 \times n = 117$ $n = 13$

25. $n \div 2 = 2$ $n = 4$ **26.** $n \div 4 = 6$ $n = 24$ **27.** $n \div 8 = 11$ $n = 88$ **28.** $n \div 14 = 3$ $n = 42$

29. $6 \div n = 3$ $n = 2$ **30.** $18 \div n = 6$ $n = 3$ **31.** $24 \div n = 4$ $n = 6$ **32.** $90 \div n = 6$ $n = 15$

REVIEW EXERCISES

C.   Write whether each angle is *right, acute, obtuse,* **or** *straight. (Lesson 154)*

33. 95 degrees   obtuse   **34.** 90 degrees   right   **35.** 88 degrees   acute

36. 180 degrees   straight **37.** 14 degrees   acute   **38.** 105 degrees   obtuse

D.   Solve these reading problems on profit. *(Lesson 129)*

39. The Stauffer family raised a calf to sell. They paid $125.00 for the calf, $155.27 for feed, and $4.50 for other expenses. The calf sold for $350. How much profit did they make on the calf? $65.23

40. Marlin's father received $175.00 from a carpentry project. He had paid $85.00 for lumber and $28.50 in other expenses. What was his profit? $61.50

41. The Brubaker family has a small bookstore. They sold three copies of *The Price of Peace* for $8.75 each. They had paid $18.38 for the books, and their other expenses for the books were $2.25. How much profit did they make on the three books?

$5.62

42. The Weaver family had a garden project one summer. They spent $35.00 for seeds, $25.00 for gasoline, and $60.00 for renting a tractor. Their produce sales were $325.56. What was their profit? $205.56

E.   Change these English linear measures as indicated. *(Lesson 32)*

43. 13 ft. = <u>156</u> in.   **44.** 15 ft. = <u> 5 </u> yd.   **45.** 60 in. = <u> 5 </u> ft.

46. 19 yd. = <u> 57 </u> ft.   **47.** 3 mi. = <u>15,840</u> ft.   **48.** 300 in. = <u> 25 </u> ft.

163. Using Number Sentences to Solve Reading Problems

To find the correct answer to a reading problem, you must follow several orderly steps. First, read the problem carefully to be sure you understand all the facts. Second, be sure you know what question is being asked. Third, decide what operation or operations you will use to find the answer. Then solve the problem. Check your solution by asking, "Does this answer seem reasonable?"

Writing a number sentence is one part of an orderly method to solve a reading problem. A number sentence is a mathematical statement with an equal sign, stating that two amounts are equal. Usually one number in the sentence is unknown. Because the rest of the numbers are known and the amounts on both sides of the equal sign are equal, the unknown number can be found.

The reading problems in this lesson could easily be solved without number sentences. Writing number sentences for these problems will prepare you to use number sentences for solving more difficult problems. To write a number sentence for a reading problem, use the following steps.

1. Read the problem carefully. Notice the facts that are needed to find the answer, and the key words that suggest what operation to use.

2. Choose a letter to represent the unknown number. The letter n is often used in number sentences.

3. Write a number sentence to show how the solution can be found. A number sentence must contain an equal sign. Have the number sentence end with "$= n$" (or whatever letter you have chosen).

4. Solve the equation and write the answer, including the letter.

5. Check your answer by using the solution to replace the letter in the original number sentence. If it makes the number sentence true, your answer is correct.

Example A

On the way to church one evening, the Zehr family saw 11 deer. On the way home, they counted 7 deer. How many deer did they see in all?

Step 1: The needed facts are 11 deer and 7 deer.
　　　　The words *in all* suggest addition.

Step 2: Use n to stand for the unknown number.

Step 3: $11 + 7 = n$

Step 4: $n = 18$

Step 5: $11 + 7 = 18$ (true)

LESSON 163

Objective

- To teach *writing number sentences to solve reading problems.

Review

1. *Triangles* (Lesson 156). Review the fact that the total number of degrees in all the angles of a triangle is 180 degrees. Identify each type of triangle.
   a. angle $a = 41°$, angle $b = 69°$, angle $c = 70°$ (acute)
   b. angle $a = 90°$, angle $b = 42°$, angle $c = 48°$ (right)
   c. angle $a = 35°$, angle $b = 105°$, angle $c = 40°$ (obtuse)

2. *Finding unit prices* (Lesson 130). Answers should be rounded to the nearest cent.
   a. 50 lb. potatoes for $8.00. ($0.16 per pound)
   b. 10 lb. potatoes for $2.35. ($0.24 per pound)

3. *English units of weight* (Lesson 33).
   a. 5 lb. = (80) oz.
   b. 96 oz. = (6) lb.
   c. 7 t. = (14,000) lb.
   d. 24,000 lb. = (12) tons

Introduction

Review solving number sentences from Lesson 162.
   a. $15 + 8 = n$ $(n = 23)$
   b. $23 + n = 35$ $(n = 12)$
   c. $17 - 3 = n$ $(n = 14)$
   d. $43 - n = 18$ $(n = 25)$
   e. $6 \times 9 = n$ $(n = 54)$
   f. $12 \times n = 132$ $(n = 11)$
   g. $45 \div 9 = n$ $(n = 5)$
   h. $96 \div n = 12$ $(n = 8)$

Teaching Guide

The steps for writing number sentences to solve reading problems are much the same as for solving other reading problems. What is new is the writing of a number sentence to show how the problem will be solved. Show how to apply these steps to the reading problems on the next page.

1. Read the problem carefully. Notice the facts that are needed to find the answer, and the key words that suggest what operation to use.

2. Choose a letter to represent the unknown number. The letter n is often used in number sentences.

3. Write a number sentence to show how the solution can be found. A number sentence must contain an equal sign. Have the number sentence end with "$= n$" (or whatever letter you have chosen).

4. Solve the equation and write the answer, including the letter.

5. Check your answer by using the solution to replace the letter in the original number sentence. If it makes the number sentence true, your answer is correct.

Problem A

The Reinford family lives 2 miles from school and 8 miles from church. How much farther is it to church than to school?

1. The needed facts are 2 miles and 8 miles. "How much farther" suggests subtraction.
2. Use n to stand for the unknown number.
3. $8 - 2 = n$
4. $n = 6$ miles
5. $8 - 2 = 6$ (true)

Problem B

Mother Shirk drove 3 1/2 miles to school to get the school children. From school the Shirks went 4 1/4 miles to the church building, where they did the cleaning. How far in all did Mother drive to get from home to the church building?

1. The needed facts are 3 1/2 miles and 4 1/4 miles. "In all" suggests addition.
2. Use n to stand for the unknown number.
3. $3\ 1/2 + 4\ 1/4 = n$
4. $n = 7\ 3/4$ miles
5. $3\ 1/2 + 4\ 1/4 = 7\ 3/4$ (true)

Problem C

The Reinford family has four times as far to church as to school. They have 8 miles to church. How far do they live from school?

1. The needed facts are 8 miles and "four times as far." Since 8 miles is 4 times the unknown distance, the required operation is division.
2. Use n to stand for the unknown number.
3. $8 \div 4 = n$
4. $n = 2$ miles
5. $8 \div 4 = 2$ (true)

Problem D

The Stauffers planted 4 1/2 rows of peas in their garden. They planted 2 1/2 times as many rows of sweet corn. How many rows of sweet corn did they plant?

1. The needed facts are 4 1/2 rows and "2 1/2 times as many." Since the unknown number is 2 1/2 times as great as 4 1/2, the required operation is multiplication.
2. Use n to stand for the unknown number.
3. $2\ 1/2 \times 4\ 1/2 = n$
4. $n = 11\ 1/4$ rows
5. $2\ 1/2 \times 4\ 1/2 = 11\ 1/4$ (true)

> **Example B**
>   Going to church, the Zehr family saw 11 deer. Coming home, they saw 7 deer. What was the difference in the number of deer they saw?
>   Step 1: The needed facts are 11 deer and 7 deer.
>   The word *difference* suggests subtraction.
>   Step 2: Use n to stand for the unknown number.
>   Step 3: $11 - 7 = n$
>   Step 4: $n = 4$
>   Step 5: $11 - 7 = 4$ (true)

CLASS PRACTICE

Write a number sentence for each reading problem. Use your number sentences to solve the problems.

a. Lamar husked 126 ears of corn. His brother Dale husked 178 ears. How many more ears of corn did Dale husk than Lamar? $178 - 126 = n$ $n = 52$ ears

b. The Wenger family husked 420 ears of corn that morning. How many dozen ears is that? $420 \div 12 = n$ $n = 35$ dozen

c. The Gospel of Luke has 24 chapters. The Epistle to the Philippians has $\frac{1}{6}$ as many chapters. How many chapters are in Philippians? $\frac{1}{6} \times 24 = n$ $n = 4$ chapters

d. In a certain Bible, the Book of Obadiah begins on page 1,275 and the Book of Revelation on page 1,785. How many pages is it from Obadiah to the first page of Revelation? $1,785 - 1,275 = n$ $n = 510$ pages

WRITTEN EXERCISES

A. *Read each problem, and study the number sentence that is written for it. Use the number sentence to find the solution. Include the letter n in your answer.*

1. Dale is 14 years old, and his brother David is 11 years old. How much older is Dale than David? $14 - 11 = n$ $n = 3$ years

2. In a regular Sunday morning service, the Oakville congregation sings three songs before the devotional, one song while the offering is being lifted, one song before the sermon, and one song before dismissal. How many songs do they sing in all?
    $3 + 1 + 1 + 1 = n$ $n = 6$ songs

3. The average attendance at the Harrison Mennonite Church is 120. In the Palatinate in Europe, only one-sixth of that number was allowed to assemble in an Anabaptist worship service during the late 1600s. How many people were allowed to meet in an Anabaptist worship service? $120 \div 6 = n$ $n = 20$ people

4. Rosene spent 15 minutes every day memorizing Bible verses. How much time did she spend memorizing Bible verses in a month of 30 days? $15 \times 30 = n$
    $n = 450$ minutes (or) $7\frac{1}{2}$ hours

B.   **Write a number sentence for each of these reading problems. Use your number sentences to solve the problems.**

5.   In one classroom of the Locust Dale Mennonite School, there are 9 students in sixth grade and 12 students in seventh grade. How many students are in the entire room?

$9 + 12 = n$ $n = 21$ students

6.   The Oakville Mennonite School has three classrooms. There are 21 students in grades 1–3, 14 students in grades 4–6, and 17 students in grades 7–10. How many students attend the school? $21 + 14 + 17 = n$ $n = 52$ students

7.   How many more seventh grade students than sixth grade students attend the Locust Dale School? (Use the facts in problem 5.) $12 - 9 = n$ $n = 3$ students

8.   How many more students are in the grades 1–3 classroom at Oakville than in the grades 4–6 classroom? (Use the facts in problem 6.) $21 - 14 = n$ $n = 7$ students

9.   One afternoon Father planted a 15-acre field of corn. He wants to plant 6 times that much corn in all. How many acres of corn does Father want to plant?

$15 \times 6 = n$ $n = 90$ acres

10.   Father planted corn at the rate of 22,000 seeds per acre. How many seeds did he plant in the 15-acre field? $22,000 \times 15 = n$ $n = 330,000$ seeds

11.   The Martins shipped three calves to market. The total weight of the calves was 465 pounds. What was the average weight of each calf? $465 \div 3 = n$ $n = 155$ pounds

12.   Father calculated that the corn sprouted at a rate of 20,000 plants per acre. If each plant produces one ear and the yield is 176 bushels per acre, how many plants does it take to produce 1 bushel of corn? (Round your answer to the nearest whole number.)

$20,000 \div 176 = n$ $n = 114$ plants

REVIEW EXERCISES

C.   **Find the size of the missing angle in each triangle.** *(Lesson 156)*

13. $a = 46°$
     $b = 55°$
     $c = \underline{79°}$

14. $a = 70°$
     $b = 90°$
     $c = \underline{20°}$

15. $a = 45°$
     $b = 38°$
     $c = \underline{97°}$

16. $a = 115°$
     $b = 48°$
     $c = \underline{17°}$

D.   **Use a protractor to measure these angles to the nearest 5 degrees.** *(Lesson 155)*

17.

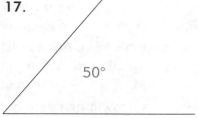

50°

18.

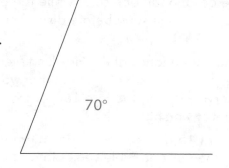

70°

Further Study

The letter *n* is commonly used as a symbol for an unknown number because it is the first letter of the word *number*. The letter *x* is also used frequently, but it has the disadvantage of being the symbol for multiplication. Although the letter *x* is not generally used to indicate multiplication in algebra (6*x* is used rather than 6 × *x*), the fact that *x* is used in general mathematics leaves open the possibility for confusion. Therefore, the literal number used in this lesson is *n* rather than *x*.

19. 10°

20. 130°

E.   Find the unit price of each item, to the nearest cent. *(Lesson 130)*

21. 5 grapefruits for $1.00 $0.20

22. 7 oranges for $1.00 $0.14

23. calf feed at $10.00 per hundredweight (100 lb.) $0.10

24. milk at $13.05 per hundredweight (100 lb.) $0.13

F.   Change these measures as indicated. *(Lesson 33)*

25. 3 lb. = __48__ oz.   **26.** 128 oz. = __8__ lb.   **27.** 18 lb. = __288__ oz.

28. 5 tons = __10,000__ lb.   **29.** 24,000 lb. = __12__ tons   **30.** 8 tons = __16,000__ lb.

164. Review of Chapters 1 and 2

A. *If the number is written with digits, write it with words. If the number is written with words, write it with digits. (Lesson 1)*

1. 4,500,000

   four million, five hundred thousand

2. 15,615,000,000

   fifteen billion, six hundred fifteen million

3. four billion, two hundred million

   4,200,000,000

4. fifteen trillion

   15,000,000,000,000

B. *Write the place value of each underlined digit. (Lesson 2)*

5. 1**2**,132,375

   million

6. **2**2,000,000

   ten million

7. 4,**2**02,500

   hundred thousand

8. 8,0**3**0,100

   ten thousand

C. *Round the following numbers as indicated. (Lesson 3)*

To nearest:	ten	hundred
48	9. 50	10. 0
115	11. 120	12. 100

To nearest:	thousand	hundred thousand	million
1,415,939	13. 1,416,000	14. 1,400,000	15. 1,000,000
4,529,321	16. 4,529,000	17. 4,500,000	18. 5,000,000

D. *Express the Roman numerals as Arabic numerals, and the Arabic numerals as Roman numerals. (Lesson 4)*

19. CCXXXIV
    234

20. MMCMIX
    2,909

21. 435
    CDXXXV

22. 1,119
    MCXIX

E. *For each blank, write the correct term for that number in the problem. Choose from the list at the right. (Lessons 5, 8, 15, 21)*

```
535 ← 23. addend          468 ← 25. minuend
+426                     − 149 ← 26. subtrahend
961 ← 24. sum             319 ← 27. difference
```

```
                                    ┌──── 31. quotient
346 ← 28. multiplicand       30 R 14 ← 32. remainder
×273 ← 29. multiplier     89)2,684 ←──── 33. dividend
94,458 ← 30. product          ↑          34. divisor
```

quotient
addend
multiplicand
minuend
sum
remainder
dividend
difference
multiplier
divisor
product
subtrahend

LESSON 164

Objective

- To review the addition, subtraction, and multiplication skills taught in Chapters 1 and 2.

Teaching Guide

The suggestions below apply to all the review lessons in this chapter (Lessons 164–169).

The Scriptural injunction to teach "line upon line, line upon line" could apply to teaching math. These review lessons are an accumulation of all the material covered in the Grade 6 text. They are designed both to review the material taught throughout the year and to prepare the students for the Final Test (Lesson 170).

Your approach to these lessons should be similar to that for chapter reviews. Discuss in class the material in the chapters indicated. Be especially careful to review any areas in which your students had particular problems. Then give the written assignment.

These review lessons have plenty of material. You will probably not want to assign the entire lesson as one day's work. The lessons have the same format as the chapter reviews: each odd-numbered exercise is usually similar to the next higher even-numbered exercise. Therefore, the same approach can be used as that recommended for the chapter reviews.

a. Use the odd-numbered problems for review in class, and assign the even-numbered problems.

b. Divide the lesson in two. Assign the odd-numbered problems one day and the even-numbered problems the next day.

F. Solve these problems. *(Lessons 5, 8, 15–18, 21–25)*

35.	36.	37.	38.
483 812 149 821 + 523 2,788	3,814 5,321 6,818 + 1,231 17,184	421,915 + 362,630 784,545	$4,581.91 + 3,814.21 $8,396.12

39.	40.	41.	42.
5,611 − 3,822 1,789	28,912 − 15,781 13,131	452,981 − 157,699 295,282	$6,712.91 − 3,481.97 $3,230.94

43.	44.	45.	46.
45 × 36 1,620	217 × 421 91,357	389 × 203 78,967	2,131 × 1,212 2,582,772

47. 6)7,981 → 1,330 R 1 48. 12)5,161 → 430 R 1 49. 85)43,919 → 516 R 59 50. 123)42,181 → 342 R 115

G. Write true or false for each statement. *(Lesson 26)*

51. 13,887 is divisible by 3. true
52. 15,020 is divisible by 4. true
53. 603,136 is divisible by 6. false
54. 13,887 is divisible by 9. true

H. Find the average of each set of numbers. Express any remainder as a fraction. *(Lesson 27)*

55. 7, 9, 1, 3, 8, 1 $4\frac{5}{6}$
56. 21, 28, 22, 20, 23, 15 $21\frac{1}{2}$
57. 16, 15, 13, 12, 16 $14\frac{2}{5}$
58. 35, 38, 30, 41, 38, 22   34

I. Write what information is needed to solve each problem. *(Lesson 12)*

59. Father planted 4 more rows of peas than Daniel did. How many rows of peas did Father plant? How many rows Daniel planted

60. In Alta's math lesson, 10% of the problems were done incorrectly. How many answers were incorrect? How many problems were in the lesson

J. Solve these reading problems.

61. Linda spends 2 hours mowing each time she mows the lawn. How many hours does she spend mowing if she mows 26 times in a year? 52 hours

62. Father and Mark loaded 125 bales of hay onto a wagon. The hay weighed 5,125 pounds. What was the average weight per bale? 41 pounds

63. Mark sold 5 bales of hay to a customer for $0.08 per pound. The bales weighed 45 pounds, 43 pounds, 48 pounds, 44 pounds, and 45 pounds. How much should Mark charge for the hay? $18.00

64. Mark's father shipped a truckload of hay to market. The truck weighed 24,000 pounds when it was empty, and 33,250 pounds when it was loaded with hay. How many pounds of hay were on the truck? 9,250 pounds

165. Review of Chapters 3 and 8

A.   *Write the abbreviation for each unit of measure. (Lessons 32–36, 98–101)*

1. yard   yd.   **2.** mile   mi.   **3.** inch   in.   **4.** quart   qt.

5. ounce   oz.   **6.** bushel   bu.   **7.** square mile   sq. mi.   **8.** acre   a.

9. decimeter   dm   **10.** dekagram   dkg **11.** milliliter   ml   **12.** kilogram   kg

13. hectometer   hm **14.** centimeter   cm **15.** square meter   m² **16.** hectare   ha

B.   *Match these prefixes to their meanings. (Lesson 97)*

17. centi-   g   **a.** 10
18. deka-   a   **b.** 100
19. milli-   f   **c.** 1,000
20. hecto-   b   **d.** 10,000
21. deci-   h   **e.** $\frac{1}{10,000}$
22. kilo-   c   **f.** $\frac{1}{1,000}$
                                                             g. $\frac{1}{100}$
                                                             h. $\frac{1}{10}$

C.   *Change these English measures as indicated. (Lessons 32–34)*

23. 1 mi. = _5,280_ ft.   **24.** 12 ft. = _144_ in.
25. 16 yd. = _48_ ft.   **26.** 64 oz. = _4_ lb.
27. 3 tons = _6,000_ lb.   **28.** 10 pt. = _5_ qt.
29. 9 gal. = _36_ qt.   **30.** 11 bu. = _44_ pk.
31. 5 sq. ft. = _720_ sq. in.   **32.** 45 sq. ft. = _5_ sq. yd.

D.   *Change these metric measures as indicated. (Lessons 98–101)*

33. 12,800 m = _12.8_ km   **34.** 47 cm = _0.47_ m   **35.** 4.9 kg = _4,900_ g
36. 2,300 mg = _2.3_ g   **37.** 350 ml = _0.35_ l **38.** 25 kl = _25,000_ l
39. 6.3 l = _6,300_ ml   **40.** 550 ha = _5.5_ km²

E.   *Change these measures of time as indicated. (Lesson 37)*

41. 7 min. = _420_ sec.   **42.** 240 min. = _4_ hr.
43. 60 mo. = _5_ yr.   **44.** 24 decades = _240_ yr.

LESSON 165

Objective

- To review the English and metric units taught in Chapters 3 and 8.

Review

Give Lesson 165 Speed Test (Multiplication). Time limit: 2 minutes. This is a continuation of reviewing the basic facts, which began in Lesson 159.

Teaching Guide

See the comments for Lesson 164.

An Ounce of Prevention

Be sure that numbers 17–22 are either reviewed in class or assigned as written work.

F. Copy and solve these problems on compound measures. *(Lessons 39, 40)*

45.   4 ft.   7 in.
        + 6 ft.   8 in.
        ———————
         11 ft.   3 in.

46.   6 ft.   3 in.
        + 5 ft. 11 in.
        ———————
         12 ft.   2 in.

47.   6 yd.   1 ft.
        – 4 yd.   2 ft.
        ———————
          1 yd.   2 ft.

48.   5 lb.   4 oz.
        – 2 lb.   6 oz.
        ———————
          2 lb. 14 oz.

49.   3 ft. 11 in.
               × 5
        ———————
         19 ft.   7 in.

50.   3 gal. 3 qt.
               × 5
        ———————
         18 gal. 3 qt.

51.   4 ft. 1 in.
        6)24 ft. 6 in.

52.   3 bu. 3 pk.
        5)18 bu. 3 pk.

G. Fill in this chart relating to time zones. *(Lesson 38)*

	Pacific Standard Time	Mountain Standard Time	Central Standard Time	Eastern Standard Time
53.	2:00 P.M.	3:00 P.M.	4:00 P.M.	5:00 P.M.
54.	10:30 A.M.	11:30 A.M.	12:30 P.M.	1:30 P.M.

H. Solve these reading problems.

55. The Wenger family is planning a trip to a distant church. The distance on the map is 6 inches, and the scale of the map is 1 inch = 23 miles. What is the actual distance between the Wenger family's home and the church?   138 miles

56. The scale on a local map is 1 inch = $1\frac{1}{2}$ miles. What is the distance from the Marshville Christian Day School to the Mountainside Mennonite Church if the distance on the map is 4 inches?   6 miles

57. Mark's father is drawing a blueprint for a house he is planning to build. The length of the house on the blueprint is 24 inches. The scale of the blueprint is 1 inch = 2 feet. How long will the house actually be?   48 feet

58. Mark saw that on the blueprint of this house, the kitchen was $7\frac{1}{2}$ inches wide. How wide will the kitchen actually be? (1 inch = 2 feet.)   15 feet

I.   *Study the following bar graph, and answer the questions below.* (Lesson 109)

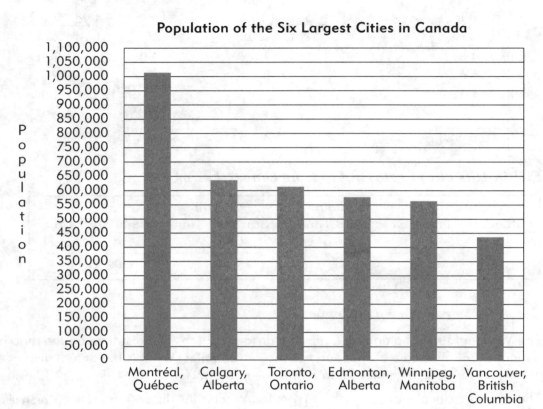

Population of the Six Largest Cities in Canada

Source: *Rand McNally Road Atlas*, 1995

59. Which city in Canada has the largest population?   Montreal, Quebec

60. About how many people live in Toronto?   610,000

61. About how many people live in Vancouver?   430,000

62. About how many people live in Winnipeg?   560,000

(Allow reasonable variation.)

LESSON 166

Objective

- To review fractions as taught in Chapters 4 and 5.

Teaching Guide

See the comments for Lesson 164.

166. Review of Chapters 4 and 5

A.   *Write the correct term to match each example.*

1. $3\frac{1}{2}$ and $1\frac{2}{3}$ mixed numbers   reciprocals
2. the 4 in $\frac{3}{4}$ denominator   greatest common factor
3. $\frac{8}{5}$ and $\frac{11}{3}$ improper fractions   mixed numbers
4. 6 is the ___ of 12 and 18   greatest common factor   lowest common multiple
5. 7 and 15   whole numbers   whole numbers
6. the 7 in $\frac{7}{9}$ numerator   denominator
7. 20 is the ___ of 4 and 5   lowest common multiple   numerator
8. $\frac{3}{4}$ and $\frac{4}{3}$ reciprocals   proper fractions
9. $\frac{1}{4}$ and $\frac{5}{6}$ proper fractions   improper fractions

B.   *Write whether each number is prime or composite.* *(Lesson 45)*

10. 48 composite   **11.** 49 composite   **12.** 50 composite   **13.** 51 composite

C.   *Find the prime factors of these composite numbers.* *(Lesson 46)*

14. 15   **15.** 20   **16.** 30   **17.** 40
    $15 = 3 \times 5$ $20 = 2 \times 2 \times 5$ $30 = 2 \times 3 \times 5$ $40 = 2 \times 2 \times 2 \times 5$

D.   *Find the greatest common factor of each pair.* *(Lesson 47)*

18. 16, 20   4   **19.** 28, 42   14   **20.** 18, 45   9   **21.** 12, 36   12

E.   *Find the lowest common multiple of each pair.* *(Lesson 48)*

22. 6, 9   18   **23.** 12, 18   36   **24.** 12, 16   48   **25.** 8, 10   40

F.   *Change these mixed numbers to improper fractions.* *(Lesson 50)*

26. $4\frac{1}{4}$ $\frac{17}{4}$ **27.** $3\frac{3}{5}$ $\frac{18}{5}$ **28.** $4\frac{2}{3}$ $\frac{14}{3}$ **29.** $5\frac{3}{8}$ $\frac{43}{8}$

G.   *Change these improper fractions to mixed numbers.* *(Lesson 50)*

30. $\frac{18}{4}$ $4\frac{1}{2}$ **31.** $\frac{22}{5}$ $4\frac{2}{5}$ **32.** $\frac{23}{8}$ $2\frac{7}{8}$ **33.** $\frac{22}{7}$ $3\frac{1}{7}$

H.   *Write the reciprocals of these fractions.* *(Lesson 65)*

34. $\frac{7}{8}$ $\frac{8}{7}$ **35.** $\frac{5}{7}$ $\frac{7}{5}$ **36.** $\frac{4}{9}$ $\frac{9}{4}$ **37.** $\frac{5}{6}$ $\frac{6}{5}$

I.   *Solve these fraction problems. (Lessons 52–56, 59–67)*

38. $\begin{array}{r}\frac{3}{4}\\[2pt]+\ \frac{2}{3}\\\hline 1\frac{5}{12}\end{array}$ **39.** $\begin{array}{r}\frac{5}{6}\\[2pt]+\ \frac{3}{5}\\\hline 1\frac{13}{30}\end{array}$ **40.** $\begin{array}{r}4\frac{1}{3}\\[2pt]+\ 2\frac{3}{8}\\\hline 6\frac{17}{24}\end{array}$ **41.** $\begin{array}{r}5\frac{3}{8}\\[2pt]+\ 3\frac{7}{12}\\\hline 8\frac{23}{24}\end{array}$

42. $\begin{array}{r}\frac{3}{4}\\[2pt]-\ \frac{1}{3}\\\hline \frac{5}{12}\end{array}$ **43.** $\begin{array}{r}\frac{5}{6}\\[2pt]-\ \frac{1}{5}\\\hline \frac{19}{30}\end{array}$ **44.** $\begin{array}{r}2\frac{1}{2}\\[2pt]-\ 1\frac{3}{4}\\\hline \frac{3}{4}\end{array}$ **45.** $\begin{array}{r}2\frac{2}{3}\\[2pt]-\ 1\frac{5}{6}\\\hline \frac{5}{6}\end{array}$

46. $\begin{array}{r}5\\[2pt]-\ 1\frac{2}{3}\\\hline 3\frac{1}{3}\end{array}$ **47.** $\begin{array}{r}6\\[2pt]-\ 3\frac{7}{9}\\\hline 2\frac{2}{9}\end{array}$ **48.** $\frac{3}{4}$ of 17 $12\frac{3}{4}$ **49.** $\frac{3}{5}$ of 20   12

50. $1\frac{3}{5} \times \frac{3}{4}$ $1\frac{1}{5}$ **51.** $4\frac{1}{8} \times \frac{2}{3}$ $2\frac{3}{4}$ **52.** $3\frac{1}{5} \times 1\frac{7}{8}$ 6   **53.** $4\frac{1}{3} \times 2\frac{2}{5}$ $10\frac{2}{5}$

54. $8 \div \frac{1}{4}$ 32   **55.** $9 \div \frac{3}{5}$ 15   **56.** $\frac{3}{4} \div \frac{3}{8}$ 2   **57.** $\frac{5}{6} \div \frac{5}{12}$ 2

58. $3 \div 1\frac{1}{4}$ $2\frac{2}{5}$ **59.** $5 \div 3\frac{1}{8}$ $1\frac{3}{5}$ **60.** $4\frac{1}{4} \div 3\frac{1}{8}$ $1\frac{9}{25}$ **61.** $3\frac{3}{8} \div 1\frac{5}{6}$ $1\frac{37}{44}$

J.   *Solve by changing the compound measures to mixed numbers. (Lesson 68)*

62. $3\frac{1}{2} \times 3$ ft. 6 in. $12\frac{1}{4}$ ft.   **63.** $1\frac{1}{3} \times 4$ ft. 8 in. $6\frac{2}{9}$ ft.

64. 3 yd. 2 ft. $\div 1\frac{1}{4}$ $2\frac{14}{15}$ yd.   **65.** 4 yd. 1 ft. $\div 2\frac{1}{2}$ $1\frac{11}{15}$ yd.

K.   *Estimate answers to these reading problems. Then find the exact answers. (Lesson 69)*   (Estimates are in parentheses.)

66. How far did a passenger train travel in 6 hours if its average speed was 55 miles per hour? For your estimate, round the speed to the nearest ten.   (360 miles) 330 miles

67. A school building has the shape of a rectangle 93 feet long and 78 feet wide. What is the area of the building? Round both the length and the width to the nearest ten for your estimate.   (7,200 square feet)   7,254 square feet

68. One week the Landis family drove the following distances in their family car: 48 miles, 36 miles, 33 miles, 81 miles, 44 miles, 15 miles, and 58 miles. How far did they drive in all that week? Round each number to the nearest ten for your estimate.

(320 miles)   315 miles

69. John needs some pieces of wood 1 foot 11 inches long. How many pieces can he cut from an 8-foot board? Round to the nearest foot for your estimate, and drop any fraction in your exact answer.   (4 pieces)   4 pieces

70. The Weber family receives $12.25 per hundredweight (100 pounds) of milk that they ship. If there are $11\frac{3}{4}$ gallons of milk in a hundredweight, how much do they receive per gallon? For your estimate, round to the nearest whole gallon and the nearest whole dollar. Round the exact answer to the nearest cent.   ($1.00) $1.04

LESSON 167

Objective

- To review decimals, ratios, and proportions as taught in Chapters 6 and 7.

Teaching Guide

See the comments for Lesson 164.

An Ounce of Prevention

Be sure to review conversions between fractions and decimals.

167. Review of Chapters 6 and 7

A.   Write these decimals, using words. *(Lesson 72)*

1. 3.4   **2.** 9.83   **3.** 8.088   **4.** 7.007

1. three and four tenths   2. nine and eighty-three hundredths

3. eight and eighty-eight thousandths   4. seven and seven thousandths

B.   Change these fractions to decimals. *(Lesson 73)*

5. $\frac{3}{4}$ **6.** $\frac{4}{5}$ **7.** $\frac{19}{20}$ **8.** $\frac{23}{40}$ **9.** $\frac{37}{40}$ **10.** $\frac{47}{50}$

  0.75   0.8   0.95   0.575   0.925   0.94

C.   Change these decimals to fractions in lowest terms. *(Lesson 74)*

11. 0.6   **12.** 0.25   **13.** 0.85   **14.** 0.35   **15.** 0.41   **16.** 0.89

  $\frac{3}{5}$ $\frac{1}{4}$ $\frac{17}{20}$ $\frac{7}{20}$ $\frac{41}{100}$ $\frac{89}{100}$

D.   Copy each set of decimals, compare them, and write > or < between them.
(Lesson 75)

17. 3.2 $>$ 3.097   **18.** 2.004 $<$ 2.011   **19.** 5 $<$ 5.001   **20.** 3.98 $>$ 3.979

E.   Copy and solve these problems. *(Lessons 76, 77, 79, 80, 85–87)*

21. 3.412 + 2.801 6.213	**22.** 3.802 + 4.098 7.900	**23.** 4.5121 6.311 15.2214 + 4.2 30.2445	**24.** 4.4 3.512 0.26 + 5.0981 13.2701
25. 7.26 - 4.89 2.37	**26.** 8.731 - 5.981 2.750	**27.** 9.2 - 4.891 4.309	**28.** 3 - 1.212 1.788
29. 32.5 × 1.5 48.75	**30.** 4.11 × 2.2 9.042	**31.** 0.71 × 0.04 0.0284	**32.** 0.12 × 0.06 0.0072

33. $6\overline{)14.22}$ = 2.37   **34.** $12\overline{)4.92}$ = 0.41   **35.** $3.3\overline{)7.26}$ = 2.2   **36.** $0.41\overline{)1.435}$ = 3.5

F.   Solve mentally by moving the decimal point. *(Lessons 78, 84)*

37. 4.2 × 10   **38.** 15.773 × 100   **39.** 4.213 × 1,000   **40.** 4.5 × 100
          42   1,577.3   4,213   450

41. 5.75 ÷ 10   **42.** 13.66 ÷ 100   **43.** 345.6 ÷ 1,000   **44.** 6.8 ÷ 1,000
          0.575   0.1366   0.3456   0.0068

G.   Round each decimal to the nearest tenth. *(Lesson 88)*

45. 4.65   4.7   **46.** 3.099   3.1   **47.** 4.96   5.0   **48.** 5.771   5.8

H.   Round each decimal to the nearest hundredth. *(Lesson 88)*

49. 5.717   5.72   **50.** 8.897   8.90   **51.** 6.588   6.59   **52.** 8.9871   8.99

I.   Express each common fraction as a decimal fraction rounded to the nearest hundredth. *(Lesson 89)*

53. $\frac{5}{7}$ 0.71   **54.** $\frac{5}{8}$ 0.63   **55.** $\frac{9}{14}$ 0.64   **56.** $\frac{7}{16}$ 0.44

J.   Change these fractions to decimals. Divide to the hundredths' place, and express the remainder as a fraction in lowest terms. *(Lesson 89)*

57. $\frac{3}{7}$ $0.42\frac{6}{7}$ **58.** $\frac{3}{16}$ $0.18\frac{3}{4}$ **59.** $\frac{7}{9}$ $0.77\frac{7}{9}$ **60.** $\frac{5}{12}$ $0.41\frac{2}{3}$

K.   Compare each of the following by writing a ratio in lowest terms. *(Lesson 92)*

61. 125 copies of the *Star of Hope* to 3 men distributing them.   125:3
62. 45 library books to 20 students.   9:4
63. 12 baseball gloves to 26 students.   6:13
64. 8,500 bricks to 4 bricklayers.   2,125:1

L.   Find the missing numbers in these proportions. *(Lesson 93)*

65. $\frac{2}{3} = \frac{n}{18}$ $n = 12$ **66.** $\frac{2}{10} = \frac{n}{25}$ $n = 5$ **67.** $\frac{4}{6} = \frac{10}{n}$ $n = 15$ **68.** $\frac{6}{8} = \frac{15}{n}$ $n = 20$

M.   Solve each reading problem by writing a proportion. *(Lesson 94)*

69. One year the Carpenter family picked 8 quarts of strawberries for every 10 strawberry plants they had planted the year before. At that rate, how many quarts of strawberries did they get from 55 plants? $\frac{8}{10} = \frac{n}{55}$ $n = 44$ quarts

70. Brother Weber calculated that 2 students use 13 tablets every school year. There are 45 students in the school. At that rate, how many tablets should he order? Round your answer to the nearest whole number. $\frac{2}{13} = \frac{45}{n}$ $n = 293$ tablets

71. Last week the Reimer family shipped their 5 largest steers, which weighed a total of 6,500 pounds. If they ship 12 steers of the same average weight this week, what will be their total weight? $\frac{5}{6,500} = \frac{12}{n}$ $n = 15,600$ pounds

72. The Lauvers were on a trip to visit an uncle's family. Paul calculated that they were traveling 13 miles every 15 minutes. At that rate, how many miles per hour were they traveling? $\frac{13}{15} = \frac{n}{60}$ $n = 52$ miles per hour

LESSON 168

Objectives

- To review percents as taught in Chapter 9.
- To review concepts associated with money as taught in Chapter 10.

Review

Give Lesson 168 Speed Test (Multiplication). Time limit: 2 minutes. This is a continuation of reviewing the basic facts, which began in Lesson 159.

Teaching Guide

See the comments for Lesson 164. The cash expense record (numbers 46–53) should be assigned in its entirety.

168. Review of Chapters 9 and 10

A. *Write the missing numbers so that each number is expressed as a percent, a decimal, and a fraction.* (Lessons 112–115)

Percent	Decimal	Fraction
25%	**1.** 0.25	**2.** $\frac{1}{4}$
3. 40%	**4.** 0.4	$\frac{2}{5}$
55%	0.55	**5.** $\frac{11}{20}$
6. 68%	0.68	**7.** $\frac{17}{25}$

B. *Add or subtract these percents as shown.* (Lessons 116, 119)

8. 100% – 12%   **9.** 100% – 34%   **10.** 100% + 16%   **11.** 100% + 8%
    88%   66%   116%   108%

C. *Find these percentages.* (Lessons 117, 118)

12. 25% of 84 21   **13.** $33\frac{1}{3}$ % of 39 13   **14.** 15% of 24 3.6   **15.** 16% of 65 10.4
16. 88% of 62 54.56   **17.** 95% of 90 85.5   **18.** 8% of 35 2.8   **19.** 4% of 55 2.2

D. *Find the amount after each increase or decrease.* (Lesson 119)

20. 20% decrease from $4.00 $3.20   **21.** 10% decrease from $3.00 $2.70
22. 5% decrease from 12   11.4   **23.** 12% increase over $15.00 $16.80
24. 15% increase over $45.00 $51.75   **25.** 15% increase over 30   34.5

E. *Find the discount and the sale price of each item.* (Lesson 120)

	Regular Price	Percent of Discount				Regular Price	Percent of Discount		
26.	$42.50	10%	$4.25	$38.25	**27.**	$10.00	15%	$1.50	$8.50
28.	$16.00	20%	$3.20	$12.80	**29.**	$19.00	25%	$4.75	$14.25

F. *Find the commissions on these sales.* (Lesson 121)

	Sales	Rate			Sales	Rate	
30.	$40.00	12%	$4.80	**31.**	$75.00	10%	$7.50
32.	$25.00	8%	$2.00	**33.**	$140.00	7%	$9.80
34.	$95.00	8%	$7.60	**35.**	$115.00	5%	$5.75

G. Find these percents. *(Lessons 122, 123)*

36. 5 is _25_ % of 20   **37.** 9 is _20_ % of 45   **38.** 8 is _32_% of 25

39. 6 is _8_ % of 75   **40.** 12 is _15_% of 80   **41.** 5 is _4_ % of 125

H. Copy and complete the following chart. *(Lesson 127)*

	Amount of Sale	Amount Given	1¢	5¢	10¢	25¢	$1	$5	Total Change
42.	$0.48	$5.00	2			2	4		$4.52
43.	$3.42	$10.00	3	1		2	1	1	$6.58

I. Write what you would say as you count the change to the customer.
(Lesson 127)

	Amount of sale	Amount given
44.	$6.30	$10.00
45.	$4.37	$5.00

44. $6.30 out of $10.00, $6.40, $6.50, $6.75, $7.00, $8.00, $9.00, $10.00

45. $4.37 out of $5.00, $4.40, $4.50, $4.75, $5.00

J. Find all the totals for this expense record. *(Lesson 128)*

Record of Cash Expenses

Month	Lumber	Hardware	Paint	Other	Totals
January	$25 38	$5 75	$18 95	$9 77	**46.** $59 85
February	44 61	4 16	8 65	15 46	**47.** 72 88
March	35 99	15 44	0 00	11 77	**48.** 63 20
Totals	**49.** $105 98	**50.** $25 35	**51.** $27 60	**52.** $37 00	**53.** $195 93

K. Find the total expenses and the profit for each line. *(Lesson 129)*

	Income	Materials	Electricity & Telephone	Small Tools	Total Expenses	Profit
54.	$115.69	$27.71	$3.41	$6.99	$38.11	$77.58
55.	$141.35	$59.37	$7.86	$4.99	$72.22	$69.13

L. Find the unit price for each item, to the nearest cent. *(Lesson 130)*

56. 5 lb. cheese for $9.95 $1.99   **57.** 5 gal. ice cream for $18.95 $3.79

58. 12 reams paper for $45.00 $3.75   **59.** 2½ doz. eggs for $1.75 $0.70

M. *Compute the interest in each case.* (*Lessons 131–133*)

	Principal	Rate	Time	
60.	$200	8%	4 yr.	$64.00
61.	$700	7%	3 yr.	$147.00
62.	$200	9%	6 mo.	$9.00
63.	$500	7%	4 mo.	$11.67

N. *Solve these reading problems.*

64. Mother and Charlotte are shopping. The price of eggs is $0.75 per dozen or $1.85 for $2\frac{1}{2}$ dozen. Which is the better buy? $1.85 for $2\frac{1}{2}$ dozen

65. A set of 4 books can be purchased for $20 per volume, or $70 for the whole set. How much is saved per volume by purchasing the entire set at one time? $2.50

66. A small carpentry job involved the following expenses: lumber, $27.95; supplies, $8.75; and other expenses, $8.50. The total income was $80.00. What was the profit? $34.80

67. Mother bakes bread to sell each week. One week the bread sales totaled $23.75. Expenses were as follows: ingredients, $4.75; electricity, $1.15; and other expenses, $2.35. What was the profit? $15.50

68. Brother Lloyd lent $500.00 to Brother David. At the end of two years, Brother David paid back the principal plus interest at 5%. How much did Brother David pay to Brother Lloyd? $550.00

69. A savings account with 4% interest had a balance of $450.00. If the interest was added to the balance, how much money was in the account after 6 months? $459.00

169.   Review of Chapters 11 and 12

A.   Write the correct term for each description. *(Lesson 137)*

1. A polygon with 5 sides   pentagon
2. A polygon with 3 sides   triangle
3. A polygon with 4 equal sides and 4 right angles   square
4. A polygon with 6 sides   hexagon
5. Any 4-sided polygon whose corners are right angles   rectangle
6. A polygon with 8 sides   octagon
7. A 4-sided polygon whose opposite sides are parallel but whose corners are not right angles   parallelogram

B.   Name the following geometric figures. *(Lesson 137)*

8.   ·   point   9.   △   triangle   10. ⟷   line

11. ⟶   ray   12.   intersecting lines   13.   parallel lines

14. ——   line segment   15.   right angle   16.   rectangle

C.   Find the perimeter of each polygon in inches. *(Lesson 138)*

17.   8 inches

18.   10 inches

D.   Find the areas indicated. *(Lessons 140, 141)*

19. The polygon in number 17   20.   The polygon in number 18
                              4 sq. in.   6 sq. in.

LESSON 169

Objective

- To review the concepts of geometry taught in chapters 11 and 12.

Review

Give Lesson 169 Speed Test (Division). Time limit: 2 minutes. This is a continuation of reviewing the basic facts, which began in Lesson 159.

Teaching Guide

See the comments for Lesson 164.

E. **Find the perimeters of polygons having these dimensions.** *(Lessons 138, 139)*

21. square
s = 12 in.

48 in.

22. square
s = 35 ft.

140 ft.

23. rectangle
l = 16 in.
w = 14 in.
60 in.

24. rectangle
l = 500 ft.
w = 200 ft.
1,400 ft.

25. triangle
s = 22 in.
s = 25 in.
s = 18 in.
65 in.

26. triangle
s = 11 in.
s = 19 in.
s = 17 in.
47 in.

27. hexagon
each side
= 7 in.

42 in.

28. octagon
each side
= 6 in.

48 in.

F. **Find the areas of polygons having these dimensions.** *(Lessons 140–143)*

29. square
s = 7 in.

49 sq. in.

30. square
s = 15 ft.

225 sq. ft.

31. rectangle
l = 12 in.
w = 9 in.
108 sq. in.

32. rectangle
l = 85 ft.
w = 50 ft.
4,250 sq. ft.

33. parallelogram
b = 15 in.
h = 6 in.
90 sq. in.

34. parallelogram
b = 35 ft.
h = 18 ft.
630 sq. ft.

35. triangle
b = 20 in.
h = 12 in.
120 sq. in.

36. triangle
b = 45 in.
h = 32 in.
720 sq. in.

G. **Study this graph to answer the question below.** *(Lesson 144)*

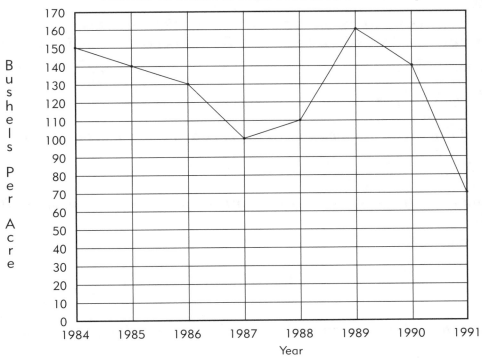

Bushels of Corn Per Acre Produced on the Troyer Farm

What was the yield per acre for each of the following years?

37. 1984 150 bu.   **38.** 1986 130 bu.   **39.** 1988 110 bu.   **40.** 1991 70 bu.

H.   Write the correct term for each description. *(Lessons 148, 154, 157)*

41. The distance around a circle.   circumference

42. The distance from one edge of a circle, through the center, to the opposite edge.

                                                                     diameter

43. Any part of the curved line of a circle.   arc

44. Half of a circle.   semicircle

45. An angle with more than 90 degrees but less than 180 degrees.   obtuse angle

46. An angle with 180 degrees.   straight angle

47. An angle with less than 90 degrees.   acute angle

48. A 90-degree angle.   right angle

49. A triangle with all angles less than 90 degrees.   acute triangle

50. A triangle with one 90-degree angle.   right triangle

51. A triangle with one angle of more than 90 degrees but less than 180 degrees.

                                                                     obtuse triangle

I.   Write the missing numbers. *(Lesson 148)*

52. radius = 7 in.; diameter = __14__ in.

53. diameter = 15 in.; radius = __$7\frac{1}{2}$__ in.

J.   Find the circumferences of circles with these diameters. Use π = 3.14 for numbers 54 and 55. Use π = $\frac{22}{7}$ for numbers 56 and 57. *(Lesson 149)*

54. 16 in.   50.24 in.   55. 15 in.   47.1 in.

56. 14 in.   44 in.   57. 21 in.   66 in.

K.   Find the areas of circles with these radii. Use π = 3.14. *(Lesson 150)*

58. 6 in.   113.04 sq. in.   59. 8 m   200.96 m²

L.   Find the volumes of rectangular solids having these dimensions. *(Lessons 151, 153)*

60. l = 9 in.   61. l = 16 cm
     w = 5 in. w = 12 cm
     h = 3 in.   135 cu. in. h = 9 cm   1,728 cm³

M.   Find the volumes of cubes having these edges. *(Lessons 152, 153)*

62. 3 ft.   27 cu. ft.   63. 12 cm   1,728 cm³

LESSON 170

Objective

- To give a final test on the math concepts taught in grade 6.

Teaching Guide

1. Correct Lesson 169.

2. Review any areas of special difficulty.

3. Administer the test. Be sure to give the students enough time to finish the final test, since it is longer than usual.

N. *Using your protractor, measure the degrees in these angles. All the answers are multiples of 5 degrees. (Lesson 155)*

64.

60°

65.

120°

O. *Each exercise gives two angles of a triangle. Find the degrees in the third angle. (Lesson 156)*

66. angle 1 = 48 degrees
    angle 2 = 38 degrees   94 degrees

67. angle 1 = 60 degrees
    angle 2 = 60 degrees   60 degrees

P. *Use the information on the circle graph to answer these questions.*

68. What percent of the students are in fifth grade?   37%

69. What percent of the students are in sixth grade?   42%

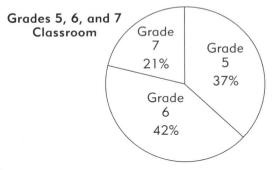

Grades 5, 6, and 7 Classroom

Grade 7
21%

Grade 5
37%

Grade 6
42%

Q. *Solve these sets of parallel reading problems. (Lesson 145)*

70. Sarah is using a 2-gallon bucket to fill a watering trough. How many buckets of water will she need to put 22 gallons of water into the trough?   11 buckets

71. Audrey is using a $2\frac{1}{2}$-gallon bucket to fill a watering trough. How many buckets of water will she need to put 35 gallons of water into the trough?   14 buckets

72. The Musser family traveled to Bible school for the closing program. They traveled the 260-mile distance in 5 hours. What was their average rate of speed?

       52 miles per hour

73. The Newswanger family also went to the Bible school program. They traveled 15 miles in $\frac{1}{3}$ hour. What was their average rate of speed?   45 miles per hour

R.   *Draw a sketch to find the solution for each reading problem.*

74. Father is using concrete blocks to start building a fireplace. The blocks are 16 inches long, and the fireplace will be 4 feet wide. With one mortar joint between each pair of blocks, how many mortar joints are needed to lay a four-foot course of blocks?

2 joints

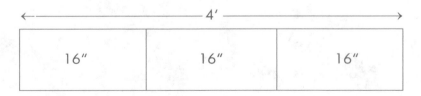

75. The first evening, Father laid two courses of concrete blocks as the foundation of the fireplace. He then laid 5 courses of bricks on top of the blocks. One course of blocks is 8 inches high, and one course of bricks is $2\frac{3}{4}$ inches high. How high was the fireplace by the end of the evening?

$29\frac{3}{4}$ inches

$2\frac{3}{4}''$

$2\frac{3}{4}''$

$2\frac{3}{4}''$

$2\frac{3}{4}''$

$2\frac{3}{4}''$

$8''$

$8''$

---

170. Final Test   (See page T–415.)

QUIZZES and SPEED TESTS

Answer Key

Quizzes and Speed Tests 5–68
are found in Book 1.

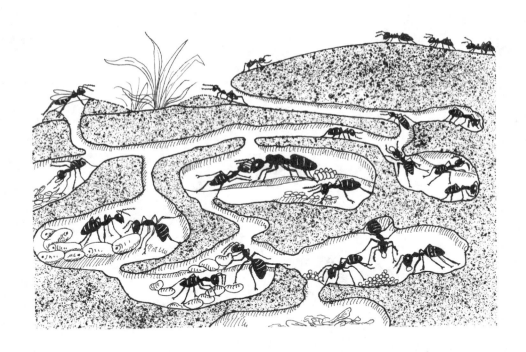

"Consider her ways, and be wise."
(Proverbs 6:6)

Dividing Fractions

Divide these fractions. Use cancellation whenever possible.

1. $4 \div \frac{1}{4} =$ 16

2. $8 \div \frac{1}{5} =$ 40

3. $9 \div \frac{2}{3} =$ $13\frac{1}{2}$

4. $12 \div \frac{3}{4} =$ 16

5. $\frac{7}{8} \div \frac{1}{4} =$ $3\frac{1}{2}$

6. $\frac{5}{9} \div \frac{5}{6} =$ $\frac{2}{3}$

7. $2\frac{3}{4} \div 3 =$ $\frac{11}{12}$

8. $4\frac{1}{5} \div \frac{3}{5} =$ 7

9. $3\frac{1}{3} \div 1\frac{1}{3} =$ $2\frac{1}{2}$

10. $5\frac{1}{4} \div 2\frac{1}{2} =$ $2\frac{1}{10}$

Quiz

Name _____   Date _____   Score _____

Changing Fractions to Decimals and Decimals to Fractions

A. *Change each fraction to a decimal. See if you can do numbers 1–3 by memory.*

1. $\frac{1}{4}$ = ____0.25____

2. $\frac{4}{5}$ = ____0.8____

3. $\frac{1}{2}$ = ____0.5____

4. $\frac{3}{8}$ = ____0.375____

5. $\frac{5}{8}$ = ____0.625____

6. $\frac{7}{16}$ = ____0.4375____

B. *Change these decimals to fractions in lowest terms.*

7. 0.45 = ____$\frac{9}{20}$____

8. 0.6 = ____$\frac{3}{5}$____

9. 0.46 = ____$\frac{23}{50}$____

10. 0.875 = ____$\frac{7}{8}$____

Speed Test

Adding and Subtracting Decimals

1. 45.3
    + 5.9
    51.2

2. 3.8
    + 7.232
    11.032

3. 4.919
    + 7.9
    12.819

4. 18.999
    + 15.33
    34.329

5. 3.3
    14.444
    + 5.06
    22.804

6. 45.6
    − 8.8
    36.8

7. 56.3
    − 14.9
    41.4

8. 8.791
    − 0.9
    7.891

9. 7.5
    − 3.099
    4.401

10. 8.3
    − 7.992
    0.308

Multiplying and Dividing by 10, by 100, and by 1,000

	Multiply	by 10	by 100	by 1,000
1.	345	3,450	34,500	345,000
2.	4.5	45	450	4,500
3.	345.83	3,458.3	34,583	345,830
4.	0.0032	0.032	0.32	3.2

	Divide	by 10	by 100	by 1,000
5.	345	34.5	3.45	0.345
6.	5.6	0.56	0.056	0.0056
7.	34.6	3.46	0.346	0.0346
8.	723.4	72.34	7.234	0.7234

Quiz

Name _____   Date _____   Score _____

Multiplying and Dividing Decimals

1. $4.50
    × 12
    $54.00

2.   3.5
    × 4.6
    16.10

3.   8.3
    × 0.37
    3.071

4.   0.15
    × 0.15
    0.0225

5.   0.07
    × 0.07
    0.0049

6. $3.25
    9)$29.25

7. 7.08
    2.4)16.992

8. 2.14
    3.5)7.49

9. 15.25
    0.2)3.05

10. 1.066
    0.15)0.1599

Multiplying Mentally by Changing Decimals to Fractions

1. $0.25 \times 24 =$ _____6_____

2. $0.33\frac{1}{3} \times 60 =$ _____20_____

3. $0.5 \times 52 =$ _____26_____

4. $0.66\frac{2}{3} \times 60 =$ _____40_____

5. $0.75 \times 28 =$ _____21_____

6. $0.2 \times 40 =$ _____8_____

7. $0.4 \times 35 =$ _____14_____

8. $0.6 \times 35 =$ _____21_____

9. $0.25 \times 20 =$ _____5_____

10. $0.8 \times 25 =$ _____20_____

Name _____   Date _____   Score _____

Metric Units of Linear Measure

A. Match these prefixes with the correct definitions.

_b_	**1.** centi-	**a.**	tenth
_f_	**2.** kilo-	**b.**	hundredth
_e_	**3.** hecto-	**c.**	thousandth
_d_	**4.** deka-	**d.**	ten
_c_	**5.** milli-	**e.**	hundred
_a_	**6.** deci-	**f.**	thousand

B. Measure each line to the nearest centimeter.

(Lines pictured here are 87% of pupil's copy.)

7. ———————————— 6 cm

8. ———————————————————— 14 cm

9. —————————————————— 12 cm

10. —————————————————————— 16 cm

C. Change these metric units as indicated.

11. 4 m = _____400_____ cm   **12.** 4 m = _____4,000_____ mm

13. 25 km = _____25,000_____ m   **14.** 85 mm = _____0.085_____ m

15. 18 mm = _____1.8_____ cm   **16.** 330 m = _____0.33_____ km

Quiz

Name _____   Date _____   Score _____

Metric Units of Weight, Capacity, and Area

1. 50 g = __0.05__ kg

2. 300 mg = __0.3__ g

3. 1.5 m.t. = __1,500__ kg

4. 3,700 ml = __3.7__ l

5. 350 l = __0.35__ kl

6. 2.5 l = __2,500__ ml

7. 750 ha = __7.5__ km^2

8. 5 ha = __50,000__ m^2

9. 0.45 m^2 = __4,500__ cm^2

Metric Units of Measure

1.   5 m = __500__ cm

2.   8 kg = __8,000__ g

3.   4 kl = __4,000__ l

4.   6 km = __6,000__ m

5.   15 cm = __0.15__ m

6.   9 km^2 = __900__ ha

7.   160 ha = __1.6__ km^2

8.   6 m^2 = __60,000__ cm^2

9.   35 mm = __3.5__ cm

10.   5.5 l = __5,500__ ml

11.   150 m = __0.15__ km

12.   8.8 cm = __88__ mm

Quiz

Name _____ Date _____ Score _____

Conversions Between Metric and English Units

Metric to English	English to Metric
Linear Measure	**Linear Measure**
1 cm = 0.39 in.	1 in. = 2.54 cm
1 m = 39.4 in.	1 ft. = 0.3 m
1 m = 3.28 ft.	1 mi. = 1.61 km
1 km = 0.62 mi.	
Weight	**Weight**
1 g = 0.035 oz.	1 oz. = 28.3 g
1 kg = 2.2 lb.	1 lb. = 0.45 kg
Capacity	**Capacity**
1 l = 1.06 qt. (liquid)	1 qt. (liquid) = 0.95 l
Area	**Area**
1 ha = 2.5 a.	1 a. = 0.4 ha
1 km² = 0.39 sq. mi.	1 sq. mi. = 2.59 km²

Use the tables above to make the conversions indicated.

1. 6 m = __19.68__ ft.

2. 9 in. = __22.86__ cm

3. 3 mi. = __4.83__ km

4. 9 km = __5.58__ mi.

5. 15 lb. = __6.75__ kg

6. 6 oz. = __169.8__ g

7. 150 g = __5.25__ oz.

8. 25 kg = __55__ lb.

9. 7 qt. = __6.65__ l

10. 15 l = __15.9__ qt.

11. 7 ha = __17.5__ a.

12. 7 a. = __2.8__ ha

13. 4 sq. mi. = __10.36__ km²

14. 8 km² = __3.12__ sq. mi.

Distance, Rate, and Time

	Rate	Time	Distance
1.	59 m.p.h.	3 hr.	177 mi.
2.	45 m.p.h.	4 hr.	180 mi.
3.	48 m.p.h.	7 hr.	336 mi.
4.	51 m.p.h.	9 hr.	459 mi.
5.	51 m.p.h.	15 hr.	765 mi.
6.	353 m.p.h.	6 hr.	2,118 mi.
7.	44 m.p.h.	5 hr.	220 mi.
8.	52 m.p.h.	6 hr.	312 mi.
9.	48 m.p.h.	2.5 hr.	120 mi.
10.	49 m.p.h.	12 hr.	588 mi.

LESSON 117   Quiz

Name _____   Date _____   Score _____

Expressing Percents as Decimals and Fractions

Write each percent as a decimal and as a fraction in lowest terms.

	Percent	Decimal	Fraction
1.	20%	0.2	$\frac{1}{5}$
2.	18%	0.18	$\frac{9}{50}$
3.	35%	0.35	$\frac{7}{20}$
4.	53%	0.53	$\frac{53}{100}$
5.	60%	0.6	$\frac{3}{5}$
6.	30%	0.3	$\frac{3}{10}$
7.	12%	0.12	$\frac{3}{25}$
8.	51%	0.51	$\frac{51}{100}$

Finding a Percentage of a Number

A.   Do as many of these mentally as you can.

1.   25% of 80 = _____20_____   2. $33\frac{1}{3}$% of 60 = _____20_____

3.   50% of 96 = _____48_____   4.   20% of 40 = _____8_____

5. $66\frac{2}{3}$% of 36 = _____24_____   6.   80% of 15 = _____12_____

B.   Solve these problems.

7.   24% of 40 = _____9.6_____   8.   52% of 55 = _____28.6_____

9.   15% of 46 = _____6.9_____   10.   95% of 60 = _____57_____

Quiz

Name _____   Date _____   Score _____

Working With Percents

A.   Write each percent as a decimal and as a fraction in lowest terms.

	Percent	Decimal	Fraction
1.	75%	0.75	$\frac{3}{4}$
2.	52%	0.52	$\frac{13}{25}$
3.	28%	0.28	$\frac{7}{25}$

B.   Write each decimal as a percent.

4. 0.52 = __52%__   5. 0.3 = __30%__   6. 0.7 = __70%__   7. 0.03 = __3%__

C.   Write each fraction as a percent. Express any remainder as a fraction.

8. $\frac{4}{5}$ = __80%__   9. $\frac{5}{8}$ = __$62\frac{1}{2}$%__   10. $\frac{5}{16}$ = __$31\frac{1}{4}$%__   11. $\frac{12}{20}$ = __60%__

D.   Find the percentages of these whole numbers.

12. 30% of 60 = __18__   13. 28% of 40 = __11.2__   14. 15% of 70 = __10.5__

15. 45% of 40 = __18__   16. 65% of 60 = __39__   17. 85% of 80 = __68__

Counting Change

A. *Fill in this chart, showing the number of coins and bills you would use and the total amount of change.*

	Amount of Sale	Amount Given	1¢	5¢	10¢	25¢	$1	$5	Total Change
1.	$0.48	$1.00	2			2			$0.52
2.	$1.17	$2.00	3	1		3			$0.83
3.	$3.55	$5.00			2	1	1		$1.45
4.	$4.27	$10.00	3		2	2		1	$5.73
5.	$12.36	$15.00	4		1	2	2		$2.64

B. *Write what you would say as you count the change to the customer.*

Amount of Sale   Amount Given

6. $1.34 $2.00 $1.34; $1.35; $1.40; $1.50; $1.75; $2.00

7. $2.69 $5.00 $2.69; $2.70; $2.75; $3.00; $4.00; $5.00

8. $3.48 $5.00 $3.48; $3.50; $3.75; $4.00; $5.00

9. $3.45 $10.00 $3.45; $3.50; $3.75; $4.00; $5.00; $10.00

10. $4.71 $10.00 $4.71; $4.75; $5.00; $10.00

Quiz

Name _____   Date _____   Score _____

Computing Interest

1. $p = \$900,$ $r = 9\%,$ $t = 2$ yr., $i =$ _____ $\$162.00$

2. $p = \$800,$ $r = 12\%,$ $t = 5$ yr., $i =$ _____ $\$480.00$

3. $p = \$750,$ $r = 10\%,$ $t = 3$ yr., $i =$ _____ $\$225.00$

4. $p = \$850,$ $r = 8\%,$ $t = 4$ yr., $i =$ _____ $\$272.00$

5. $p = \$2,000,$ $r = 12\%,$ $t = \frac{1}{2}$ yr., $i =$ _____ $\$120.00$

6. $p = \$2,500,$ $r = 9\%,$ $t = \frac{1}{2}$ yr., $i =$ _____ $\$112.50$

7. $p = \$1,200,$ $r = 10\%,$ $t = \frac{2}{3}$ yr., $i =$ _____ $\$80.00$

8. $p = \$3,500,$ $r = 8\%,$ $t = 6$ mo., $i =$ _____ $\$140.00$

9. $p = \$500,$ $r = 14\%,$ $t = 4$ mo., $i =$ _____ $\$23.33$

10. $p = \$650,$ $r = 7\%,$ $t = 3$ mo., $i =$ _____ $\$11.38$

Name _____ Date _____ Score _____

Finding Perimeters

Find the perimeters of polygons with these dimensions.

1. Triangle   14 in.
   5 in. by 3 in. by 6 in.

2. Triangle   40 ft.
   12 ft. by 12 ft. by 16 ft.

3. Rectangle   54 ft.
   12 ft. by 15 ft.

4. Rectangle   84 mi.
   28 mi. by 14 mi.

5. Rectangle   16 ft. 4 in.
   4 ft. 8 in. by 3 ft. 6 in.

6. Rectangle   30.4 km
   8.7 km by 6.5 km

7. Square   64 in.
   each side = 16 in.

8. Square   192 ft.
   each side = 48 ft.

9. Pentagon   26 ft.
   sides = 4 ft., 6 ft.,
   3 ft., 8 ft., 5 ft.

10. Hexagon   180 ft.
   two sides = 15 ft.
   two sides = 30 ft.
   two sides = 45 ft.

Finding Perimeters

A. Find the perimeters of squares with these dimensions.

1. 6-in. sides	**2.** 12-in. sides	**3.** each side = $4\frac{1}{2}$ ft.
24 in.	48 in.	18 ft.

B. Find the perimeters of rectangles with these dimensions.

4. 8 in. by 5 in.	**5.** 15 ft. by 18 ft.	**6.** 90 ft. by 80 ft.
26 in.	66 ft.	340 ft.

7. 55 ft. by 45 ft.	**8.** 6 mi. by 4 mi.	**9.** 88 m by 53 m
200 ft.	20 mi.	282 m

C. Find the perimeters of these triangles.

10. side a = 12 in.	**11.** side a = 400 ft.	**12.** side a = 15 km
side b = 9 in.	side b = 400 ft.	side b = 25 km
side c = 7 in.	side c = 694 ft.	side c = 32 km
28 in.	1,494 ft.	72 km

Finding Areas

A. Find the areas of rectangles with these dimensions.

1. $l = 5$ ft.
    $w = 4$ ft.

    20 sq. ft.

2. $l = 15$ in.
    $w = 8$ in.

    120 sq. in.

3. $l = 35$ ft.
    $w = 25$ ft.

    875 sq. ft.

4. $l = 45$ ft.
    $w = 28$ ft.

    1,260 sq. ft.

B. Find the areas of squares with these dimensions.

5. $s = 4$ ft.

    16 sq. ft.

6. $s = 18$ in.

    324 sq. in.

7. $s = 92$ ft.

    8,464 sq. ft.

C. Find the areas of triangles with these dimensions. The formula is $a = \frac{1}{2}bh$.

8. $b = 8$ in.
    $h = 6$ in.

    24 sq. in.

9. $b = 23$ in.
    $h = 18$ in.

    207 sq. in.

10. $b = 32$ ft.
     $h = 16$ ft.

     256 sq. ft.

LESSON 152

Quiz

Name _____   Date _____   Score _____

Working With Circles

A. *Find the circumferences of circles with these diameters. The formula is c = π × d.*
(π = 3.14)

1. 4 in.   12.56 in.   2. 3 ft.   9.42 ft.

3. 5 yd.   15.7 yd.   4. 10 in.   31.4 in..

5. 20 ft.   62.8 ft.

B. *Find the areas of circles with these radii. The formula is a = πr². (π = 3.14)*

6. 2 in.   12.56 sq. in.   7. 3 in.   28.26 sq. in.

8. 4 ft.   50.24 sq. ft.   9. 10 in.   314 sq. in.

10. 20 in.   1,256 sq. in.

LESSON 155   Quiz

Name _____   Date _____   Score _____

Computing Volume

A.   Find the volumes of rectangular solids with these dimensions.

1. 4 in. by 3 in. by 2 in.
    24 cu. in.

2. 8 in. by 7 in. by 6 in.
    336 cu. in.

3. 12 ft. by 9 ft. by 10 ft.
    1,080 cu. ft.

4. 15 ft. by 13 ft. by 8 ft.
    1,560 cu. ft.

5. 30 ft. by 20 ft. by 10 ft.
    6,000 cu. ft.

B.   Find the volumes of cubes with these dimensions.

6. $e = 8$ in.
    512 cu. in.

7. $e = 6$ in.
    216 cu. in.

8. $e = 9$ ft.
    729 cu. ft.

9. $e = 15$ ft.
    3,375 cu. ft.

10. $e = 14$ ft.
    2,744 cu. ft.

Speed Test

Multiplying Decimals

1.   2.6
    × 1.5
    3.90

2.   3.4
    × 0.43
    1.462

3.   3.5
    × 0.12
    0.420

4.   6.6
    × 0.05
    0.330

5.   1.1
    × 1.1
    1.21

6.   2.5
    × 1.3
    3.25

7.   1.85
    × 0.68
    1.2580

8.   0.22
    × 0.25
    0.0550

9.   0.15
    × 0.12
    0.0180

10.   0.04
    × 0.05
    0.0020

Speed Test

Addition Facts

1.	8 +1 9	4 +7 11	6 +8 14	2 +3 5	3 +8 11	3 +3 6	2 +1 3	7 +0 7	3 +6 9	8 +0 8
2.	4 +2 6	2 +9 11	7 +5 12	0 +8 8	7 +3 10	9 +6 15	5 +0 5	4 +4 8	1 +6 7	2 +0 2
3.	8 +8 16	5 +8 13	1 +7 8	9 +2 11	9 +3 12	0 +1 1	6 +2 8	5 +6 11	5 +2 7	7 +2 9
4.	9 +4 13	0 +3 3	5 +3 8	6 +4 10	4 +5 9	4 +3 7	7 +6 13	1 +3 4	3 +2 5	1 +4 5
5.	0 +9 9	8 +6 14	3 +9 12	3 +5 8	1 +0 1	9 +1 10	3 +0 3	2 +6 8	7 +9 16	8 +5 13
6.	2 +2 4	4 +0 4	6 +7 13	2 +5 7	7 +1 8	9 +5 14	3 +7 10	9 +7 16	5 +9 14	3 +1 4
7.	9 +8 17	0 +4 4	8 +3 11	6 +9 15	5 +1 6	4 +8 12	0 +2 2	0 +5 5	3 +4 7	9 +0 9
8.	7 +7 14	6 +5 11	2 +4 6	0 +0 0	1 +9 10	6 +3 9	4 +1 5	5 +5 10	5 +7 12	7 +8 15
9.	4 +6 10	9 +9 18	1 +5 6	6 +1 7	6 +0 6	4 +9 13	1 +8 9	0 +6 6	8 +7 15	1 +2 3
10.	2 +8 10	0 +7 7	8 +9 17	2 +7 9	1 +1 2	8 +2 10	5 +4 9	8 +4 12	6 +6 12	7 +4 11

LESSON 162

Speed Test

Time: 2 minutes

Subtraction Facts

1.	13 −6 = 7	8 −0 = 8	7 −1 = 6	8 −3 = 5	12 −7 = 5	6 −1 = 5	6 −5 = 1	5 −0 = 5	11 −9 = 2	17 −8 = 9
2.	6 −6 = 0	13 −5 = 8	12 −9 = 3	10 −7 = 3	7 −5 = 2	3 −1 = 2	16 −7 = 9	10 −4 = 6	4 −3 = 1	14 −7 = 7
3.	11 −2 = 9	6 −4 = 2	6 −3 = 3	13 −8 = 5	8 −7 = 1	15 −6 = 9	9 −8 = 1	12 −4 = 8	8 −1 = 7	4 −4 = 0
4.	8 −6 = 2	2 −0 = 2	12 −5 = 7	9 −0 = 9	8 −4 = 4	7 −6 = 1	8 −2 = 6	9 −7 = 2	13 −4 = 9	4 −1 = 3
5.	14 −6 = 8	14 −5 = 9	9 −4 = 5	3 −3 = 0	9 −6 = 3	2 −1 = 1	11 −4 = 7	16 −8 = 8	8 −8 = 0	11 −3 = 8
6.	12 −8 = 4	9 −5 = 4	7 −0 = 7	3 −2 = 1	10 −5 = 5	2 −2 = 0	16 −9 = 7	7 −2 = 5	12 −6 = 6	10 −9 = 1
7.	7 −3 = 4	15 −7 = 8	9 −3 = 6	11 −7 = 4	5 −4 = 1	5 −1 = 4	14 −9 = 5	1 −0 = 1	9 −9 = 0	11 −5 = 6
8.	6 −2 = 4	1 −1 = 0	11 −8 = 3	13 −9 = 4	6 −0 = 6	10 −6 = 4	15 −9 = 6	7 −4 = 3	0 −0 = 0	10 −8 = 2
9.	14 −8 = 6	10 −2 = 8	13 −7 = 6	9 −2 = 7	8 −5 = 3	4 −2 = 2	9 −1 = 8	11 −6 = 5	10 −1 = 9	12 −3 = 9
10.	5 −5 = 0	5 −3 = 2	4 −0 = 4	7 −7 = 0	17 −9 = 8	10 −3 = 7	3 −0 = 3	18 −9 = 9	15 −8 = 7	5 −2 = 3

Speed Test

Multiplication Facts

1.
6	5	2	7	3	8	4	9	12	0
× 7	× 6	× 3	× 9	× 6	× 6	× 9	× 5	× 12	× 3
42	30	6	63	18	48	36	45	144	0

2.
4	8	4	2	6	1	6	11	12	10
× 6	× 1	× 7	× 1	× 6	× 2	× 2	× 1	× 5	× 8
24	8	28	2	36	2	12	11	60	80

3.
3	6	0	5	1	8	10	1	3	7
× 7	× 5	× 8	× 9	× 6	× 8	× 9	× 3	× 8	× 8
21	30	0	45	6	64	90	3	24	56

4.
2	9	5	11	5	11	7	9	4	12
× 2	× 8	× 0	× 11	× 7	× 10	× 0	× 9	× 0	× 6
4	72	0	121	35	110	0	81	0	72

5.
0	9	5	12	6	12	5	11	8	9
× 9	× 4	× 2	× 3	× 8	× 8	× 1	× 9	× 4	× 6
0	36	10	36	48	96	5	99	32	54

6.
10	4	9	1	8	2	3	3	2	7
× 4	× 8	× 3	× 9	× 9	× 8	× 9	× 1	× 4	× 6
40	32	27	9	72	16	27	3	8	42

7.
3	9	12	8	3	9	1	0	7	3
× 0	× 0	× 7	× 2	× 4	× 7	× 1	× 5	× 4	× 2
0	0	84	16	12	63	1	0	28	6

8.
5	1	12	2	11	8	5	0	11	7
× 4	× 7	× 4	× 5	× 8	× 3	× 8	× 6	× 12	× 5
20	7	48	10	88	24	40	0	132	35

9.
7	9	12	7	4	2	5	6	4	8
× 7	× 2	× 9	× 3	× 2	× 0	× 3	× 9	× 4	× 5
49	18	108	21	8	0	15	54	16	40

10.
1	3	12	7	5	6	0	11	8	2
× 4	× 3	× 11	× 2	× 5	× 4	× 1	× 6	× 7	× 6
4	9	132	14	25	24	0	66	56	12

Multiplication Facts

1.	2 ×8 16	5 ×0 0	12 ×11 132	10 ×4 40	11 ×9 99	8 ×4 32	9 ×6 54	5 ×8 40	5 ×9 45	9 ×7 63
2.	9 ×4 36	5 ×2 10	9 ×8 72	3 ×0 0	3 ×1 3	2 ×4 8	7 ×6 42	5 ×3 15	11 ×11 121	8 ×3 24
3.	4 ×8 32	9 ×3 27	1 ×6 6	5 ×4 20	0 ×5 0	7 ×4 28	3 ×2 6	7 ×7 49	12 ×3 36	2 ×0 0
4.	9 ×0 0	6 ×5 30	5 ×7 35	5 ×5 25	0 ×6 0	11 ×12 132	7 ×5 35	1 ×4 4	1 ×9 9	6 ×4 24
5.	1 ×7 7	8 ×8 64	6 ×8 48	8 ×6 48	6 ×9 54	4 ×4 16	8 ×5 40	5 ×6 30	8 ×2 16	4 ×9 36
6.	9 ×2 18	11 ×10 110	6 ×7 42	1 ×2 2	11 ×6 66	8 ×7 56	2 ×6 12	8 ×1 8	2 ×5 10	6 ×2 12
7.	3 ×3 9	12 ×8 96	4 ×6 24	7 ×9 63	12 ×12 144	0 ×3 0	7 ×0 0	8 ×9 72	7 ×3 21	10 ×9 90
8.	2 ×3 6	12 ×7 84	3 ×7 21	2 ×1 2	12 ×5 60	10 ×8 80	5 ×1 5	3 ×4 12	7 ×2 14	0 ×1 0
9.	4 ×7 28	12 ×4 48	2 ×2 4	1 ×3 3	3 ×8 24	7 ×8 56	3 ×9 27	11 ×8 88	3 ×6 18	9 ×5 45
10.	0 ×8 0	12 ×9 108	0 ×9 0	9 ×9 81	4 ×0 0	12 ×6 72	1 ×1 1	4 ×2 8	6 ×6 36	11 ×1 11

Speed Test

Division Facts

1. $3\overline{)36}$ = 12 $8\overline{)16}$ = 2 $6\overline{)66}$ = 11 $10\overline{)100}$ = 10 $3\overline{)0}$ = 0 $11\overline{)77}$ = 7 $1\overline{)9}$ = 9 $3\overline{)21}$ = 7

2. $7\overline{)42}$ = 6 $11\overline{)33}$ = 3 $7\overline{)84}$ = 12 $4\overline{)24}$ = 6 $8\overline{)48}$ = 6 $7\overline{)0}$ = 0 $8\overline{)56}$ = 7 $4\overline{)12}$ = 3

3. $10\overline{)30}$ = 3 $11\overline{)22}$ = 2 $5\overline{)10}$ = 2 $8\overline{)0}$ = 0 $10\overline{)80}$ = 8 $5\overline{)15}$ = 3 $12\overline{)108}$ = 9 $9\overline{)9}$ = 1

4. $5\overline{)25}$ = 5 $4\overline{)36}$ = 9 $7\overline{)35}$ = 5 $1\overline{)4}$ = 4 $10\overline{)90}$ = 9 $1\overline{)5}$ = 5 $9\overline{)45}$ = 5 $3\overline{)27}$ = 9

5. $9\overline{)63}$ = 7 $1\overline{)7}$ = 7 $5\overline{)35}$ = 7 $9\overline{)18}$ = 2 $7\overline{)14}$ = 2 $6\overline{)18}$ = 3 $10\overline{)40}$ = 4 $12\overline{)84}$ = 7

6. $9\overline{)36}$ = 4 $2\overline{)16}$ = 8 $12\overline{)96}$ = 8 $12\overline{)48}$ = 4 $2\overline{)10}$ = 5 $3\overline{)3}$ = 1 $6\overline{)0}$ = 0 $11\overline{)66}$ = 6

7. $3\overline{)18}$ = 6 $7\overline{)7}$ = 1 $9\overline{)81}$ = 9 $6\overline{)42}$ = 7 $6\overline{)36}$ = 6 $3\overline{)12}$ = 4 $9\overline{)54}$ = 6 $7\overline{)63}$ = 9

8. $5\overline{)0}$ = 0 $2\overline{)12}$ = 6 $4\overline{)32}$ = 8 $1\overline{)0}$ = 0 $3\overline{)6}$ = 2 $5\overline{)30}$ = 6 $2\overline{)6}$ = 3 $2\overline{)14}$ = 7

9. $4\overline{)20}$ = 5 $11\overline{)121}$ = 11 $8\overline{)8}$ = 1 $7\overline{)21}$ = 3 $8\overline{)72}$ = 9 $6\overline{)24}$ = 4 $8\overline{)32}$ = 4 $8\overline{)24}$ = 3

10. $10\overline{)120}$ = 12 $8\overline{)40}$ = 5 $2\overline{)0}$ = 0 $12\overline{)72}$ = 6 $10\overline{)60}$ = 6 $8\overline{)64}$ = 8 $9\overline{)0}$ = 0

11. $4\overline{)16}$ = 4 $9\overline{)72}$ = 8 $7\overline{)28}$ = 4 $11\overline{)88}$ = 8 $7\overline{)56}$ = 8 $10\overline{)110}$ = 11 $4\overline{)28}$ = 7

12. $6\overline{)48}$ = 8 $12\overline{)60}$ = 5 $11\overline{)99}$ = 9 $3\overline{)15}$ = 5 $5\overline{)45}$ = 9 $5\overline{)40}$ = 8 $12\overline{)24}$ = 2

13. $2\overline{)8}$ = 4 $11\overline{)132}$ = 12 $11\overline{)110}$ = 10 $12\overline{)144}$ = 12 $6\overline{)54}$ = 9 $7\overline{)49}$ = 7 $12\overline{)132}$ = 11

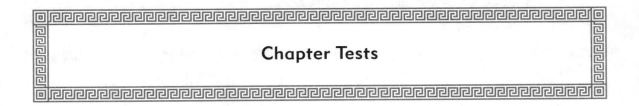

Chapter Tests

Answer Key

```
┌─────────────────────────────────────────────────────────────┐
│  96.  Chapter 7 Test                                         │
└─────────────────────────────────────────────────────────────┘
```

A.   Solve these problems. Check 1–4 by casting out nines.

1.   565
      × 89
     50,285

2.   876
      × 71
     62,196

3. $81\overline{)5{,}721}$ 70 R 51

4. $76\overline{)31{,}118}$ 409 R 34

5. $\frac{3}{4} \times 3\frac{1}{2}$ $2\frac{5}{8}$

6. $3\frac{2}{3} \times 2\frac{1}{4}$ $8\frac{1}{4}$

7. $8 \div \frac{3}{4}$ $10\frac{2}{3}$

8. $3\frac{1}{2} \div 4\frac{1}{4}$ $\frac{14}{17}$

B.   Divide these numbers as indicated.

9. $44.5 \div 10 =$ _4.45_

10. $3.62 \div 100 =$ _.0362_

11. $95.6 \div 1{,}000 =$ _.0956_

C.   Divide until each problem comes out evenly. Check by casting out nines.

12. $5\overline{)14.5}$ 2.9

13. $14\overline{)\$43.26}$ $3.09

14. $4.2\overline{)15.12}$ 3.6

15. $3.9\overline{)6.201}$ 1.59

16. $1.5\overline{)0.0141}$ 0.0094

17. $0.42\overline{)0.63}$ 1.5

D.   Round these numbers as indicated.

To the nearest tenth

18. 0.68   _0.7_

19. 3.828   _3.8_

To the nearest hundredth

20. 4.079   _4.08_

21. 5.799   _5.80_

To the nearest cent

22. $3.557   _$3.56_

23. $5.797   _$5.80_

E.   *Change each fraction to a decimal. Divide to the hundredths' place, and express the remainder as a fraction in lowest terms.*

24. $\frac{5}{12}$ $0.41\frac{2}{3}$

25. $\frac{8}{15}$ $0.53\frac{1}{3}$

F.   *Change these fractions to decimals rounded to the nearest hundredth.*

26. $\frac{7}{9}$ 0.78

27. $\frac{9}{16}$ 0.56

G.   *Find whether each proportion is true, and write* yes *or* no.

28. ___no___ $\frac{8}{7} = \frac{14}{12}$

29. ___no___ $\frac{14}{8} = \frac{16}{9}$

30. ___yes___ $\frac{12}{8} = \frac{15}{10}$

31. ___yes___ $\frac{30}{12} = \frac{40}{16}$

H.   *Find the missing numbers in these proportions.*

32. $\frac{8}{6} = \frac{n}{15}$; $n =$ ___20___

33. $\frac{9}{15} = \frac{21}{n}$; $n =$ ___35___

I.   *Solve each reading problem by using a proportion. Show your work; the proportion will be counted as part of the answer.*   (Proportion arrangements may vary.)

34. Father delivers eggs on his egg route 7 times in two weeks. At that rate, how many times does he deliver eggs in 8 weeks?

$$\frac{7}{2} = \frac{n}{8} \qquad n = 28 \text{ times}$$

35. The sixth grade uses the *Christian Hymnal* for morning devotions. They have 2 hymnals for every 3 students. If there are 18 students in the room, how many *Christian Hymnals* do they have?

$$\frac{2}{3} = \frac{n}{18} \qquad n = 12 \text{ hymnals}$$

36. The fifth and sixth grades together have 3 *Christian Hymnals* for every 5 students in the room. There are 15 *Christian Hymnals* in the room. How many students are there?

$$\frac{3}{5} = \frac{15}{n} \qquad n = 25 \text{ students}$$

37. The sixth grade has 7 pencils for every 3 students. How many pencils do the 18 students have in all?

$$\frac{7}{3} = \frac{n}{18} \qquad n = 42 \text{ pencils}$$

111. Chapter 8 Test

A.   Match these prefixes and their meanings.

1. __e__ deka-   2. __c__ milli-

3. __f__ hecto-   4. __g__ kilo-

5. __b__ centi-   6. __a__ deci-

a. 0.1   e. 10
b. 0.01   f. 100
c. 0.001   g. 1,000
d. 0.0001   h. 10,000

B.   Measure these lines to the nearest centimeter. (Lines pictured here are 87% of pupil's copy.)

7. 3 cm ——————————   8. 8 cm ————————————————————

C.   Change these metric measures as indicated.

9. 2,500 m = __2.5__ km   10. 3.4 cm = __34__ mm   11. 3.5 kg = __3,500__ g

12. 1,800 mg = __1.8__ g   13. 1,500 l = __1.5__ kl   14. 3 m² = __30,000__ cm²

15. 140 kg = __0.14__ m.t.   16. 0.35 l = __350__ ml   17. 400 ha = __4__ km²

D.   Use these tables to change the measures below as indicated.

Metric to English		English to Metric	
Linear Measure *Area*		*Linear Measure* *Area*	
1 m = 3.28 ft. 1 ha = 2.5 a.		1 ft. = 0.3 m 1 a.= 0.4 ha	
1 km = 0.62 mi. 1 km² = 0.39 sq. mi.		1 mi. = 1.61 km 1 sq. mi. = 2.59 km²	
Weight *Capacity*		*Weight* *Capacity*	
1 kg = 2.2 lb. 1 l = 1.06 qt. (liquid)		1 lb. = 0.45 kg 1 qt. (liquid) = 0.95 l	

18. 4 m = __13.12__ ft.   19. 6 mi. = __9.66__ km   20. 11 kg = __24.2__ lb.

21. 30 lb. = __13.5__ kg   22. 16 ha = __40__ a.   23. 25 km² = __9.75__ sq. mi.

E.   Find the actual distance represented by each measurement if the scale of a map is 1 inch = 32 miles.

24. 9 in. = __288 miles__   25. $3\frac{1}{4}$ in. = __104 miles__

F.   Find the actual length represented by each measurement if the scale of a blueprint is $\frac{1}{4}$ inch = 1 foot.

26. 7 in. = __28 feet__   27. $2\frac{3}{4}$ in. = __11 feet__

G. *Refer to this bar graph to answer the question below.*

Population of the Five Largest States in the Russian Federation

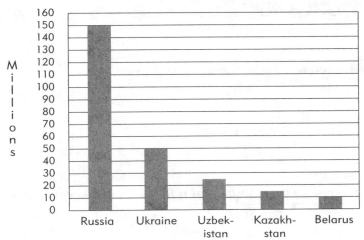

Source: *World Almanac,* 1995

What is the approximate population of each state?

28. Russia   150,000,000   **29.** Ukraine   50,000,000

30. Uzbekistan   25,000,000   **31.** Kazakhstan   15,000,000

32. Belarus   10,000,000

H. *Solve these reading problems. Use the formula* $d = r \times t$ ***for numbers 33–35.***

33. It takes the Martin family $\frac{1}{4}$ hour to drive to church at an average speed of 48 miles per hour. How far do they live from church?
　　　　　　　　　　　12 miles

34. The Weavers went to visit Uncle Laban's one weekend. They drove 297 miles in 6 hours. What was their average speed?
　　　　　　　　　49.5 miles per hour

35. One Friday a group of people traveled to Boston, Massachusetts, to hold street meetings. They drove 456 miles at an average speed of 48 miles per hour. What was their traveling time?
　　　　　　　　　　9.5 hours

36. One day Father planted 21 acres of corn. How many hectares of corn did he plant? (Use the table in part D.)
　　　　　　　　　　8.4 hectares

┌───┐
│ **126. Chapter 9 Test**   │
└───┘

A. *Express these decimals and fractions as percents.*

1. 0.37 = <u>37%</u>

2. 0.09 = <u>9%</u>

3. 0.135 = <u>$13\frac{1}{2}$%</u>

4. $\frac{3}{5}$ = <u>60%</u>

5. $\frac{5}{8}$ = <u>$62\frac{1}{2}$%</u>

6. $\frac{13}{16}$ = <u>$81\frac{1}{4}$%</u>

B. *Write each percent as a decimal and a fraction in lowest terms.*

	Percent	Decimal	Fraction
7.	59%	0.59	$\frac{59}{100}$
8.	26%	0.26	$\frac{13}{50}$

C. *Add or subtract these percents as shown.*

9. 100% + 18% = <u>118%</u>

10. 100% – 6% = <u>94%</u>

11. 100% – 95% = <u>5%</u>

D. *Find these percentages.*

12. 35% of 60 = <u>21</u>

13. 25% of 44 = <u>11</u>

14. 38% of 52 = <u>19.76</u>

15. 25% of 69 = <u>17.25</u>

16. 4% of 17 = <u>0.68</u>

17. 8% of 35 = <u>2.8</u>

E.   Find the price after each increase or decrease.

18. 10% decrease from $18.00 = $16.20

19. 15% increase over $20.00 = $23.00

F.   Find these percents.

20. 5 is ___25___ % of 20   21. 8 is ___$66\frac{2}{3}$___ % of 12   22. 7 is ___20___ % of 35

G.   Solve these reading problems.

23. Father took a corn planter to an auction, and it sold for $950.00. How much commission did the auctioneer receive if the rate of commission was 6%?

       ___$57.00___

24. A salesman sold $775.00 worth of fertilizer at a commission of 8%. How much did he earn?

       ___$62.00___

25. Nevin correctly solved 30 out of 32 problems in his math assignment. What was his score as a percent? Round your answer to the nearest whole percent.

       ___94%___

26. One week, 4 of the 7 days were sunny. What percent of the days of that week were sunny? Express any remainder as a fraction.

       ___$57\frac{1}{7}$%___

27. Father bought a hammer that was on sale at a 20% discount. The original price of the hammer was $11.95. Find the discount, and find the sale price.

     Discount = ___$2.39___   Sale Price = ___$9.56___

28. Martha bought a songbook that was regularly priced at $8.95. The songbook was on sale at 15% off. Find the discount, and find the sale price.

     Discount = ___$1.34___   Sale Price = ___$7.61___

┌──┐
│   │
│   **136. Chapter 10 Test**   │
│   │
└──┘

A. *Solve these problems.*

1. $\frac{5}{6} \times \frac{3}{5} = \frac{1}{2}$

2. $3\frac{3}{4} \times \frac{3}{4} = 2\frac{13}{16}$

3. $5\frac{1}{2} \div \frac{5}{8} = 8\frac{4}{5}$

4. $\begin{array}{r} 6.7 \\ \times\,0.28 \\ \hline 1.876 \end{array}$

5. $\begin{array}{r} 15.83 \\ \times\,3.15 \\ \hline 49.8645 \end{array}$

6. $5.4\overline{)9.612}$ quotient 1.78

B. *Fill in the following chart.*

	Amount of Sale	Amount Given	1¢	5¢	10¢	25¢	$1	$5	Total Change
7.	$1.15	$2.00			1	3			$0.85
8.	$2.84	$5.00	1	1	1		2		$2.16
9.	$1.48	$10.00	2			2	3	1	$8.52

C. *Write what you would say as you give change to a customer.*

	Amount of Sale	Amount Given	

10. $0.57 $1.00 $0.57; $0.57 out of $1.00, $0.60, $0.65, $0.75, $1.00

11. $3.42 $5.00 $3.42; $3.42 out of $5.00, $3.45, $3.50, $3.75, $4.00, $5.00

12. $3.29 $10.00 $3.29; $3.29 out of $10.00, $3.30, $3.40, $3.50, $3.75, $4.00, $5.00, $10.00

D. Complete this cash expense record.

Months	Feed		Fuel		Utilities		Other		Totals	
Jan.–June	$748	29	$274	89	$153	63	$115	72	13. $1,292	53
June–Dec.	816	98	199	36	121	63	189	56	14. 1,327	53
Totals	15 $1,565	27	16. $474	25	17. $275	26	18. $305	28	19. $2,620	06

E. Find the total expenses and the profit in each line.

	Income	Materials	Electricity & Telephone	Small Tools	Total Expenses	Profit
20.	$127.92	$26.93	$8.25	$4.63	$39.81	$88.11
21.	$315.58	$102.36	$9.36	$15.96	$127.68	$187.90
22.	$525.36	$146.63	$12.44	$8.99	$168.06	$357.30

F. Find the unit price for each item, to the nearest cent.

23. 12 dinner rolls for $1.39

$0.12

24. 50 lb. potatoes for $7.00

$0.14

G. Find the interest.

25. $700 at 9% for 1 year

$63.00

26. $500 at 12% for 4 years

$240.00

27. $1,500 at 8% for ½ year

$60.00

28. $900 at 8% for 9 months

$54.00

H.   *Solve these reading problems.*

29. Father sold a hay rake for $900.00 at a public sale. He paid $35 to have the rake hauled to the auction, and the auctioneer's commission was 8%. What did Father receive for the hay rake after the commission and the hauling were deducted?

<u> $793.00   </u>

30. David began plowing a field at 1:00 P.M., with 32 gallons of fuel in the tractor. Until what time will the fuel last if the tractor uses 8 gallons of fuel per hour?

<u>   5:00 P.M.   </u>

31. The Wenger family has a small greenhouse. During the month of April their sales were $732.89. Their expenses were as follows: heat, $25.00; supplies, $35.25; and seeds and plants, $65.00. What was their profit for that month?

<u> $607.64   </u>

32. Stanley put $225.00 into a savings account with an interest rate of 5%. When the money was in the bank for one year, what was the new balance if the bank computed the interest and added it to the account?

<u> $236.25   </u>

33. Laura bought 3 loaves of bread at the store. She paid with a 5-dollar bill and received $2.15 in change. What was the price for each loaf of bread?

<u> $0.95   </u>

147. Chapter 11 Test

A.   Match the terms to the definitions. You will not use all the letters.

1. __d__   A polygon with 8 sides

2. __e__   A polygon with 4 equal sides and 4 square corners

3. __g__   A polygon with 6 sides

4. __b__   Any 4-sided polygon with square corners

5. __a__   A polygon with 5 sides

6. __f__   A polygon with 3 sides

a. pentagon

b. rectangle

c. circle

d. octagon

e. square

f. triangle

g. hexagon

B.   Match the terms to the illustrations. You will not use all the letters.

a.   •

7. __h__   right angle

b.

8. __f__   parallel lines

c.   ——————

9. __c__   line segment

d.   ⟶

10. __a__   point

e.   ↕↔

11. __e__   intersecting lines

f.

12. __g__   line

g.   ⟷

13. __d__   ray

h.   ⌐→

C. *For numbers 14 and 15, find the perimeter of each figure. For numbers 16 and 17, find the area of each figure. Measure in inches.* (Figures pictured are 87% of pupil's copy.)

Figure A

Figure B

14. Figure A: $p = $ ___10 in.___
16. Figure A: $a = $ ___6 sq. in.___

15. Figure B: $p = $ ___8 in.___
17. Figure B: $a = $ ___4 sq. in.___

D. *Find the perimeters of polygons having these dimensions.*

18. square
   $s = 15$ in.
   ___60 in.___

19. square
   $s = 50$ ft.
   ___200 ft.___

20. rectangle
   $l = 18$ in.
   $w = 12$ in.
   ___60 in.___

21. rectangle
   $l = 400$ ft.
   $w = 250$ ft.
   ___1,300 ft.___

22. triangle
   $s = 12$ in.
   $s = 15$ in.
   $s = 18$ in.
   ___45 in.___

23. triangle
   $s = 25$ in.
   $s = 20$ in.
   $s = 16$ in.
   ___61 in.___

24. pentagon
   each side = 5 in.
   ___25 in.___

25. hexagon
   each side = 4 in.
   ___24 in.___

E. *Find the areas of polygons having these dimensions.*

26. square
   $s = 7$ in.
   ___49 sq. in.___

27. square
   $s = 15$ ft.
   ___225 sq. ft.___

28. rectangle
   $l = 12$ in.
   $w = 9$ in.
   ___108 sq. in.___

29. rectangle
   $l = 85$ ft.
   $w = 50$ ft.
   ___4,250 sq. ft.___

30. parallelogram
   $b = 15$ in.
   $h = 6$ in.
   ___90 sq. in.___

31. parallelogram
   $b = 35$ ft.
   $h = 18$ ft.
   ___630 sq. ft.___

32. triangle
   $b = 9$ in.
   $h = 7$ in.
   ___$31\frac{1}{2}$ sq. in.___

33. triangle
   $b = 45$ in.
   $h = 32$ in.
   ___720 sq. in.___

F.   Study this graph, and answer the question below.

Enrollment at the Lakeside Christian School

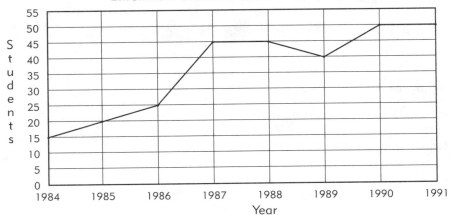

What was the enrollment during each of the following years?

34. 1984 ___15___   **35.** 1986 ___25___   **36.** 1988 ___45___   **37.** 1991 ___50___

G.   Solve these sets of parallel reading problems.

38. The Landis family drove 100 miles in $2\frac{1}{2}$ hours to attend a distant church service. What was their average rate of travel?

_____40 miles per hour_____

39. The Weber family took a hike through the woods one Saturday afternoon. They walked $3\frac{1}{2}$ miles in $1\frac{1}{2}$ hours. What was their average rate of walking?

_____$2\frac{1}{3}$ miles per hour_____

40. Several families were planning to bring a hot lunch to the Rock Point Mennonite School. If 14 quarts of fruit juice have been prepared, how many 2-quart pitchers can be filled with juice?

_____7 pitchers_____

41. If a pitcher of juice holds 8 cups and each glass is filled with $\frac{2}{3}$ cup, how many glasses can be filled from one pitcher of juice?

_____12 glasses_____

161. Chapter 12 Test

A. *Use the circle on the right to do these exercises.*

1. Line segment _____RQ_____ shows the diameter of the circle.

2. The part of the circle between point __R__ and point __P__ is an arc. (Several correct answers are possible.) P, Q or R, Q

3. Line segment _____OP____ shows the radius of the circle.

4. What is the circumference of the circle? (Measure the diameter, and compute with the decimal form of π.) _9.42 in._

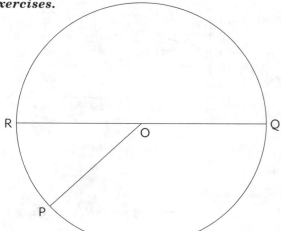

B. *Match the terms to the descriptions. You will not use all the letters.*

5. ___c___ A 90-degree angle

6. ___f___ A triangle with three angles that are each less than 90 degrees

7. ___b___ A 180-degree angle

8. ___a___ An angle that has less than 90 degrees

9. ___d___ A triangle with one angle that is more than 90 degrees but less than 180 degrees.

  a. acute angle
  b. straight angle
  c. right angle
  d. obtuse triangle
  e. right triangle
  f. acute triangle

C. *Write the missing numbers.*

10. radius = 5 inches; diameter = ___10___ inches

11. diameter = 11 inches; radius = ___$5\frac{1}{2}$___ inches

D. *Find the circumferences of circles with these diameters, using the decimal form of π. The formula is $c = \pi d$.*

12. 6 inches _18.84 in._

13. 11 inches _34.54 in._

E. *Find the areas of circles with these radii, using the decimal form of π. The formula is $a = \pi r^2$.*

14. 4 inches _50.24 sq. in._

15. 5 meters _78.5 m²_

476

F.   *Find the volume of rectangular solids with these dimensions.*

16. l = 8 in., w = 6 in., h = 7 in. 336 cu. in.

17. l = 15 cm, w = 11 cm, h = 8 cm 1,320 cm³

G.   *Find the volumes of cubes with these edges.*

18. e = 9 in. 729 cu. in.

19. e = 15 cm 3,375 cm³

H.   *Use your protractor to measure the degrees of these angles. All the answers are multiples of 5 degrees.*

20.

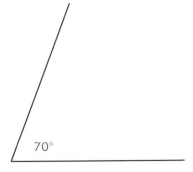

70°

21.

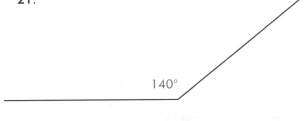

140°

I.   *Each problem gives the degrees for two angles of a triangle. Find the size of the third angle.*

22. Angle 1—55 degrees
Angle 2—88 degrees
Angle 3 =   37   degrees

23. Angle 1—38 degrees
Angle 2—52 degrees
Angle 3 =   90   degrees

J.   *Name the types of triangles described above.*

24. The triangle in number 22 is a(n) _____ acute _____ triangle.

25. The triangle in number 23 is a(n) _____ right _____ triangle.

K.   *Fill in the following chart to calculate the degrees for each sector of a circle graph.*

Number of Students in Grades 6 and 7

		Students	*Ratios*	*Percents*	*Degrees*
26.	*Grade 6*	12	$\frac{12}{23}$	52%	187°
27.	*Grade 7*	11	$\frac{11}{23}$	48%	173°
28.	*Totals*	23	$\frac{23}{23}$	100%	360°

L. *Use the information on the circle graph to answer these questions.*

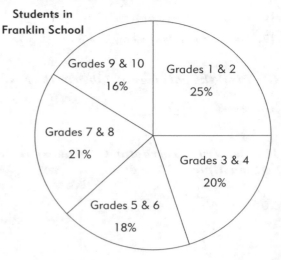

Students in
Franklin School

29. What percent of the students in the school are in grades 1 and 2? __25%__

30. What percent of the students are in grades 5 and 6? __18%__

31. What percent of the students are in grades 7 and 8? __21%__

32. What percent of the students are in grades 9 and 10? __16%__

M. *Draw a sketch, and find the solution for each problem.*

33. Ruth hung three sheets on the clothesline. Each sheet was fastened with four clothespins, and the last clothespin holding one sheet was the first clothespin holding the next sheet. How many clothespins did she use?

 __10 clothespins__

34. Sarah is cutting a 12-inch piece of material into 2-inch strips. How many times will Sarah need to cut the material?

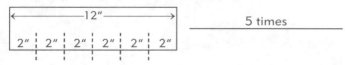 __5 times__

35. A rail fence along the front of a property needs to be replaced. There are 5 upright posts, each joined to the next one by 2 rails. How many rails will be needed?

__8 rails__

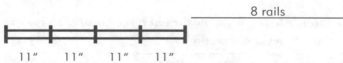

36. In problem 35, how long will the fence be if the 5 upright posts are placed 11 feet apart?

__44 feet__

```
╔════════════════════════════════════════════════════════╗
║  170.  Chapter 13 Test (Final)                           ║
╚════════════════════════════════════════════════════════╝
```

A. Math calculation. *Solve these problems.*

1.
```
   6,381
   3,919
     866
 + 2,818
  13,984
```

2.
```
   6,012
 - 3,816
   2,196
```

3.
```
 $3,908.21
 - 2,299.88
 $1,608.33
```

4.
```
    455
   × 73
  33,215
```

5.
```
    385
  × 218
  83,930
```

6. $169 \text{ R } 3$
$41)\overline{6,932}$

7. $420 \text{ R } 99$
$115)\overline{48,399}$

8.
$$\frac{5}{8}$$
$$+ \frac{1}{2}$$
$$1\frac{1}{8}$$

9.
$$1\frac{5}{6}$$
$$+ 3\frac{3}{4}$$
$$5\frac{7}{12}$$

10.
$$\frac{4}{5}$$
$$- \frac{1}{2}$$
$$\frac{3}{10}$$

11.
$$4\frac{1}{4}$$
$$- 3\frac{5}{6}$$
$$\frac{5}{12}$$

12. $\frac{1}{2} \times \frac{3}{4}$ $\frac{3}{8}$

13. $3\frac{1}{3} \times 2\frac{1}{4}$ $7\frac{1}{2}$

14. $25 \div \frac{2}{3}$ $37\frac{1}{2}$

15. $4\frac{1}{2} \div 1\frac{1}{9}$ $4\frac{1}{20}$

16.
```
   2.7172
 + 4.91
   7.6272
```

17.
```
   4.515
   3.2
  11.12
 + 0.4187
  19.2537
```

18.
```
  41.21
 - 17.8
  23.41
```

19.
```
   4.7
 - 1.791
   2.909
```

20.
```
   51.5
  × 8.5
 437.75
```

21.
```
    1.2
 × 0.06
  0.072
```

22. 4.56×100
456

23. $34.1 \div 1,000$
0.0341

24. 4.1
$1.4)\overline{5.74}$

25. 825
$0.02)\overline{16.5}$

26. $\frac{10}{12} = \frac{n}{30}$
$n = 25$

27. $\frac{6}{7} = \frac{21}{n}$
$n = 24\frac{1}{2}$

28. 40% of 60

24

29. 55% of 72

39.6

30. 25% decrease from $30

$22.50

31. 6 is __15__ % of 40

32. 9 is __$37\frac{1}{2}$__ % of 24

B. Math terms. *Write the answers.*

33. The answer to an addition problem is the _____sum_____ .

34. The answer to a subtraction problem is the _____difference_____ .

35. The answer to a multiplication problem is the _____product_____ .

36. The answer to a division problem is the _____quotient_____ .

37. In $\frac{3}{4}$, the denominator is __4__ .

38. Circle the one that is an improper fraction: $\frac{3}{4}$ $\left(\frac{4}{3}\right)$ $1\frac{1}{4}$

C. Numeration. *Do these exercises.*

39. Write the number 6,101,453 using words. Six million, one hundred one thousand, four hundred fifty-three

40. Round 135 to the nearest ten. _____140_____

41. Round 42,999,238 to the nearest million. _____43,000,000_____

42. Write 149 as a Roman numeral. _____CXLIX_____

43. Write MCCLXVII as an Arabic numeral. _____1,267_____

44. Is 43,383 divisible by 3? _____yes_____

45. Is 527,124 divisible by 4? _____yes_____

46. The greatest common factor of 27 and 45 is _____9_____ .

47. The lowest common multiple of 16 and 20 is _____80_____ .

48. Round 0.47 to the nearest tenth. _____0.5_____

49. Round 0.399 to the nearest hundredth. _____0.40_____

D.   Units of measure. *Write the answers.*

50. 6 ft. = ___72___ in.

51. 3 mi. = ___15,840___ ft.

52. 5 gal. = ___20___ qt.

53. 6 hr. = ___360___ min.

54. 160 cm = ___1.6___ m

55. 7 km = ___7,000___ m

56. 3 km² = ___300___ ha

57. 18 sq. ft. = ___2___ sq. yd.

58.
```
    4 lb.   6 oz.
  – 2 lb.   9 oz.
    1 lb.  13 oz.
```

59.
```
    3 ft.  5 in.
       × 4
   13 ft.  8 in.
```

E.   Geometry. *Write the answers.*

60. A pentagon is a closed figure having ___5___ straight sides.

61. A triangle with one 109-degree angle is a(n) ___obtuse___ triangle.

62. A ___parallelogram___ is a four-sided figure whose opposite sides are parallel but whose corners are not right angles.

63. Item ___d___ below is a ray.

64. Item ___c___ shows parallel lines.

a.   b.   c.   d.   e.   f.

65. Square: each side = 18 in.; perimeter = ___72 in.___

66. Rectangle: length = 25 ft.; width = 20 ft.; perimeter = ___90 ft.___

67. Square: each side = 18 ft.; area = ___324 sq. ft.___

68. Rectangle: length = 25 ft.; width = 20 ft.; area = ___500 sq. ft.___

69. Triangle: base = 8 in.; height = 7 in.; area = ___28 sq. in.___

70. Cube: each edge = 9 in.; volume = ___729 cu. in.___

71. Rectangular solid: l = 8 cm; w = 6 cm; h = 4 cm; v = ___192 cm³___

F.   **Reading problems.** *Find the answers.*

72. The Martin family has a small produce stand during the summer. One summer they had an income of $425.52. Their expenses were $32.43 for seeds, $35.52 for insecticides, and $18.99 for other expenses. What was their profit?

<u> $338.58   </u>

73. The Martins sold sweet corn at their stand for $1.50 per dozen. What was the selling price per ear of corn?

<u> $12\frac{1}{2}$¢   </u>

74. One day when Elsie was tending the produce stand, a customer bought $3.43 worth of produce. The customer gave Elsie $10.00. Fill in the blanks below to show the bills and coins that Elsie should return in change.

1¢	5¢	10¢	25¢	$1.00	$5.00
2	1		2	1	1

75. The Martins' truck patch is 40 feet wide. The rows are placed $2\frac{1}{2}$ feet apart. The first row and the last row are $2\frac{1}{2}$ feet from the sides of the garden. How many rows are in the truck patch? (Draw a sketch.)

<u>   15 rows   </u>

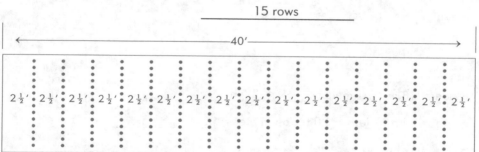

76. The silo on the Wenger farm has a diameter of 20 feet. What is its circumference? The formula is $c = \pi \times d$.

<u>   62.8 ft.   </u>

77. The face of a certain clock has a radius of 7 inches. What is the area of the clock face? The formula is $a = \pi r^2$.

<u>   154 (153.86) sq. in.   </u>

INDEX

Index numbers correspond to pupil page numbers found in the top corner of the pages.

SYMBOLS

>   is greater than

<   is less than

∧   caret (indicates decimal point location)

∠   angle

∟   right angle

π   pi (relationship of circumference to diameter of a circle: near 3.14 or $3\frac{1}{7}$)

FORMULAS

$d = rt$ distance = rate × time

$i = prt$ interest = principal × rate × time

perimeter

$p = 2l + 2w$ perimeter of a rectangle = (2 × length) + (2 × width)

$p = 4s$ perimeter of a square = 4 × side

$p = a + b + c$ perimeter of a triangle = sum of all sides

$c = \pi d$ circumference of a circle = pi × diameter

area

$a = lw$ area of a rectangle = length × width

$a = s \times s$ area of a square = side × side

$a = bh$ area of a parallelogram = base × height

$a = \frac{1}{2}bh$ area of a triangle = ½ × base × height

$a = \pi r^2$ area of a circle = pi × radius × radius

volume

$v = lwh$ volume of a rectangular solid = length × width × height

$v = e \times e \times e$ volume of a cube = edge × edge × edge

circle formulas

$d = 2r$ diameter of a circle = 2 × radius

$c = \pi d$ circumference of a circle = pi × diameter

$a = \pi r^2$ area of a circle = pi × radius × radius

Tables of Measure

Bible Measure

Length

1 finger = $\frac{3}{4}$ inch

1 handbreadth = 3 inches

1 span = 3 handbreadths (9 inches)

1 cubit = 2 spans (18 in. or $1\frac{1}{2}$ feet)

1 fathom = 4 cubits (6 feet)

1 furlong = about $\frac{1}{9}$ mile

Weight

1 gerah = $\frac{1}{50}$ ounce

1 bekah = 10 gerahs ($\frac{1}{5}$ ounce)

1 shekel = 2 bekahs ($\frac{2}{5}$ ounce)

1 maneh = 50 shekels (20 ounces)

1 talent = 60 manehs (75 pounds)

Liquid Measure

1 log = almost 1 pint

1 hin = 12 logs ($5\frac{1}{3}$ quarts)

1 bath = 6 hins (8 gallons)

1 homer = 10 baths (80 gallons)

Dry Measure

1 cab = $2\frac{3}{4}$ pints

1 omer = 5 pints

1 seah = 6 cabs or $3\frac{1}{3}$ omers (1 peck)

1 ephah = 3 seahs ($3\frac{1}{4}$ pecks)

1 homer = 10 ephahs (8 bushels)

Tables of Measure

Metric Measure

Length

basic unit: **meter**

1 millimeter = 0.001 meter
1 centimeter = 0.01 meter
1 decimeter = 0.1 meter
1 dekameter = 10 meters
1 hectometer = 100 meters
1 kilometer = 1,000 meters

Capacity

basic unit: **liter**

1 milliliter = 0.001 liter
1 centiliter = 0.01 liter
1 deciliter = 0.1 liter
1 dekaliter = 10 liters
1 hectoliter = 100 liters
1 kiloliter = 1,000 liters
1 bushel = 4 pecks

Weight

basic unit: **gram**

1 milligram = 0.001 gram
1 centigram = 0.01 gram
1 decigram = 0.1 gram
1 dekagram = 10 grams
1 hectogram = 100 grams
1 kilogram = 1,000 grams

Temperature, Celsius scale

0° = freezing point
100° = boiling point

Metric-to-English Conversion

Linear Measure

1 centimeter = 0.39 inch
1 meter = 39.4 inches
1 meter = 3.28 feet
1 kilometer = 0.62 mile

Weight

1 gram = 0.035 ounce
1 kilogram = 2.2 pounds

Capacity

1 liter = 1.06 quarts (liquid)

Area

1 hectare = 2.5 acres
1 square kilometer = 0.39 square mile

English-to-Metric Conversion

Linear Measure

1 inch = 2.54 centimeters
1 foot = 0.3 meter
1 mile = 1.61 kilometers

Weight

1 ounce = 28.3 grams
1 pound = 0.45 kilogram

Capacity

1 quart (liquid) = 0.95 liter

Area

1 acre = 0.4 hectare
1 square mile = 2.59 square kilometers